James Hutton – Present and Future

Geological Society Special Publications
Series Editor
A. J. FLEET
R. E. HOLDSWORTH
A. C. MORTON
M. S. STOKER

It is recommended that reference to all or part of this book should be made in one of the following ways:

CRAIG, G. Y. & HULL, J. H. (eds) 1999. *James Hutton – Present and Future*. Geological Society, London, Special Publications, **150**.

MCINTYRE, D. B. 1999. James Hutton's Edinburgh: a précis. *In:* CRAIG, G. Y. & HULL, J. H. (eds) *James Hutton – Present and Future*. Geological Society, London, Special Publications, **150**, 1–12.

GEOLOGICAL SOCIETY SPECIAL PUBLICATION NO. 150

James Hutton – Present and Future

EDITED BY

G. Y. CRAIG & J. H. HULL
Royal Society of Edinburgh, UK

1999
Published by
The Geological Society
London

THE GEOLOGICAL SOCIETY

The Society was founded in 1807 as The Geological Society of London and is the oldest geological society in the world. It received its Royal Charter in 1825 for the purpose of 'investigating the mineral structure of the Earth'. The Society is Britain's national society for geology with a membership of around 8500. It has countrywide coverage and approximately 1500 members reside overseas. The Society is responsible for all aspects of the geological sciences including professional matters. The Society has its own publishing house, which produces the Society's international journals, books and maps, and which acts as the European distributor for publications of the American Association of Petroleum Geologists, SEPM and the Geological Society of America.

Fellowship is open to those holding a recognized honours degree in geology or cognate subject and who have at least two years' relevant postgraduate experience, or who have not less than six years' relevant experience in geology or a cognate subject. A Fellow who has not less than five years' relevant postgraduate experience in the practice of geology may apply for validation and, subject to approval, may be able to use the designatory letters C Geol (Chartered Geologist).

Further information about the Society is available from the Membership Manager, The Geological Society, Burlington House, Piccadilly, London W1V 0JU, UK. The Society is a Registered Charity, No. 210161.

Published by The Geological Society from:
The Geological Society Publishing House
Unit 7, Brassmill Enterprise Centre
Brassmill Lane
Bath BA1 3JN
UK
(*Orders*: Tel. 01225 445046
Fax 01225 442836)

First published 1999

The publishers make no representation, express or implied, with regard to the accuracy of the information contained in this book and cannot accept any legal responsibility for any errors or omissions that may be made.

British Library Cataloguing in Publication Data
A catalogue record for this book is available from the British Library.

ISBN 1-86239-026-6

Distributors

USA
AAPG Bookstore
PO Box 979
Tulsa
OK 74101-0979
USA
(*Orders*: Tel. (918) 584-2555
Fax (918) 560-2652)

Australia
Australian Mineral Foundation
63 Conyngham Street
Glenside
South Australia 5065
Australia
(*Orders*: Tel. (08) 379-0444
Fax (08) 379-4634)

India
Affiliated East-West Press PVT Ltd
G-1/16 Ansari Road
New Delhi 110 002
India
(*Orders*: Tel. (11) 327-9113
Fax (11) 326-0538)

Japan
Kanda Book Trading Co.
Cityhouse Tama 204
Tsurumaki 1-3-10
Tama-shi
Tokyo 206-0034
Japan
(*Orders*: Tel. (0423) 57-7650
Fax (0423) 57-7651)

Typeset by E & M Graphics, Midsomer Norton, Bath, UK.

Printed by Cambridge University Press, Cambridge, UK.

Contents

Royal Society of Edinburgh Organizing Committee for the Hutton Bicentennial Conference

Acknowledgements

Principal donor
Lothian and Edinburgh Enterprise Ltd

Major donors
British Geological Survey
Centre for Marine and Petroleum Technology
Dundas and Wilson WS
Edinburgh Convention Bureau
Glenmorangie plc
Laings (Scotland) Ltd
The Lady Lyell
Scottish Association for Marine Science
Scottish & Newcastle plc
Scottish Office
Scottish Natural Heritage
The Scottish Post Office Board

Sponsors
Brewin Dolphin and Co Ltd
R and K Drysdale Ltd
Dunstaffnage Marine Laboratory, Oban
City of Edinburgh
Dept of Geology and Geophysics, University of Edinburgh
Edinburgh Geological Society
Hunters Coaches
Open University
James Thin
University of Edinburgh

Joint sponsors with the Geological Society (London)
Amerada Hess Ltd
Amoco Services Ltd
ARCO British Ltd
BP Exploration Operating Company Ltd
Chevron Europe Ltd
Conoco (Europe) Ltd
IKODA Ltd
Kerr McGee Oil (UK) Ltd
Oryx UK Energy Company
Ready Mixed Concrete (UK) Ltd
Shell UK Exploration and Production
Statoil (UK) Ltd

Preface

The roots of the Bicentennial Hutton–Lyell Conference to commemorate the death of James Hutton in 1797 and the birth of Charles Lyell in that same year may well have arisen from an incautious remark made by one of us (G. Y. Craig) at a Geological Society of America Annual Convention meeting in Dallas, Texas. 'Open your mouth and you will end up as a volunteer' has a nasty habit of coming true. But it has all come to pass and the participants seemed to have enjoyed themselves thoroughly, listening to and arguing with our distinguished international speakers. Enjoyment also came in large measures from our sponsors, acknowledged on p. vi. Their generosity enabled us to pay the speakers' travelling costs and accommodation, to say nothing of the lunchtime hospitality given to all participants. And for once the warmth of Edinburgh hospitality was matched by the weather. We can say this without conceit because neither of us is Edinburgh born!

The London Lyell meeting was held from 30 July to 3 August 1997. The book of the proceedings, *Lyell: the Past is the Key to the Present*, has recently been published by the Geological Society Publishing House. The Edinburgh meeting (from 5–9 August) was held at the Royal College of Physicians in Queen Street, because the Royal Society of Edinburgh could not at that time accommodate the expected number of registrants. Over 180 delegates attended, including 30 who had travelled north after the Lyell meeting.

The meeting began with an outline of Edinburgh as it was in Hutton's day; other keynote speakers over the five sessions examined Hutton's philosophy and his influence on current research. In spite of what has sometimes been written about him, James Hutton was essentially a practical man – farmer, industrial chemist, canal adviser and field geologist. It was entirely appropriate then that half the meeting should be devoted to visits to some of Hutton's classical localities, including Arthur's Seat and Salisbury Crags which are literally within a stone's throw of the site of Hutton's house in Edinburgh. Fellows of the Edinburgh Geological Society, especially Andrew McMillan, played an important part in planning and leading the excursions. Hutton's unconformity at Siccar Point ('*the Original Abyss of Time*') was led by David McAdam and Stuart Munro of the British Geological Survey and by Doreen Grove of Historic Scotland. A party of more than 90 not only saw exciting rocks but also Dunglass Collegiate Church where Sir James Hall, 'Father of Experimental Geology' is buried. After a copious lunch provided by Drysdale's Swedes (in their swede-packing plant on a particularly hot day), most of the party were in a distinctly tranquil state as they viewed the impressive remains of Tantallon Castle, former home of the warring Douglas family.

On the last day, Donald McIntyre and David Stephenson enthusiastically showed one party the classic geological localities of granite and schist in the beautiful valley of Glen Tilt in Perthshire, where Hutton was first able to demonstrate that granites were intrusive. The information-packed journey also illustrated much of local Scottish history. Ian Rolfe took the second group to Kinnordy House in Angus, where Sir Charles Lyell was born. Members examined the sites that gave rise to Lyell's first two papers, including outcrops of the serpentine 'dyke' and Kinnordy Loch, which at one time was drained and dug for agricultural marl. Lunch was graciously provided by the Lady Lyell and Lord Lyell. Leonard Wilson and Ian Rolfe had gone to much effort to lay out exhibits of Lyell's notes and work in the beautiful library.

A plaque was unveiled to commemorate the site of Hutton's house at St John's Hill in the Pleasance, at a delightful ceremony introduced by David Land, President of the Edinburgh Geological Society. The unveiling was attended by the Lord Provost of Edinburgh, the Principal of Edinburgh University, the President of the Royal Society of Edinburgh, Fraser Morrison, Chairman of the Morrison Construction Group and a gathering of well over a hundred guests, including descendants of James Hutton. Norman Butcher very efficiently organized the ceremony. An evening reception was hosted by the Scottish Office in the Signet Library, with Malcolm Chisholm, MP, the then Scottish Minister for Local Government and Transport, giving the welcoming address. The conference dinner was held in the Playfair Library of the University of Edinburgh, at which the guest speaker was Lord Lyell, great-great-great-nephew of Sir Charles Lyell.

Lastly we wish to thank the all-too-frequently-unsung heroines of the Royal Society of Edinburgh staff, especially Catherine Lyall, Sandra McDougall and Luana Pritchard, who did so much of the hard work and made the life of the Organizing Committee so much easier. Additionally Vicki Ingpen is thanked for her unstinting assistance in the publication of this volume.

The Geological Society has undertaken the publication of this book as well as the Lyell volume. We think that the result is a pleasantly related house style befitting the joint nature of the conference. The Editors and authors would like to acknowledge the assistance of the following referees and thank them for their helpful and constructive comments on the papers accepted for publication: Dr Iain Brown, Sir Alan Cook, Professor Gordon Craig, Professor Barry Dawson, Professor Colin Donaldson, Professor Colin Graham, Mr John Hull, Dr Michael Johnson, Dr Dick Kroon, Dr William Napier, Professor Bruce Proudfoot, Dr Roger Scrutton and Professor Brian Upton.

Finally we are most grateful to Derek Blundell, Chairman of the Geological Society Lyell Meeting, for his unfailing and courteous help.

Gordon Craig
John Hull

James Hutton's Edinburgh: a précis

DONALD B. MCINTYRE

Beaumont House, Flat 17, 15 North St John's Place, Perth PH1 5SZ, UK

Abstract: James Hutton (1726–1797) was born and bred in Edinburgh. Having decided to be a farmer, he went to Norfolk aged 24 to learn new methods of husbandry. From that base, he travelled widely and developed an interest in geology. In 1767 he left his Berwickshire farm and returned to Edinburgh, where he became a valued member of the remarkable group of men who founded the Royal Society of Edinburgh and made the city the unrivalled intellectual centre of the age.

Edinburgh was a capital without the distractions of king and parliament. When the Industrial Revolution began, many disciplines were already represented by men of world renown who knew each other – many, indeed, were related. There were still no boundaries between narrowly defined disciplines; there was shared interest in all knowledge.

Geological structure had constricted Edinburgh's growth, keeping the compact Old Town on its ancient defensive ridge. The North Bridge, completed soon after Hutton's return to Edinburgh, made possible the planned New Town, in dramatic architectural and intellectual contrast to the mediaeval city. The beauty and interest of Edinburgh's scenery is the result of an active geological past. Consequently, in a small and accessible space, rocks of different character are exposed in a natural geological laboratory.

James Hutton did not live in an ivory tower. War, rebellion and revolution, both political and industrial, all had their influence. In a turbulent world, a decade of peace (1783–1793) was another factor making possible Hutton's great contribution to modern geology.

This essay sketches the historical, social and political background of the Edinburgh of Hutton's time. Space permits only a précis here, but I am grateful to *Earth Sciences History* for publishing the full documentation (with references, bibliography and genealogical trees) (McIntyre 1997). At the suggestion of the Conference Organising Committee and Scottish Natural Heritage, a book on Hutton as a field geologist was published by the Stationery Office during the week of the conference (McIntyre & McKirdy 1997, *James Hutton: The Founder of Modern Geology*). Although addressed to a general readership, this book contains previously unpublished Huttonian material. Dennis Dean's augmented edition of Hutton's own eminently readable account (Hutton 1997, *James Hutton in the Geology in the Field and in the Study*) was also published during the conference. These resources on Hutton's geology being available (along with Dean 1992), this account deals with the environment that made his geology possible.

In one of his novels Walter Scott describes how an Edinburgh advocate gave letters of introduction to a visitor who 'was gratified with seeing that [the letters] were addressed to some of the first literary characters in Scotland. "To David Hume, Esq." "To John Home, Esq." "To Dr Ferguson." "To Dr Black." "To Lord Kaimes." "To Mr. Hutton." "To John Clerk, Esq., of Eldin." "To Adam Smith, Esq." "To Dr. Robertson." Upon my word, my

McIntyre, D. B. 1999. James Hutton's Edinburgh: a précis.
In: Craig, G. Y. & Hull, J. H. (eds) *James Hutton – Present and Future*. Geological Society, London, Special Publications, **150**, 1–12.

legal friend has a good selection of acquaintances … [A man] must rub up his faculties a little, and put his mind in order, before he enters this sort of society.' My paper is intended to serve as a letter of introduction to that company.

It is helpful to keep the following dates in mind: 1726 Hutton was born; 1750 he returned from the Continent; 1767 he moved back to Edinburgh; 1785 his *Theory of the Earth* was read to the Royal Society of Edinburgh (published 1788); 1795 his extended *Theory of the Earth* was published; and 1797 Hutton died.

The *dramatis personae* includes pioneers not in science only, but lawyers, statesmen, soldiers, sailors, engineers, historians and other literary men. Consider William Smellie, a largely self-taught man with an enormous breadth of interest and accomplishment. Although apprenticed to a printer at the age of 12, five years later he won the Silver Medal of the Philosophical Society (parent of the Royal Society of Edinburgh) for the most accurate edition of a Latin classic. At the age of 20 he helped to found the Newtonian Club. In 1777 he founded the Crochallan Club, one of the most popular of Edinburgh's convivial clubs. Smellie was printer for both David Hume and Robert Burns. He played an important part in producing the first edition of the *Encyclopaedia Britannica*, to which he contributed many major scientific articles. Smellie was a founding member of the Royal Society of Edinburgh, an accomplished botanist and antiquary, and a versatile linguist – teaching himself Hebrew in order to print a Hebrew dictionary.

Henry Home, Lord Kames, was a judge, writer, influential critic, and agricultural innovator. He was a friend of Benjamin Franklin and David Hume, and a friend and sponsor of Adam Smith. Yet, though Smellie was 44 years his junior, Kames adopted him as a friend and trusted him as a literary confidant. In the end, Smellie wrote biographies of Kames Hume, and Smith.

Benjamin Franklin knew Edinburgh well. In 1759, he met Adam Smith, William Robertson and Adam Ferguson, and was Lord Kames' guest at his country house near David Hume's home at Ninewells, not far from where Hutton was farming. Perhaps Hutton and Franklin met during that visit. When Franklin returned to Edinburgh in 1771, he stayed with Hume in his new house in St David Street and was the guest of Lord Kames in Perthshire. Among Franklin's 'distinguished acquaintances in the medical faculty' he named Joseph Black, William Cullen and James Russell, all of whom were Hutton's close friends. As Hutton was then living in Edinburgh, he and Franklin might well have met.

Franklin and his son were among the nine Honorary Fellows elected when the Royal Society of Edinburgh was constituted in 1783. Recommending Edinburgh to an American acquaintance, Franklin wrote, 'At this time there happen to be collected a set of as truly great men, professors of the several branches of knowledge, as have ever appeared in any age or country.' He also noted an Edinburgh characteristic: the '*disputatious turn* – Persons of good sense, I have observed, seldom fall into it except lawyers, university men, and men of all sorts that have been bred in Edinborough'.

Despite Hutton's innovations in farming, his pioneering work in industrial chemistry, his tests for coal and culm, his friendship with James Watt, and his involvement with the Forth and Clyde Canal, he has been criticized as an impractical theorist, 'loftily dismissive of utilitarian science' – as much a theologian as a scientist. This is wrong: Hutton was an experienced field geologist with a deep interest in useful applications.

Hutton had an 'exquisite relish for whatever is beautiful and sublime in science', and the implications of his geological discoveries 'were matter, not of transient delight but of solid and permanent happiness'. He loved to share the pleasure he had from his discoveries. After finding granite veins in Arran, it was characteristic of him that he returned to Brodick for John Clerk, junior (son of his friend, John Clerk of Eldin): 'Not contented with this view of those two alpine bodies, in that jaunt which I had taken alone, I wished to give Mr Clerk the same satisfaction.'

In his last letter to Kames, Franklin wrote 'I almost envy the Abilities you continue to possess of instructing, delighting, and being useful at so late a Period in Life.' Ian Simpson Ross, in his biography of Kames, remarked that '*Delighting*, *instructing*, and *being useful* were the great aims of all the men of letters of the Enlightenment'. This was surely true for James Hutton.

Notable Edinburgh characters, chiefly lawyers and disputants

The Court of Session is Scotland's highest law court, and advocates raised to the Bench are known by honorary titles, often taken from their family estates. The General Assembly, the Church of Scotland's highest court, meets once a year in Edinburgh, where its debates provided opportunities for young advocates serving as Elders. As the legal profession outnumbered the ministers and professors, lawyers dominated the city's intellectual life. The spirited character of Hutton's Edinburgh is illustrated by highlighting the careers of some of these men.

Alexander Wedderburn, who as a young man was a protégé of Adam Smith and David Hume, became an influential figure in Lord North's government and rose to be Lord Chancellor of England, presiding over the House of Lords. Without intending the result, Wedderburn did much to shape Franklin's attitude towards American independence.

It has been said that the two most remarkable figures at the Scots bar 'in their own or any other time' were Henry Erskine and John Clerk, junior – Hutton's field assistant in Arran. Erskine succeeded Viscount Melville ('the uncrowned King of Scotland') as Lord Advocate and Dean of the Faculty of Advocates, and was considered the Scottish bar's most eloquent speaker as well as its leader. Erskine's brother, Thomas, began his career as a midshipman before rising to the top of the English bar. He became Lord Chancellor, and it is said that 'he was probably the greatest advocate the English bar has ever seen'. Edinburgh provided England with a third Lord Chancellor in Lord Brougham, who, while still a student, published papers with the Royal Society of London. He also reviewed Hutton's *Theory of the Earth*.

Sydney Smith, the founder of the *Edinburgh Review*, gave a shrewd summary of the questioning attitude characteristic of the Scottish Enlightenment: 'If you were sailing from Alicant to Aleppo in a storm, and if (after sailors had held up the image of a Saint and prayed to it) the storm were to abate, you would be more sorry for the encouragement of superstition than rejoiced for the preservation of your life; (and so would every other man born and bred in Edinburgh.'

As Lord Justice Clerk, Lord Braxfield presided over some of the most infamous trials in Scottish legal history. The fate of the Martyrs for Parliamentary Reform, condemned for sedition, shows how little freedom of speech was tolerated in the 1790s – this at the time when Hutton was writing his *Theory of the Earth*.

The reason John Clerk, junior, did not become a geologist was that in 1788 – the year after he had accompanied Hutton to Arran – he found fame as an advocate in the sensational trial of Deacon Brodie. Brodie was the Edinburgh Councillor whose double life inspired Robert Louis Stevenson to write his well-known tale, *Dr Jekyll and Mr Hyde*. A contemporary account of the trial was written by William Creech, a member of the jury and Scotland's leading publisher. Brodie was defended by Henry Erskine, while John Clerk was counsel for Brodie's assistant.

Lord Monboddo, another judge, gave weekly *learned* suppers, which were regularly attended by Hutton, Joseph Black (Professor of Chemistry and practising physician) and William Smellie.

The Enlightenment from 1759 to 1799

A review of some of the intellectually significant events of this period in Scotland provides a context for Hutton, who was 34 years old in 1760, and 69 in 1795.

1759: Adam Smith published his *Theory of Moral Sentiments*. When Hutton and Smith first met is discussed in the paper.
Franklin received an LLD degree from St Andrews and was admitted 'Burges & Gildbrother of Edinburgh'.
Robert Burns was born.

1760: John Roebuck founded the Carron Ironworks.

1760–1764: Joseph Black distinguished between quantity and intensity of heat. His major contribution to chemistry was his use of quantitative methods.

1761: Sir James Hall of Dunglass (founder of experimental geology) was born.

1762: David Hume completed his *History of England*.
Revd William Robertson, the historian, became Principal of Edinburgh University, a position he held with success for 31 years.
John Robison (aged 23) was the Board of Longitude's representative in charge of Harrison's chronometer on its test voyage to Jamaica.

1763: Watt repaired a model of the Newcomen steam engine.

1764: Adam Smith left on the Grand Tour with the young third Duke of Buccleuch.

1767: Adam Ferguson published his *Essay on the History of Civil Society*.

1768: Construction of the Forth and Clyde canal began. Hutton was a member of the Management Committee from 1767 to 1775.

1769: Watt took out his first patent.

1771: Walter Scott was born in Edinburgh.
The *Encyclopaedia Britannica* was published.
Benjamin Franklin visited Edinburgh as Hume's guest.

1772: Hutton found 'alkali in a stony body', and Black's pupil, Daniel Rutherford, discovered nitrogen.

1773: Samuel Johnson and James Boswell visited Edinburgh on their way to the Hebrides and again on their return journey.
On Adam Smith's recommendation, Adam Ferguson became tutor to the Earl of Chesterfield and was absent on the Continent for two years.

1774: Watt joined Matthew Boulton in Birmingham, where Hutton visited him.

1776: David Hume died aged 65.
Adam Smith's *The Wealth of Nations* and the first volume of Edward Gibbon's *The Decline and Fall of the Roman Empire* were published
Franklin helped to draft the Declaration of Independence, which was signed by two Edinburgh graduates, the Revd John Witherspoon and Benjamin Rush.

1777: Hutton's work on the distinction between coal and culm was published.

1779: Hume's *Dialogues Concerning Natural Religion* was published posthumously.

1780–1781: Playfair became acquainted with Hutton.

1783: Ferguson's *History of the Progress and Termination of the Roman Republic* was published.
The Royal Society of Edinburgh received its Royal Charter.

1783–1786: Sir James Hall visited Lavoisier.

1784: Barthélémy Faujas de Saint Fond visited Hutton, Black and Smith.

1785: Hutton's *Theory of the Earth* was read to the Royal Society of Edinburgh.
Hutton and John Clerk of Eldin found granite veins in Glen Tilt.
Black's pupils founded the Edinburgh University Chemical Society – the earliest chemical society in the world.

1786: Hutton and John Clerk of Eldin made a geological excursion to Galloway.

1786–1788: Robert Burns visited Edinburgh.

1787: William Creech published Burns' poems.
Hutton, Black, Adam Ferguson and Dugald Stewart were present when Burns and Scott had their only meeting.
Hutton visited Arran with John Clerk, junior.
Hutton discovered the unconformity at Jedburgh.

1788: Hutton's *Theory of the Earth* was published in the first volume of the *Transactions of the Royal Society of Edinburgh*.
Franklin's letter on geology was read to the American Philosophical Society. On 19 October 1943, Arthur Holmes began his first lecture in Edinburgh on Advanced Physical Geology by referring to Franklin's theory of the Earth's fluid interior, before developing his own views on convection in the mantle.
Sir James Hall lectured on Lavoisier's *New Theory of Chemistry*.

1789: The foundation stone of Robert Adam's new building for the University was laid with ceremony.

1790: An accident at the Leith glass-house provided the impetus for Hall's experiments, which he began in 1790.
Hutton and Hall gave papers on granite to the Royal Society of Edinburgh.
Adam Smith died aged 67. Black and Hutton were his executors, and Hutton recorded Smith's farewell words.
Eight months after publication of Lavoisier's *Traité élémentaire de Chimie*, a translation by Black's student Robert Kerr was published in Edinburgh.

1791: Sir James Hall revisited Lavoisier in Paris.

1792: The Chemical Society of Philadelphia, the first in America, was founded by Black's former student, Benjamin Rush.

1794: Lavoisier was sent to the guillotine.

1795: Hutton's *Theory of the Earth* was published in two volumes.

1796: Burns died aged 37.

1797: Hutton died on 26 March aged 70.

1798: Sir James Hall began a series of experiments on which he worked, often seven days a week, until 1805. By melting basalt and cooling the molten glass slowly he produced a stony, crystalline substance 'in texture completely resembling whinstone'. Hall showed this specimen to the Royal Society of Edinburgh on 5 February 1798. The present writer was privileged to display this specimen (labelled by Hall himself) at the Third International

Symposium on Experimental Petrology and Geochemistry in 1990, marking the bicentennial of the beginning of Hall's experimental work.

1799: Black died aged 71.

Historical background

After the Treaty of Union in 1707, the Scottish Parliament left Edinburgh. The Treaty, however, preserved Scotland's law, church and universities, which is why lawyers, clergymen and academics were prominent throughout Hutton's lifetime. On the death of Queen Anne, the only living descendants of Charles I were Catholic. To find a Protestant successor, the Whig government turned to the Elector of Hanover, whose grandmother was a daughter of James VI. The Elector was invited to London in 1714 as King George I, though he knew nothing of the language or culture of his new subjects.

Scotland was forced to accept the Hanoverian Succession, but many believed that Scotland had the right to choose its own king, and unsuccessful Jacobite Risings took place in 1715–1716, and 1719. In order to subdue the Highlands, in 1725 General Wade began construction of a network of military roads. The difficulty of travel in those days is not appreciated by those who deny Hutton's importance as a field geologist: Hutton travelled on foot, on horseback and in a chaise from the English Channel to Caithness.

A fourth and more serious Jacobite Rising took place in 1745–1746. Prince Charles Edward Stuart landed in the West Highlands and within two months had defeated General Cope at Prestonpans, and held court in Holyrood Palace. When Hutton and Clerk of Eldin visited Glen Tilt in 1785, their host was the fourth Duke of Athol, the grandson of Prince Charles' Lieutenant-General.

Benjamin Franklin arrived in France on 4 December 1776 to negotiate a Franco–American alliance. After Burgoyne surrendered at Saratoga on 17 October 1777, Lord North attempted to save the British Empire by making a conciliatory offer to the American Congress. The full paper describes the steps that culminated in French and British frigates racing one another across the Atlantic to bring the proposals of their respective governments before the American Congress.

Lord North despatched a Peace Commission, nominally under the Earl of Carlisle, in a desperate attempt to persuade Congress to accept his proposals. Adam Ferguson, as the Commission's Secretary, crossed the Atlantic in the company of Lord Cornwallis, newly appointed as Second-in-Command of the British forces in America.

The first engagement between British and French forces during the American War of Independence was an indecisive naval battle in July 1778 off Brest (Ushant). For reasons described in the full paper, Admiral Keppel, the British Commander-in-Chief, was court-martialled on the charge of misconduct and neglect of duty. These were capital offences: Byng, the last Admiral so charged, had been shot on the quarterdeck.

The court-martial began on 7 January 1779 and lasted for five weeks. Keppel, who was defended with great ability by Tom Erskine, was acquitted. Every captain in the fleet testified, and the reports were read and discussed with great interest in Edinburgh. No naval battle had been documented so thoroughly, and it was his study of these reports that made John Clerk of Eldin immerse himself in naval tactics. Indeed, this is probably why Hutton and Clerk's most productive geological activity was during the decade of peace from 1783 to 1793.

In 1781 Admiral de Grasse surprised the British forces by bringing his entire fleet to the Chesapeake. Travelling with him was the newly appointed French Minister

Plenipotentiary to the United States. Cornwallis was at that time fortifying Yorktown, close to the mouth of Chesapeake Bay, quite unaware that Washington was preparing to besiege him and that de Grasse was about to arrive with French troops, siege artillery, and supplies, supported by 28 battleships. When news of Cornwallis' surrender reached London, it signalled the end of Lord North's Government, and the Tories were swept out of every level of government. Adam Ferguson knew Cornwallis, and the news of the surrender at Yorktown must have been heard with great attention by Hutton's circle of friends in Edinburgh.

The principles of Clerk of Eldin's naval tactics were employed in 1782 by Admiral Rodney in the battle near the islands called the Saints, between Guadeloupe and Dominica. Rodney defeated the French fleet and took Admiral de Grasse prisoner. By winning command of the sea, Britain gained one of its few bargaining points in the negotiations that culminated in the Treaty of Paris on 3 September 1783 – signed little more than two months after the Royal Society of Edinburgh held its first general meeting.

Louis XVI was guillotined on 21 January 1793, and 11 days later the French revolutionary government declared war on Britain. Except for the time between October 1801 and May 1803, the two countries were at war for the next 22 years. Romantics, such as Wordsworth and Coleridge, welcomed the Revolution. Having sympathized with the Americans in their struggle against what was perceived to be a tyrannical government, they found it natural to support the cause of freedom. It was not, indeed, until French armies invaded Switzerland in 1798 that Wordsworth and Coleridge recoiled in dismay.

In Edinburgh the authorities dealt severely with anyone appearing to show sympathy with the French Revolution – or even with the idea of universal suffrage at home. Revisionists, judging Hutton on the basis of his theological references, may not fully appreciate the situation that obtains when speech is not as free as we may innocently think it always has been. In *The Decline and Fall of the Roman Empire*, Hutton's contemporary, Edward Gibbon, used irony 'with consummate art and felicity' because 'an attack on Christianity laid a writer open to prosecution and penalties under the statutes of the realm'. In the 1690s the Principal and half the Professors in Edinburgh University were dismissed for refusing to subscribe to every clause in the Westminster Confession of Faith. In the 1950s, Professors at the University of California lost their jobs for refusing to sign an Oath; as S. E. Morison said, 'Nobody who did not live through [the Senator McCarthy era] will ever believe what a sound and fury [it] made up' – and so it was in Hutton's Edinburgh.

Physical setting

Edinburgh Castle is built on a plug of basalt in the feeding pipe of a Lower Carboniferous volcano long since destroyed by erosion. The Castle rock stands high because it is more resistant than the surrounding sedimentary rocks, which dip at a low angle to the east. During the Ice Age, when an ice sheet moved eastwards across the Edinburgh area, the Castle rock protected the sedimentary rocks in its lee. This, along with an easterly dip, accounts for the mile-long ridge of the High Street from the Castle to the Palace of Holyrood. The ridge is accentuated by a hollow, gouged by the ice, that is now the site of Princes Street Gardens and the Grassmarket. This ridge was early chosen as a defensive site.

It has been estimated that Edinburgh's population grew from about 31 000 in 1755 to some 67 000 in 1800. The Old Town, protected by the City Wall, was confined to the ridge, and tall tenements housed a compressed population. During Hutton's adult lifetime the city broke out from its enclosed defensive position, and the contrast between the narrow closes of the Old Town and Robert Adam's elegant buildings in the New Town is striking. In 1772 the North Bridge was completed, inviting expansion northwards from the city's medieval bounds. David Hume was one of the first to build in the New Town, and it was there that Franklin was his guest.

Landmarks in Hutton's career

1726–1747: Edinburgh

James Hutton was born in Edinburgh on 3 June 1726. This was the year that Dr Beringer published illustrations of what he believed to be genuine fossils, but which had in fact been fabricated by his Iago-like enemies. The science of geology was still in a primitive state, and the Earth was believed to be only some 6000 years old.

Hutton entered the University as a student of humanity in November 1740, but he developed an early and lifelong interest in chemistry, and while still a student he and his friend James Davie experimented on the production of sal ammoniac from the city soot. These experiments later became the basis of a profitable chemical business.

His student years included the 1745 Jacobite Rising, an exciting time when Edinburgh was occupied by the Jacobite army. Church ministers and University Professors left their duties to bear arms against Prince Charles. Professor Maclaurin, Hutton's admired teacher, organized the defence of the city. Maclaurin, a brilliant and popular teacher, taught with authority not only as a distinguished mathematician, but as Newton's friend and expositor.

Hutton was later to see evidence all around him for what he believed to be the 'necessary' decay and destruction of rocks. But he also saw that most rocks are themselves the consolidated products of destruction of still older rocks. He concluded that, as blood circulates in the microcosm (the subject of his MD thesis), so matter circulates in the macrocosm. Hutton wrote,

> 'We are thus led to see a circulation in the matter of this globe, and a beautiful economy in the works of nature. This earth, like the body of an animal, is wasted at the same time that it is repaired. It has a state of growth and augmentation; it has another state, which is that of diminution and decay. This world is thus destroyed in one part, but it is renewed in another; and the operations by which this world is thus constantly renewed, are as evident to the scientific eye, as are those in which it is necessarily destroyed'.

Hutton must have been familiar with the similar words that Hume put into the mouth of his character Philo:

> 'Now if we survey the universe, so far as it falls under our knowledge, it bears a great resemblance to an animal or organized body, and seems actuated with a like principle of life and motion. A continual circulation of matter in it produces no disorder: A continual waste in every part is incessantly repaired: The closest sympathy is perceived throughout the entire system: And each part or member, in performing its proper offices, operates both to its own preservation and to that of the whole. The world, therefore, I infer, is an animal, and the Deity is the SOUL of the world, actuating it, and actuated by it'.

We do not know the content of the classes Hutton took from Maclaurin, but Maclaurin's *Account of Sir Isaac Newton's Philosophical Discoveries* may have planted a geological seed that flourished later in Hutton's mind.

The Bible reports that God looked on the Earth 'and saw that it was good'; Hutton and some other scientists even down to our own day have concluded that (in Hutton's words) 'The globe of this earth is evidently made for man' – the alternative was hardly possible 200 years ago.

Maclaurin's book on Newton's *Philosophical Discoveries* was known to Hume and Hutton, and we find suggestive parallels. The following is an example:

> Maclaurin: 'The plain argument for the existence of the Deity, obvious to all and carrying irresistible conviction with it, is from **the evident contrivance and fitness of things for one another**, which we meet throughout all parts of the Universe.'
>
> Hutton: 'This globe of the earth is a habitable world; and on its **fitness** for this purpose, our sense of **wisdom** in its formation must depend ... Such, indeed, is the **admirable contrivance** of the system.'

1747–1750: Paris, Leyden, London and Edinburgh

Hutton spent the years 1747–1749 studying chemistry and anatomy in Paris, and then returned to Edinburgh in the summer of 1750. As Adam Smith gave his well-attended public lectures in Edinburgh in 1748–1751, we identify 1750–1751 as the first period when Hutton and Smith could have met. Hume was studying privately at his family home in Berwickshire from 1749 to 1751, but he was already friendly with Smith and might have come to Edinburgh to hear Smith's lectures.

1750–1752: Established in Berwickshire

Having inherited farming property in Berwickshire, Hutton 'resolved to apply himself to agriculture'. His decision was confirmed when he met Sir John Hall of Dunglass (Sir James Hall's father), a gentleman 'of ingenuity and taste for science, and also much conversant with the management of country affairs'.

David Hume's older brother, John Hume at Ninewells, and Henry Home at Kames were among the first to introduce modern farming methods to Scotland. They knew each other and it seems quite likely that Hutton would visit these neighbours, with whom he had much in common and from whom he could get help and advice. Dunglass is on the main road to Edinburgh and less than nine miles from Hutton's farm at Slighhouses. Ninewells is little over three miles from Slighhouses, while Kames is less than ten miles.

Much changed in 1751–1752: Smith was appointed to the Chair of Logic in Glasgow; David Hume's older brother married; and David moved to Edinburgh, where he was elected one of the Secretaries of the revived Philosophical Society, originally founded by Maclaurin. In 1752 Hume was appointed Keeper of the historic Advocates' Library, a position that gave him access to the books he needed. Smith transferred to the Chair of Moral Philosophy in Glasgow. Robertson became leader of the Moderate party at the General Assembly, a position he held with distinction until 1780; Black transferred to Edinburgh University; and Hutton went to Norfolk.

1752–1754: Hutton in England

As Hutton was 'never disposed to do things by halves, he determined to study rural economy in the school that was then reckoned the best', and in 1752 he set off for Norfolk. While there he made many journeys on foot into different parts of England, and began making those observations that later led him to formulate his *Theory of the Earth.* He returned to Berwickshire at the end of the summer of 1754.

1754–1767: Farming in Berwickshire

Though Hutton seems to have devoted these years mainly to the improvement of his Berwickshire farms, he pondered the meaning of the geological observations he had made on his travels. Moreover his two farms are on contrasting terrains – a fact unlikely to have escaped his observation. Playfair thought that about 1760 Hutton's ideas began to come together to form a theory.

Black received his MD degree from Edinburgh in 1754, but it seems unlikely that he and Hutton became friends before 1766, when Black returned to Edinburgh as Professor of Chemistry. During the Seven Years War (1756–1763) Hume was frequently in London, and afterwards he was Secretary to the Embassy in Paris (1763–1766). Smith took the Duke of Buccleuch to the Continent in 1764. Hume returned to Ninewells in September 1766. Although this was for only a few weeks, it provided a possible opportunity for Hutton and Hume to meet.

In 1762 John Clerk of Eldin purchased a small coalfield. He was not a wealthy man: his finances were a constant source of anxiety, and we find him acknowledging his indebtedness to 'our most benevolent and worthy friend Doctor Hutton'. Clerk had to direct the colliery operations himself – an occupation providing him with practical knowledge of sedimentary rocks that was no doubt helpful to Hutton.

In 1764 Hutton made a geological tour to the north of Scotland with George Clerk-Maxwell, Clerk of Eldin's older brother.

In 1765 Hutton and Davie entered into a regular partnership for the commercial production of sal ammoniac.

1767: Return to Edinburgh

Hutton moved back to Edinburgh in 1767. Playfair tells us that this allowed Hutton to give his undivided attention to scientific pursuits, and enjoy 'the society of his literary friends, among whom were Dr Black, Mr Russel, professor of Natural Philosophy, Professor Adam Ferguson, Sir George Clerk, Mr Clerk of Elden [sic], Dr James Lind, now of Windsor, and several others'.

From 1767 to 1774 Hutton was an active member of the Management Committee for the Forth and Clyde Canal. Between the years 1772 and 1783 he contributed several papers to the Philosophical Society of Edinburgh. In one of these, read to the Society in 1778, Hutton says Ferguson had suggested the project in 1776 and 'carried' Black and Hutton to the place where the observations were to be made. We know, therefore, that by 1776 Hutton had been in the field with George Clerk-Maxwell, Watt, Ferguson and Black.

Hume returned from London in 1769 and Franklin was his guest in 1771. Hutton may have attended one of the many dinner parties given during Franklin's visit. If Hutton and Hume met, this would likely have been between 1769 and Hume's death in 1776. Perhaps the Clerk and Adam connections provided the opportunity. Robert Adam's family lived in Edinburgh, and Adam and Hume were good friends (Adam designed Hume's tomb); moreover John Clerk of Eldin was Robert Adam's brother-in-law and friend.

Adam Smith moved to Edinburgh on his appointment as Commissioner of Customs in 1778. His home was within a few minutes' walk from Hutton's house in St John's Hill. Perhaps Smith and Hutton met earlier, but it was during the years from 1778 until Smith's death in 1790 that Black and Hutton knew him well, and in the end they were his executors.

Robison returned from Russia in 1774 to take up his appointment in Natural Philosophy. Hutton would probably have met him through Black and Ferguson. The same year Robison's old friend Watt joined Boulton in Birmingham, where one of Watt's first actions was to invite Hutton to join him for a 'jaunt' to the Cheshire salt mines; an invitation that Hutton readily accepted.

Finally, we note that Hutton achieved his geological triumphs during the ten years of peace, 1783–1793, when he was accompanied first by John Clerk of Eldin and John Clerk, junior, and then by Playfair and Hall.

The Oyster Club

The distinguished French geologist, Barthélémy Faujas de Saint Fond, visited Edinburgh in October 1784, less than six months before Hutton's seminal *Theory of the Earth* was presented to the Royal Society of Edinburgh. Faujas enjoyed conversing with Hutton, this 'modest philosopher' who, Faujas said, was then 'busily employed in writing a work on the theory of the earth'. Faujas admits that he found more interest in the company of Joseph Black, the 'learned chymist', whom he visited as often as possible, and whose 'profound knowledge' he greatly respected. Faujas was entertained in a novel fashion by Adam Smith, afterwards correctly reporting that Edinburgh castle is built on a volcanic rock – however, he mistook some of the greywackes and shales of the Southern Uplands as volcanic rocks as well.

The three close friends, Adam Smith, Joseph Black and James Hutton, founded a club known as the Oyster Club, which met weekly and epitomized the best features of the Scottish Enlightenment. Among the regular members were Henry Mackenzie, Dugald Stewart, John Playfair, Sir James Hall, Robert Adam and John Clerk of Eldin. Playfair described how 'round them was soon formed a knot of those who knew how to value the familiar and social converse of these illustrious men'. As Faujas knew all three of the Club's founders, he presumably attended the Oyster Club during his Edinburgh visit.

Dr David Mackie has dated Sir Henry Raeburn's well-known portrait of Hutton to be about 1790. Looking at it, we remember that during Hutton's final years, although ill and in pain for much of the time, Hutton wrote a prodigious amount – on philosophy, physics, agriculture and his *Theory of the Earth*. Adam Smith died in 1790, James Hutton in 1797 and Joseph Black in 1799.

Epilogue

James Hutton is rightly regarded as the founder of modern geology, and a large literature is devoted to consideration of this assertion and its implication. But to think of him simply as a geologist is a mistake. He lived in a truly remarkable community of highly intelligent men, many of whom were involved in matters of national and even international importance. They were bold and original thinkers, spanning a great range of subject matter and personal experience. Moreover they were all 'equally prepared to speak and to listen'.

Hutton, with his unique contribution to knowledge of our planet's history, was close to the centre of this community, not only by virtue of his lifespan but, thanks to his generous and warm personality, by his friendships with some of the most brilliant men of the age. If we could reproduce the intellectual environment that made Hutton and his friends possible, we would have found something of greater value than the philosopher's stone.

> 'What dust of extinct lions sleeps peaceably under our feet everywhere! The soil of this world is made of the dust of Life, the geologists say.'
>
> Thomas Carlyle

References

DEAN, D. R. 1992. *James Hutton and the History of Geology*. Cornell University Press, Ithaca and London.

HUTTON, J. 1997. *James Hutton in the Field and in the Study*. Edited by D. R. Dean. Being an augmented reprinting of Vol. III of Hutton's *Theory of the Earth* (I, II, 1795), as first published by Sir Archibald Geikie (1899). Delmar, New York.

MCINTYRE, D. B. 1997. James Hutton's Edinburgh: the historical, social and political background. *Earth Sciences History*, **16**(2), 100–157.

—— & MCKIRDY, A. 1997. *James Hutton: The Founder of Modern Geology*. Stationery Office, Edinburgh.

A theory of the Earth: Hutton and Humpty Dumpty and Holmes

DON L. ANDERSON

California Institute of Technology, Division of Geological & Planetary Sciences, Pasadena, CA 91125, USA

> The volcano was not created to scare superstitious minds and plunge them into fits of piety and devotion. It should be considered as the vent of a furnace.
>
> James Hutton

Abstract: Paradoxes can be viewed as a bother or as a rich source of information. Paradoxes, fallacies and logical inconsistencies, along with the unstated assumptions behind old worldviews often form the foundation for a new worldview. This is where science differs from myth and just-so stories.

Mantle dynamicists and geochemists have developed a worldview that, in many respects, is incompatible with modern theories of planetary accretion, geodynamics and geophysics, and with the geological context of volcanoes. A primordial undegassed mantle, as both the furnace and the fuel of midplate volcanoes, occupies a central role in the geochemical models. Although modern data alone are sufficient to overturn this view, it is interesting to address it in terms of its own assumptions, fallacies and inconsistencies, and the history of ideas. This is a vast field, so, in honour of James Hutton, I focus on volcanoes, their products, their causes and their sources.

The following axioms are developed which point toward a different kind of world from the pristine primordial worldviews and the plume paradigm.

- Linear volcanic chains delineate the stress field, not the displacement field, of the lithosphere.
- Lithospheric architecture, not the core–mantle boundary, dictates the planform of convection in the mantle.
- Incipient melting is the normal state of the upper mantle.
- The lower mantle is depleted in the heat producing elements compared to the crust, upper mantle and the bulk silicate Earth.
- The Earth is depleted in volatile elements.
- High $^3He/^4He$ ratios in mantle materials imply a deficit of ^4He.
- Primordial heat contributes a significant part of the Earth's heat flow.

These axioms [**A**] are the inverse of the assumptions of the plume and primordial mantle paradigms [not-**A**] and the new and the old views are to each other as looking-glass worlds. An 'axiom' is a self-evident truth or an established rule. It is also an undemonstrated proposition concerning an undefined set of elements and relationships. The above 'axioms' [**A**] are not true axioms but [not-**A**] provide the axiomatic framework of the current world model. These [not-**A**] propositions are treated as self-evident truths so [**A**] can also be called axioms, even though they are falsifiable. The prevailing worldview, the 'standard model', attributes both melting and volcanic chains to deep mantle upwellings controlled by the bottom of the system with most of the original radioactivity and volatile inventory of the Earth in the deep mantle. This is not only inconsistent with modern data but also with the previous worldview embedded in the axioms. These axioms have not been pushed out by better ideas, or falsified; they have simply been overlooked or forgotten. Mantle dynamics is controlled from the top, not the bottom.

ANDERSON, D. L. 1999. A theory of the Earth: Hutton and Humpty Dumpty and Holmes. *In*: CRAIG, G. Y. & HULL, J. H. (eds) *James Hutton – Present and Future*. Geological Society, London, Special Publications, **150**, 13–35.

Logic is logic. That's all I say.

Oliver Wendell Holmes

Science is not a series of discoveries, the amassing of facts that speak for themselves. 'When we study the history of science, it is useful to direct our attention to the intellectual obstruction which, at a given moment, is checking the progress of thought – the hurdle which it was then particularly necessary for the mind to surmount' (Butterfield 1957). Imaginative thinking – what Butterfield called 'picking up the stick from the other end' – plays a vital role in scientific achievement. Chemistry was blocked for centuries by men who were plagued by misleading ideas and so passed their professional lives baying at an absent moon (Bolles 1997). The *terra pinguis* or *phlogiston* theory was an inversion of the real truth. Although it answered to certain *prima facie* appearances, it was a case of picking up the wrong end of the stick.

Theories of the Earth are certainly influenced by new discoveries. But change is brought about primarily by transpositions taking place in the minds of the scientists themselves (Butterfield 1957), or by the weight of accumulated paradoxes, coincidences and inconsistencies.

Aristotle stressed that logic is not so much itself a science in the ordinary sense as it is a prerequisite for any science. Logic is the science of all sciences.

Yet anti-logic is common in much of the current Earth science literature. Consider the following examples.

(1) Plumes come from the lower mantle because midocean ridge basalts (MORB) come from the upper mantle.
(2) Depleted (MORB) mantle is shallow because ridges are passive.
(3) Ocean island basalts (OIB) have high $^3He/^4He$ ratios and are therefore ^3He rich and originate in a deep primordial reservoir.

It does not take a trained logician to know that these statements are, even if true, logical nonsense, yet they form the basis of the current worldview, the 'standard model'. As might be expected, there are many paradoxes associated with the standard model.

This essay explores some of the fallacies and paradoxes associated with current paradigms of Earth evolution and identifies a few axioms (see Abstract) to replace the fallacies and myths. The paradoxes not only evaporate but they recondense as essential features of a theory of the Earth.

On Earth, there are three kinds of volcanic chains; midocean ridge, island arc and, the third kind, midplate. The first two are well understood; they are due to lithospheric extension, focusing of melt toward thin spots, and flux-induced melting. Their locations are caused by lithospheric dynamics and in the simplest terms are nothing more than magma rising to fill space that has been made available. Volcanic chains of the third kind have been called 'hotspot tracks' or 'plume tracks' and have been attributed to hot narrow jets which in turn have been attributed to fluid dynamic instabilities in a thermal boundary layer at the base of the convecting system. In this story, volcanoes of the third kind differ from ordinary volcanoes in that they (a) are active upwellings rather than passive, (b) are deeply rooted, and (c) exist independently of plate properties, cracks in the lithosphere, or large-scale flow. It is volcanoes of the third kind which I wish to address. Understanding these volcanoes is the key to understanding how the Earth furnace works. This would appear to be a mechanics or physics problem. It has become a philosophical, a logical and a geochemical problem.

Plate tectonics is a powerful concept, but it needs to be combined with mineral physics, petrology, rheology and geology in order to be fully effective. Plates are not really rigid or elastic; they have flaws and internal boundaries. Volcanoes are the expected results of plate tectonics and lithospheric dynamics; they are not a natural result of concentrated fluid jets in the mantle. Myths, fallacies, semantics and paradoxes all play a role in current worldviews and, as they have always been, they are a fascinating field of study and insight. A philosopher or logician could go through the global dynamics and mantle geochemistry literature and rewrite the theory of the Earth simply by 'picking up the other end of the stick'.

Logic

Hutton's *'Theory of the Earth'* was the first carefully reasoned and successful piece of geological argument of the form:

If P then Q
Q
Therefore P

As has been pointed out before, this is the *post hoc ergo propter hoc* or *'affirming the consequent'* fallacy. Earth scientists are always grappling with the cause vs. effect issue. For example: Do cracks in the lithosphere allow volcanoes to grow, or vice versa? Does buoyancy cause melting or does melting cause buoyancy? Breakup of continents and oceanic plates is accompanied by extensive volcanism; which causes which; or does something else cause both? This is the chicken-and-egg problem and we shall be encountering many chickens and eggs, including Humpty Dumpty. For example, does the strong outer shell of the Earth break from internal pressures (a birthing chick) or does it crack itself (Humpty Dumpty)?

A more serious fallacy is:

If P then Q
Not P
Therefore not Q

It is this fallacy upon which much of modern mantle geochemistry is built.

In words, we can illustrate one example:

If we have a midocean ridge basalt, we have a sample from the upper (convecting) mantle. If we have a different kind of basalts (ocean island basalt, continental flood basalt) we cannot have a sample from the upper (convecting) mantle.

This *modus moron* fallacy has stimulated the search for other fertile reservoirs, such as the continental lithosphere, the lower mantle and the core–mantle boundary region, to fuel volcanoes of the third kind.

The upper mantle is sometimes equated with 'the convecting mantle', 'the MORB reservoir' and 'the depleted degassed reservoir'. 'Convecting', in turn, has been assumed to imply 'well stirred, homogeneous'. Lewis Carroll, a contemporary of Charles Lyell and Sherlock Holmes, not only wrote wonderful stories, but was also a logician. Was he mocking scientists when he has Humpty Dumpty say 'When I use a word it means just what I chose it to mean – neither more nor less'? When Alice asked if you can make a word mean so many things, Humpty Dumpty responded, 'The question is which is to be master – when I make a word do a lot of work like that I always pay it extra.'

Along with the *depleted, degassed, convecting, homogeneous, upper mantle, MORB reservoir* goes the concept of an *undegassed, undepleted, primordial lower mantle*. These are the two boxes with which modern geochemists discuss the evolution of the mantle. Semantics and logic will be behind much of the following discourse. We start with Sherlock Holmes.

The science of deduction

'Eliminate all other factors, and the one which remains must be the truth.' Sherlock Holmes (created by Arthur Conan Doyle, born in Edinburgh, 1859) would have been a comfortable member of Hutton's Oyster Club. The Earth is a mystery, not a well-controlled (at least by us) physics experiment, and the principle of multiple working hypotheses is essential when working out the mystery. The introduction of black boxes, physics and mathematics into geology has not eliminated the need for keen observation and coherent logic, and more than one idea.

The prevailing current story of the deep Earth, the standard model, is based on several fallacies. The story goes roughly as follows:

> *Most of the Earth is undifferentiated and undegassed. The crust formed from the upper mantle, which is now depleted and degassed. Ocean islands tap the primordial lower mantle via hot, narrow plumes. Continental flood basalts and oceanic plateaus are the result of large bulbous 'plume heads' that rise from the core–mantle boundary. Plumes contain excess* ^{3}*He, a primordial isotope indicative of undegassed mantle. Plumes are independent of plate-scale convection and plate tectonics.*

There are many hidden assumptions in this story, most of which are obvious fallacies when stated clearly. These are some of them.

(1) *Midocean ridges are passive. They therefore tap the shallow mantle.* This is almost true but neglects the time element. Ridges are the final step in the rift-to-drift scenario and represent an approach to steady state. Only mature ridges provide 'uncontaminated' MORB and the older the ridge and the faster the spreading the more pure is the MORB. The initial magmas at a new rift, or ridge, are 'enriched' or 'contaminated' or 'OIB-like'. A global shallow enriched layer seems to be indicated; a layer that can be used up as more magma is pumped out. The MORB layer must be below this 'perisphere'. The MORB mantle is not homogeneous because it is well stirred but because it is below the enriched contaminated layer and erupts through new crust.

(2) *Since the MORB reservoir is in the upper mantle, there can be nothing else in the upper mantle.* This is the well known *modus moron* fallacy. (If P then Q, if not P, then not Q.)

(3) *MORBs are homogeneous; they therefore come from the convecting mantle. Convecting mantle is well stirred and therefore homogeneous (the omelette hypothesis).* The processes of mantle convection actually lead to differentiation. Materials in the Earth are segregated according to their densities and melting points and recycling introduces 'contaminants' into the mantle. The MORB reservoir is homogeneous partly by definition (extreme chemistries are attributed to hotspot or subduction contamination), partly

because it is deep, below some of the effects of contamination (dehydration of slab minerals), and partly because of prior removal of melts and fluids (which can homogenize the residual). The 'convecting mantle' is not a blender; it is more akin to a centrifuge.

(4) *The formation of the crust depletes only part of the mantle leaving most of it in the prima facies state.* This belief is based partly on the high U and Th abundances that are needed to balance the heat flow, assuming the Earth is in steady state (Jacobsen & Wasserburg 1979). Lord Kelvin mistakenly believed that the only contribution to heat flow was loss of primordial heat. Some workers have overreacted and now attribute all of the heat flow to radioactive decay. This actually violates the first law of thermodynamics. Up to about one-half of the present-day heat loss is due to cooling of the Earth (Schubert *et al.* 1980). Arthur Holmes (1916) attributed one-quarter of the output to original heat, the rest being radiogenic. This is in the range of the best modern estimates. When this original heat is taken into account, along with modern U and Th abundances in the crust, there is no room left for a primordial undifferentiated mantle, the *prima facies*. The idea that there is a steady-state balance between radioactive heat produced and surface heat flow also implies a cold origin for the Earth. Lord Kelvin was right in one respect; the Earth is cooling from a hot initial state.

(5) *High $^3He/^4He$ ratio basalts occur on some oceanic islands and continental flood provinces and this implies a ^3He-rich primordial reservoir.* Logically, these high ratios could be due to high ^3He or low ^4He. In fact, midocean ridge basalts (commonly attributed to 'the degassed mantle') contain more ^3He and higher He/CO_2, He/Ne and He/Ar ratios than the so-called primitive or plume basalts (Anderson 1998). Nevertheless, in current geochemical models, the following chain of inference is used.

High $^3He/^4He$ ratios imply excess ^3He, implying an undegassed reservoir implying a deep mantle source.

If, on the contrary, high $^3He/^4He$ ratios result from a deficit in ^4He, this implies a source low in U and Th and this suggests a depleted refractory reservoir such as the lithosphere or recycled lithosphere. This is the mirror image of the previous view – the looking glass world.

Modern estimates of the composition of the crust and upper mantle are consistent with modern theories of accretion, to wit:

The bulk of the Earth has been melted, differentiated and degassed. Subduction returns some volatile material to the shallow mantle. Much of the volatile inventory of the Earth may have been brought in as a late veneer (comets, carbonaceous chondrites), rather than sequestered in the deepest mantle since the origin of the Earth.

Semantics

... we cannot improve the language of any science without at the same time improving the science itself; neither can we, on the other hand, improve a science, without improving the language or nomenclature which belongs to it.

Abbé de Condillac

Seismologists divide the mantle into regions, separated by discontinuities; the upper mantle (Moho to 400 km), the transition region (400–650 km), the lower mantle and the region adjacent to the core (D″). There is no compelling evidence that these regions differ in chemistry although there are arguments for having the bulk of the mantle different from the upper part. It is reasonable that the buoyant products of mantle differentiation – crust, olivine, fluids, hydrous phases – collect in the outer Earth.

Petrologists discuss various kinds of magmas, and geochemists have identified various components in these magmas. One would like to know where these various magma types and components come from, and what are the sizes of the various mantle reservoirs.

A neat Humpty Dumpty solution to this complex problem is to relabel the seismological subdivisions as the 'depleted reservoir' (MORB mantle) and the 'primordial undegassed reservoir' (OIB mantle). Ironically, it appears that basalts thought to be from the 'primordial' reservoir are less gas rich (low ^{3}He abundances), less primordial (high $^{206}Pb/^{204}Pb$ ratios) and less ancient (low $^{4}He/^{238}U$ ratios and low ^{129}Xe) than MORB (basalts from the 'depleted degassed upper mantle').

Geologists can learn much from physicists, in spite of their experiences with Lord Kelvin and Sir Harold Jeffreys. We have learned that things are relative and that space and time can be confused. Is Iceland a plume (a point in space that is unique), or is the north Atlantic mantle being caught in the initial act of exposing itself (a unique point in time)? Since there is no fixed reference frame what is the meaning of 'relatively fixed' (compared to what)? Ridges are also 'relatively fixed', at least over periods of time comparable to the intervals of hotspot 'fixity'. Some island chains emanate from ridges (but more often, remain on or near ridges); which one moves? If 'midplate' refers to the middle of the ocean, as viewed from a continent, then a feature at midplate will move only half as fast as the other continent, making an island at this point 'relatively fixed'. Oceanic ridges ('midocean ridges') also define a 'relatively fixed' reference frame (Kaula 1975). But much has been made of the 'relative fixity' of midplate volcanoes; the observation may not require a *profound* (i.e. deep) explanation.

Current models of Earth evolution tend to mix semantics and assumptions with the observations. For example, the term *'lower mantle'* is replaced by *'undepleted undegassed primitive reservoir'* in much of the geochemical literature. Likewise *'upper mantle'* equals *'depleted degassed MORB reservoir'*, 'OIB' equals *'plume basalt'*, and *'island chains'* become *'hotspot tracks'*. High $^{3}He/^{4}He$ ratio basalts become *'high ^{3}He'* basalts or samples from the *'undegassed mantle'*. By assigning model-dependent names and locations to basalts sampled at the Earth's surface, using techniques that have no depth discrimination, closes the mind to new insights. It is possible, and quite likely, that ocean island basalts acquire their distinctive chemistry from the shallow mantle. In fact, many of the modifications to the plume hypothesis are for the purpose of making this so.

> When we hold a conclusion inviolate, some times the assumptions require certain adjustments ... but in the end assumptions are assumptions rather than conclusions, and generals who invert conclusions with assumptions lose battles and wars.
>
> H. B. Hopfenberg

Paradoxes

> A paradox may signal an inadequacy in the way we are looking at a question, thereby suggesting a new and more fruitful way of approaching it.
>
> T. Ferris

The role of the paradox in Earth science can be illustrated with examples from one small subdiscipline. There is probably no branch of Earth science where there are more paradoxes than in noble gas geochemistry. The Noble Gas Brotherhood is small and mysterious and hard to crack, but here are some of the well-guarded secrets.

(1) *The helium-heat flow paradox.* There is an order of magnitude less ^{4}He coming out of the Earth than appropriate for the heat flow and U abundance (O'Nions & Oxburgh, 1983).

(2) *The missing ^{3}He paradox.* There is one to two orders of magnitude less ^{3}He in 'plume' magmas and hotspot degassing than in ridge basalts and ridge degassing (Sano & Williams 1996; Anderson 1998). In the standard model, the former come from the 'primordial undegassed reservoir'; the latter from the 'degassed reservoir'. This seems to be the wrong way around.

(3) *The most 'primordial' (high ^{3}He/^{4}He ratio) hotspot basalts have the most atmospheric contamination* (Farley & Poreda 1993).

(4) *High ^{3}He/^{4}He ratio basalts, attributed to excess ^{3}He, have low ^{3}He/CO_2, ^{3}He/Ne and ^{3}He/Ar ratios and low absolute helium abundances* (Anderson 1998*b*,*c*). If there is 'excess ^{3}He' one expects all these ratios to be high. If ^{4}He is low, everything falls into place. Perhaps this is the 'right end of the stick'.

(5) *The lead paradox.* The lead isotopes (^{206}Pb, ^{207}Pb, ^{208}Pb) share parents (U, Th) with ^{4}He. Pb isotopes in magmas from the 'depleted upper mantle' reservoir are enriched as are basalts from the 'primitive undegassed lower mantle reservoir'. Since Pb is partially retained by residual crystals, after melt extraction, there may be no paradox if some reservoir (e.g. lower mantle) is never sampled by contemporary basalts (Anderson 1998*c*).

(6) *Fluid-filled inclusions in refractory peridotites often contain an order of magnitude more ^{3}He than OIB from 'undegassed mantle'.*

(7) *'It is very puzzling that ^{4}He/^{40}Ar ratios in MORB are higher than in Hawaiian volcanics.'* (Matsuda & Marty 1995.)

(8) *An ancient isotope, ^{129}Xe, is present in MORB but not in the materials thought to come from the ancient primordial mantle.*

(9) *Islands with high ^{3}He/^{4}He ratios usually also have, in close proximity, materials with low ^{3}He/^{4}He ratios, and the ratio often declines with time toward MORB-like values.*

Something is clearly amiss with the standard model. These paradoxes serve to falsify the primordial mantle hypothesis many times over.

All of the above paradoxes can be understood if high ^{3}He/^{4}He materials have a ^{4}He deficit and if they are dominated by fluid-filled inclusions in low U, Th refractory peridotite for helium, and by sea-water infiltration for the heavier gases. This would mean that the 'undegassed deep reservoir' of the standard model is actually a 'regassed shallow' layer, not in the least bit 'primordial' (Anderson 1998*c*).

Helium is an incompatible element (meaning that it prefers the magma to the crystal as do U and Th). However, He degasses from magma, along with CO_2 at shallow depth (~60 km), while U and Th (the parents of ^{4}He) are carried to the surface in the magma. Once degassed, CO_2 and He are trapped in crystals and fluid-filled inclusions, and cannot reach the surface except in another magma or via a deep crack. At shallow depths in the mantle, therefore, helium behaves partly as a compatible element (it is removed from the magma by the crystal) and may therefore behave as the noble metals (e.g. Os) giving

He–Os correlations that are unexpected in the standard story. *The nobles reside in crystal palaces.*

The low He/Ne, He/Ar, etc. ratios of midplate volcanoes are a natural result of the high solubility of He, relative to heavier gases, in magmas. Degassed MORB should have high ratios, as observed, while the vesicles in MORB, the possible source of hotspot gases, should have low ratios. Noble gases in so-called hotspot magmas and xenoliths, which have been attributed to ^{3}He excess from a 'deep undegassed primordial reservoir', may, in fact, be due to ^{4}He deficit and may come from a shallow, regassed, secondary, refractory reservoir. If so, ^{3}He joins the long list of elements and isotopes in 'hotspot' or 'plume' magmas which have a near-surface source. How can a hypothesis survive so many paradoxes? Read on.

Consistency and procrustean science

A foolish consistency is the hobgoblin of little minds.

Ralph Waldo Emerson

Sometimes an idea is so seductive that it is immune to new data. The deep mantle plume hypothesis of Jason Morgan (1972) was a simple, elegant idea and it was formulated in a way that made it testable and falsifiable; i.e. it was a good scientific hypothesis. The very specific predictions about plume strength, plume flux and plume heat flow have been shown to be wrong by large factors, but it is still a seductive concept. The fixity of hotspots was one of the reasons that a deep source was favoured, but hotspots are not more fixed than ridges and trenches (Kaula 1975). Once it was established that hotspots move relative to one another, or, to look at the situation in a different way, that the ends of oceanic island chains do not define a fixed reference system, statements appeared in the literature that said that it was a good thing that hotspots moved, because plumes in a convecting mantle should be swept around. There are many examples of procrustean science in the standard model.

Some early geochemical studies of continental flood basalts and ocean island basalts detected isotopic components similar to chondritic meteorites. Since this chemistry differed radically from midocean ridge basalts, it was proposed that the original layers of the Earth, the *prima facies*, still resided in the lower mantle, beyond the reach of the 'convecting mantle'. Periodically, a narrow plume of this material, a modern ichor, rises to form oceanic islands and to break up continents.

Subsequent studies showed that the main components in non-MORB magmas are similar to oceanic crust, sediments, continental crust and various metasomatic fluids. These kinds of components used to be called 'continental contamination', 'wall rock reaction', 'assimilation', 'metasomatism' and so on, implying a near-surface origin. However, the deep mantle source story survived, being amended to include recycling of surface materials to the deep mantle and rebirth as a plume. The chemistry changed but the fluid dynamic and *profound* geometric conclusions remained.

The main argument for putting the MORB reservoir into the upper mantle (the 'depleted convecting mantle') was that MORB was thought to be a common component of all hotspot magmas; it must therefore be above all the other mantle reservoirs. Therefore, hotspots must originate in the deep mantle. Many isotopic systems are now available to characterize 'hotspot' magmas and it has been found that MORB is not a common component. Island geochemistry converges on a field which is intermediate to identified endmember components (pelagic sediment, continental sediment, altered oceanic crust, depleted mantle; the so-called EM1, EM2, HIMU and DM components). This has been called FOZO (focal zone), PHEM (primitive helium mantle) and C (common) (Farley *et al.* 1992; Hanan & Graham 1996). It might better be called Q for quintessential, the fifth and required component. This common component has been attributed to a deep layer, *because it is a common component*, and must therefore be brought into the shallow mantle by plumes (Hannan & Graham 1996). There is a remarkable consistency to the conclusion about the location of the OIB reservoir, or components, which has survived a reversal of the data.

Many CFB and OIB evolve toward a MORB-like composition with time and this seems to imply that the non-MORB components are shallow and exhaustible. This is the *perisphere* model (Anderson 1998*a*,*c*). OIB-like components occur in the initial volcanics of many different tectonic provinces, again favouring a shallow and widespread source.

These examples of the persistence of a model regardless of the data have provided us with the Hacker Theorem:

> Contrary to received opinion a theory ... is not normally rejected merely because it is falsified ... falsifications and discovery of counter-examples and exceptions merely spur one on to greater ingenuity either in modifying the theory to accommodate the nuisance or in showing that the apparent counter-example can be explained away. If worst comes to worst, it can be entered in the ledger as a debt to be repaid in the future, and then conveniently shelved. (Hacker 1972.)

Bacon, Kuhn and Popper

Francis Bacon in his *Novum Organum* anticipated Karl Popper's idea of falsification by three centuries. He noted that a peculiar and perpetual error of the human intellect is to be 'more moved and excited by affirmatives than by negatives; whereas it ought properly to hold itself indifferently disposed towards both alike. Indeed in the establishment of any true axiom, the negative instance is the more forcible of the two.' As Karl Popper has shown, one can never prove that the Sun will rise, no matter how often it does so. Nor can the chicken ever be sure that the hand that feeds it will always do so, even though its neck has never been wrung before. Yet one negative example can serve to falsify an idea.

Sometimes an idea hangs on, not because it is good, or even seductive, but because it has been around a long time, or constantly repeated. If one wants to verify something written in the newspaper, should one buy 100 more copies of the paper to check it?

Again, Bacon anticipated the modern ideas of philosophers of science, this time Thomas Kuhn and his paradigm. Bacon observed 'The human understanding, when it has once adopted an opinion ... draws all things else to support and agree with it. And though there be a greater number and weight of instances to be found on the other side, yet these it either neglects and despises, or else by some distinction sets aside and rejects; in order that by this great and pernicious predetermination, the authority of its former conclusions may remain inviolate ... the first conclusion colors and brings, into conformity with itself all that come after, though far sounder and better.'

According to Karl Popper, for a statement to be scientific, it must be falsifiable. There must be some set of conceivable circumstances that, if they existed, would prove a theory false. Popper insisted that scientists must accept falsification. To immunize their ideas against refutations of their predictions is to abandon the methodology of science for nonscience, and metaphysical dreams. A theory is nonscientific if it is compatible with everything that could happen. 'Just-so' stories and myths have an explanation for everything. A theory can explain too much; it can be too good to be true. No matter what is found, it 'is consistent' with the theory.

Consistency and immunization

> It is only after you have come to know the surface of things that you can venture to seek what is underneath. ... The surface is already so vast and rich and various that it more than suffices to saturate the mind with information and meanings.
>
> Italo Calvino

One of the reasons why deep mantle plumes were invented was to bring primitive or enriched material through the depleted (MORB) upper mantle in order to fuel ocean islands. Otherwise, only MORB would be available (the *modus moron* fallacy and the old belief that MORB was a common component in all basalts).

In the perisphere model (Anderson 1996), all of the distinctive geochemical traits of ocean island basalts are in the crust and shallow mantle. Seawater, sediments, crust and lithosphere, of course, are at the top of the system and are available as contaminants. Volatile and incompatible elements, added to the plate while it is awaiting subduction, are delivered to the shallow mantle by slabs; only a fraction of this is returned to the destructive margin volcanoes above the slab. Degassing magmas and trapped melts add more material to the shallow mantle, some of it to the buoyant refractory products of previous magmatism. The upper mantle has a stratigraphy controlled by relative buoyancy, chemistry, melting point, temperature and prior history; it is the dross of mantle and crustal evolution. Some of this material is refractory, strong and dry and is called *lithosphere*. Some of this is weak and is called *asthenosphere* or *perisphere*. Some of it eventually gets dense enough to sink into the mantle. Some of it is permanently buoyant and stays near the top. OIB-like volcanic material is widespread. It occurs at new rifts and at subduction zones. It appears to come from a shallow cosmopolitan layer (Anderson 1998*a*), not from a point source of pollution.

The fertile MORB reservoir is probably below the dehydration front of subducting slabs, thereby retaining its purity and homogeneity. It does not appear at the onset of rifting, because of its depth and the intervention of enriched material, but appears when the shallow material has been removed into continental flood basalts, rift magmas, or by plate divergence. The shallow mantle, *perisphere*, is refreshed by subduction and depleted by magmatism. The distinctive geochemical signatures of 'midplate' volcanics are acquired in the crust and the shallow mantle, the sources and sinks of recycled material.

In contrast, the plume hypothesis invokes deep recycling, through the MORB reservoir, to the core–mantle boundary, where it is reheated, born again as a plume, rises through the MORB mantle and provides a point source of pollution for the shallow mantle. The widespread occurrence of enriched and recycled material is explained by flattened plume heads, fossil plume heads, large distance lateral transport, and contamination by previous plumes, sampled by later plumes (Chauvel *et al.* 1997; Hart *et al.* 1997). Plume influence in current papers is so widespread that one can no longer view the entire upper mantle, up to the base of the lithosphere, as the MORB reservoir. Thus, the plume hypothesis is self-defeating. If there is a widespread enriched shallow mantle then there is no need for a deep source, or any need for deep recycling. And the passive explanation for MORB is lost.

> Everything that is needed for OIB and CFB exists in the shallow part of the Earth. In addition, it was formed near the surface of the Earth.

Passive rifting allows melts from an already partially molten, already enriched shallow mantle to rise to the surface. Ponded melts at the base of the lithosphere may be responsible for the transient bursts of magmas that we call '*large igneous provinces*'.

Simplicity

> What can be done with fewer [assumptions] is done in vain with more.
>
> William of Ockham

William of Ockham, or as he would have preferred, Bill Ocm, is responsible for Occams Razor, the principle of parsimony. He was an Oxford don, a Franciscan, a philosopher, and a believer in simplicity. It is no surprise that he was charged with heresy.

In the plate theory, lithospheric architecture and motions cause advective currents in the hot underlying mantle. When cracks form, volcanoes or chains of volcanoes result. Cracks usually open from one end so time progressive volcanism ensues, feeding on the shallow enriched mantle. Compression closes up cracks and shuts off volcanism; continued extension evolves to oceanic ridges and a deeper source. Volcanoes of the third kind feed on shallow mantle, on the debris of plate tectonics, on a universal enriched layer below the plate.

In the original plume theory, the shallowest mantle is the deleted MORB mantle; hot mantle and undegassed primordial mantle are imported from depth. Plumes are narrow, hot and non-MORB. This was a simple, elegant, testable theory. It is no longer so.

Several examples of ongoing modifications (or, to use Popper's term, 'immunization') to the plume paradigm can be seen in a single issue of the *Journal of Chemical Geology* (Volume 139). Hart *et a*l. (1997) propose that volcanism in the West Antarctic rift system is due to present-day rifting but the shallow material tapped was emplaced under Gondwana lithosphere prior to breakup, without doming or volcanism at the time, by a large weak plume head. This 'fossil-plume' proto-lithosphere is now being sampled by passive rifting. This 'pre-volcanism', however, is part of an enormous arcuate belt extending from South America to New Zealand, a distance of 80°, parallel to a long-lived subduction boundary. The composition of the basalts in this belt are more compatible with subduction, rather than a plume source (Duncan *et al.* 1997). Plumes are invoked because of the chemical similarity of some of the basalts with OIB, where 'plumes are the reigning paradigm'. In order to explain the widespread nature of volcanism one needs multiple plumes or giant plume heads to underplate large areas of lithosphere, parallel to and above the subducting slabs, without deformation or magmatism. A long incubation period is then proposed, with the geochemistry of the underplated plume head changing with time. To explain the various volcanic products a heterogeneous two-component plume is invoked, with different solidus temperature for the two components. The laminated plume causes a stratified shallow mantle as the plume head is flattened. In order to explain the observations, the temperature gradient in the flattened plume head is assumed to parallel the solidus. The absence of uplift at the time of plume head emplacement is unexplained.

This complex scenario with its many *ad hoc* elements can be completely avoided by recognizing the proximity of subduction zones, the buoyancy of subducted products of dehydration and the likely existence of an enriched shallow mantle prior to subduction (Anderson 1996). The observations are consistent with a ubiquitous enriched shallow layer, and with volcanism progressively tapping deep mantle, as in the perisphere model. The view that the shallow mantle must be MORB-like unless deep mantle plumes are brought into it is the fallacy that drives complexities in recent plume models.

The Karoo volcanic province was once thought to define a circle about 2000 km in diameter and this was taken as evidence for a plume head origin. It is now clear that it is just part of an enormous elliptical province, 9000 km in length, traversing Gondwana from one end to the other and now called the Karoo–Ferrar province. The circular plume head idea has been falsified and the geochemical evidence favours alternative models but the immunized plume theory accepts these observations as allowable properties of plumes, since this is what happened (any theory of Earth is correct, since Earth exists). Similarly, the hottest basalts (picrites) in the Iceland province, which should be the center of the plume, are not plume-like in chemistry (primitive or enriched signatures) as predicted, but are MORB-like. This obvious falsification of the plume hypothesis has been turned into a new class of plume – 'depleted plumes'.

Along a similar line, Chauvel *et al.* (1997) discuss volcanism in the Austral chain This is a long linear volcanic chain in the South Pacific with no obvious age progression. By splitting the island population into three groups, three linear age–distance lines can be drawn. The conjecture then is that three co-linear plumes have been responsible for the volcanism, with some islands being utilized several times by different plumes. The earlier plumes contaminated the lithosphere so that later volcanoes gave signatures not of the current plume but of the earlier, now distant, plume. Why plumes should line up along the same track is not addressed. These unexpected and unpredicted observations would falsify a true scientific theory. The observations are consistent with a propagating crack or leaky transform fault model and with stress control of volcanism. There are other island chains that do not define a line, or track, or do not have an age progression (Galapagos, Azores, Cameroons, Musicians, Gulf of Alaska). By picking a few of the islands that do form a trend, and ignoring the others, or by invoking two or more plumes one can define age-progressive volcanism and can immunize the plume hypothesis against falsification.

Bathymetric maps (Smith & Sandwell 1994) show an extensive fabric in the ocean basins. Many island chains are along trends of fracture zones and some may be leaky transform faults. The microplates in the South Pacific (Easter, Juan Fernandez), along the fastest-spreading ridge on Earth, spawn a whole series of islands, seamounts and linear features. Volcanism along these trends may reflect the stress state of the lithosphere modulated by pre-existing fabric formed at the East Pacific Rise (EPR). The lack of a midocean ridge basalt component in magmas at these tensile features should be no surprise; the volumes of melts are low and the depths of melting are shallow. The long-lived and fast-spreading EPR can tap the deeper MORB level.

The long-distance transport between hotspots and various igneous provinces, often invoked to rationalize geochemical similarities between distant volcanics (e.g. Cape Verde to the Bohemian massif) is similar to the old land-bridge idea invoked by early anti-drifters to rationalize faunal similarities between continents or islands.

Recently it has been found that basalts similar to Hawaiian basalts are found 5000 km away on the East Pacific Rise (EPR) (Niu *et al.* 1996). Flow from the Hawaiian plume toward the EPR was proposed (more akin to a tunnel than a bridge!). Ironically, the component found was initially proposed as a plume component in Hawaii because, unlike other components, it had never been found on a ridge. Oyarzu *et al.* (1997) propose that basalts in Bohemia are due to plume channelling from the Cape Verde plume, 4000 km away. A widespread shallow enriched layer, perisphere, common in all tectonic environments but rare at mature ridges, where it is swept away, is the more reasonable explanation. The concepts of *fossil plume heads*, *incubating plumes*, *multiple plumes*, *plume contamination*, *plume channeling,* etc. were all devised to overcome the paradox resulting from the *modus moron* fallacy of the composition of the shallow mantle. In fact, the shallow mantle almost everywhere is contaminated by subduction, slab-derived fluids, and trapped melts and is suitable in composition for the various components in so-called hotspot magmas. There is no evidence that this material is carried into the deep mantle with the bulk of the slab.

> It is remarkable how far people may be carried in the study of a science, even when an hypothesis turns everything upside-down, but there comes a point ... where one cannot escape an anomaly, and the theory has to be tucked and folded, pushed and pinched, in order to make it conform with the observed facts. (Butterfield 1957.)

Active versus passive

Ridges are considered *passive* because, as they separate, magma flows up passively to fill the crack. Plate tectonics plays the active role; thickening plates are pulled apart or pull themselves apart.

Ocean island volcanoes are considered *active*, the result of buoyant hot jets in the mantle. Since the magma differs from MORB the source must be deep (this sentence, so far, is a fallacy).

If the upper mantle is molten almost everywhere, as implied by seismic velocities, heat flow and petrology, then extension of the plate, or opening of cracks may also result in *passive* volcanism. Melts migrate freely under inferred conditions in a mantle in a state of incipient melting and collect at levels of neutral buoyancy, or impermeability, such as the base of the crust or lithosphere. A new crack can drain the accumulated melt, or magma chamber; a transient event often ascribed to the introduction of new hot material into the shallow mantle or a hot *active* jet. Large igneous events (LIP) may simply be the starting transient event associated with plate extension. Volcanoes are sensitive strain gauges.

The largest flow rates implied for mantle magmatism, using the densities of magmas or the heights of volcanoes as gauges of the driving hydrostatic head, can be achieved with basaltic magmas flowing through 1 cm wide cracks (Spence & Turcotte 1990). If the crack is brand new, and cold, the crack needs to be 1 m wide to keep the magma from freezing. Magma chambers at the base of the lithosphere are deep enough to build the tallest volcano. Cracks do not open, and magma does not erupt, when the lithosphere is under compression. Deep mantle sources are not required to build high volcanoes.

The volumes of the largest lava outpourings (Ontong Java plateau, Shatsky Rise, Siberian flood basalts, etc.) represent only 1 per cent of the upper mantle if they drain an area three times the surface area. Since large igneous provinces occur at lithospheric discontinuities, new ridges, and triple junctions, the passive upwelling will be focused towards the thinnest or extending lithosphere, or towards lithospheric boundaries (fracture zones, sutures). The initial magma (the transient event) will, of course, be biased towards the shallow mantle material. As rifting evolves to drifting, the deeper mantle (say, 100–200 km) becomes involved and the magmas become less enriched. If the upper mantle were to be able to produce only MORB and if it were not near the melting point, then a deeper, hotter material and narrow jets may be needed, but this is a different world. A deep or narrow plume is not required to provide the volumes of magmas or rates of magmatism observed in large igneous provinces.

What limits the size of a volcano?

> On our Earth we are obviously much too small to clean out our volcanoes. That is why they bring no end of trouble upon us.
>
> The Little Prince

Athanasius Kircher (1601–1680) thought about developing a machine for cleaning out the chimneys of volcanoes to prevent them from erupting. Antoine de Saint-Exupéry's *Little Prince* had a similar idea.

The heights of volcanoes on oceanic plates vary as the square root of age of the underlying lithosphere (Vogt 1974), and, therefore, with the depth of the ultimate magma source. The highest volcanoes on Earth are in the Hawaiian chain and are on old oceanic lithosphere, with inferred magma chambers as deep as 60 km. This depth is appropriate for the height of the volcano. Most midplate volcanoes are on much younger lithosphere and most, in fact, are on or near oceanic ridges, or were on ridges not too long ago. Most volcanic chains started at spreading ridges and sometimes they migrated gradually into plate interiors and older, colder plate. Often the chains are built along pre-existing features, ridges and fracture zones. Often a volcanic chain (e.g. Emperors) stops at a fracture zone.

The prerequisites for volcanoes are a source of magma and an extensile stress which allows cracks to open to allow access of magma to the surface. Most volcanoes are built on faults, sutures and pre-existing weak zones or lithospheric boundaries, so extensional stresses do not need to be large enough to break virgin rock. Once a crack is open, and wide enough, the low viscosity of magma and the lithostatic stress are adequate to allow magma to flow at the highest observed rates. The building of a volcano is a self-limiting process. As the edifice grows, lithostatic and compressional stresses grow. It becomes harder to open cracks and to elevate magma to the summit. The load depresses the plate, causing extensional stresses radial and circumferential to the volcanic load. The presence of previous volcanoes and a regional stress field introduce asymmetry; radiating dykes provide good maps of the stress field. At some point it is easier to divert magmas to new cracks and to start new volcanoes than to pay the energy cost of building a higher volcano through the older conduit system. The new volcano buttresses the old, closing off conduits, but itself has unbuttressed flanks to allow conduit opening. Magma from the mantle migrates and ponds away from the regions of depressed lithosphere, robbing the older volcanoes to feed the young. Thus, volcanic growth is self-limiting and volcanic chains are self-propagating. Volcanic chains may indicate the orientation of the stress field, rather than the migration direction of the plate. The abrupt changes in direction, speed and productivity of the Hawaiian chain simply reflect changes in stress and a complex feedback between construction, erosion, lithospheric cracking and volcanic buttressing (Jackson & Shaw 1975). Magma being bouyant, can actually fracture the overlying plate, unless it is under compression.

The alternative view of midplate volcanism focuses on the fluid dynamics of the underlying mantle. Narrow jets (plumes) of hot mantle from the lower mantle focus on a region of the lithosphere, heating it, uplifting it and ultimately penetrating it to form a volcano. As the plate moves over the jet, the volcano moves off the source of magma and a new volcano forms. The size of a volcano is controlled by the dimension of the jet and how fast material is flowing up it. The lithosphere is passively responding to the active upwelling beneath it. The relationships between the locations of hotspots and elevations of volcanoes with lithospheric age are unexplained. The associations of volcanoes with plate and lithospheric boundaries are accidental.

Kircher and the Little Prince had definite ideas about the physics of volcanoes. In the plume hypothesis, it doesn't matter whether one cleans out one's volcanoes or not; if the volcano drifts out of range of the hot jet, it will become extinct (this is the original version of the plume hypothesis and the one that is used to explain extinct volcanoes in oceanic chains; however, if volcanoes continue to erupt for tens of millions of years after drifting off the plume, or if there is magmatism 5000 km away from the hot 'spot', then this is okay too, because this is the way it is, and the volcanoes are there to prove it).

In the alternative theory, since the shallow mantle is close to the melting point everywhere, if one cleans out one's volcanoes, one can keep them erupting. To be conservative, one can assume that the mantle temperature plays some role and that the temperature of the mantle must be above the average temperature in order to be above the melting point. Now subduction serves to cool the mantle and about half of the mantle has been so cooled since the breakup of Pangea. Almost all volcanoes of the third kind are in mantle not cooled by subduction. In fact, almost all oceanic ridges are also above such uncooled mantle. According to the plate theory, volcanoes will not exist if the shell is under compression. Rocks fail easily in extension and volcanoes prefer crust that is not under compression, even if not actively extending. When Africa goes into extension there is widespread volcanism; when it goes into compression the magmatism ceases (Bailey 1992). In this kind of world, if one keeps one's volcanoes cleaned out one can keep an eruption going; one does not drift off from a molten jet. If one can keep an open crack through the lithosphere, one has a continuous supply of magma. If one cannot do this, a volcano eventually shuts itself off but by bowing down the lithosphere it makes new cracks and new slopes on the plate bottom for the magma to drain towards. Isostasy makes an inverse island in the asthenosphere under the volcano and the surrounding inverse moat is the new source of tensile cracks and magma.

The spigot method

Hacker (1972) pointed out that those who thirst for knowledge will not discard their only cup just because it is cracked. Before worst comes to worst and the coincidences and paradoxes must be hidden away in a semantic underbrush, there is always the spigot method.

Herb Shaw (1994) describes this method, attributing it to Walderman Lindgren (1860–1939). Whenever a particular magma appeared or changed in character all one had to do was to open or close the appropriate (expedient) spigot at an appropriate (expedient) time from appropriate (expedient) source. This method has many similarities to creation myths and just-so stories. The literature of continental flood basalts, oceanic island chains, and hotspots is also similar. The plume glossary now includes incubating *plumes, starting plumes, super plumes, fossil plumes, plume heads, plume families, depleted plumes, plumelets, deflected plumes, passive plumes, cavity plumes, lateral plume flux, immature plumes, 'real' plumes, thermal plumes, chemical plumes*, and so on. In the South Pacific, there are several island chains that have been attributed to successive plumes feeding the same volcanoes. Plumes, in many respects, are like spigots turning on and off as needed to explain variations in magma flux and chemistry at oceanic islands. Variations in lithospheric stress, due to plate tectonic and local volcanic loads, provide an attractive alternative hypothesis to the many variants of plumes.

A partially molten upper mantle, variable in chemistry, temperature, volatile content and melting point, driven by lithospheric motions, focused by lithospheric architecture towards extending regions and opportunistically invading narrow cracks, which can evolve to rifting and drifting, provides a coherent global view of magmatism to replace the local just-so stories for each volcano. The Earth may be a top-down system.

Upside down or downside up?

Humpty Dumpty took the book, and looked at it carefully.
'That seems to be done right' he began.
'You're holding it upside down!' Alice interrupted.

Lewis Carroll

Volcanoes are the way that the mantle gets rid of its heat and some of its magma. The question is, are the sizes and locations of volcanoes a reflection of the vigor of mantle convection and the locations of upwelling jets, or a reflection of the stress state of the lithosphere? Are volcanic chains speedometers or piezometers? Are volcanic chains controlled by the bottom of the mantle (plume model) or the top (geology)?

The most serious perturbations to mantle flow are subduction of cold slabs, upwelling induced by spreading, and the cold fingers of Archean cratons (archons). Plates thicken as they age and pull themselves toward the consuming trenches, dragging the underlying mantle along. Mantle upwells to fill the gaps, melting or melting more as they do. Slab dehydration fluxes the mantle wedge, inducing melting and vigorous upward flow. Ridges and trenches annihilate, creating tension and cracks and extrusion.

The plates have a complex architecture which places a template atop the hot mantle. Which is the master and which is the servant? Does the hot low-viscosity mantle fluid respond passively to the overlying boundary condition or vice versa? This is the most important question facing deep Earth scientists today, but few of them are addressing both the surface and the interior of the system. Convection modellers often assume a uniform idealized boundary condition (no plates, no cracks, no continents, no geology), while top-down Earth dynamicists are comfortable with ridge push, slab pull, trench suction and plate drag as explanations for most observations including plate motions, stresses, mountain building and so on. Verhoogen (1973) argued strongly for a surface template effect. It does seem true that the lithosphere controls the locations of heat and magma escape and, to some extent, the planform of mantle convection. Focusing at continental margins helps explain the volumes of magma that otherwise seem to require high temperatures or plumes (Skogseid *et al.* 1992; King & Anderson 1995).

There are so many things that are controlled or modulated by the surface architecture that one wonders what are the features that demand a deep source. The volumes and rates and chemistry of midplate magmatism do not require deep or abnormal temperature conditions. In a homogeneous fluid, heated from below with no phase changes, no variation in properties, and with an isothermal homogeneous surface, the first features to develop are thermal instabilities in the bottom thermal boundary layer. As these rise they set up the horizontal temperature gradients that are essential for transporting heat and material by thermal convection. If the heating is not enough, or if the vertical temperature gradient is not high enough, there will be no motion. The Rayleigh number must be high enough so that the accidental and random small disturbances at the bottom can grow. This is the sort of picture that many mantle convection modellers have in mind.

When there are lateral temperature gradients or non-uniform conditions at the top of the system, it can be viewed as being differentially cooled from above. There is no minimum temperature gradient or critical Rayleigh number. The horizontal temperature gradients required for convection exist naturally; they are not a secondary result of perturbations in the lower boundary layer. The real Earth is characterized by narrow cold downwellings (slabs) and downward-protruding cold fingers (craton roots). Downwellings occur in these places; upwellings occur elsewhere, particularly at spreading ridges and extending continents. Upwelling mantle is focused toward thin lithosphere, or lithosphere under extension, because this is where heat can most easily be transported to the surface. The mantle *is* convecting, and some upwellings are caused by internal lower mantle and core heating. These are strongly modulated by plate tectonic and lithospheric structure. The question is, do narrow upwellings, carrying heat from the core, rise up to the surface, more or less unaffected by plate tectonics and 'normal' mantle convection, the plume paradigm? And what are the phenomena that require this sort of explanation? A related question is whether plate tectonic stresses–stresses due to lithospheric inhomogeneities, slab pull, ridge push, etc.–exceed convective stresses imposed from below? Are stresses other than those imposed by body forces in the plate and the sinking slab required to crack the plate and allow magmas to escape? Does the lower boundary layer drive the plates and break up continents? Sherlock Holmes has some advice: 'when you have eliminated the impossible, whatever remains, however improbable, must be the truth'.

Temperatures in the mantle

It has been believed for millennia, suspected for centuries, known for decades and forgotten for years that temperatures not too far below the crust are conducive to melting. The low-velocity zone (LVZ) of the upper mantle demands the presence of small amounts of melt (Anderson & Sammis 1970). The upper mantle, almost everywhere, is at or near the melting point. While dry, refractory rocks may avoid the melting point, 'normal' mantle rocks containing moisture or K_2O need extraordinary circumstances in order to avoid melting when exposed to normal mantle geotherms. In the upper 200 km, only subcratonic mantle and the interiors of cold slabs are possibly subsolidus (Anderson & Bass 1984). A small amount of melt, suitably arranged, has an enormous effect on seismic velocity and electrical conductivity. Decreases in seismic velocity and seismic quality factor set in at temperatures well below the ability of a petrologist to quench and detect melt. Thus, geophysicists can detect incipient melting under conditions that petrologists would call 'subsolidus' or 'weakening upon approach to the melting temperature'. Because of the mismatch in the abilities to detect melting, the oxymoron 'subsolidus melting' has been coined.

Even in the coldest parts of the mantle, seismologists have inferred the presence of melt zones (Bostock & Cassidy 1997). Under some cratons the temperature is inferred to be on the adiabat and is possibly truly subsolidus, but if the thick cratonic lithosphere were to be removed adiabatic ascent would quickly lead to partial melting (Anderson & Bass 1984). The upper mantle appears to be buffered at its melting temperature and the LVZ and the asthenosphere can be described as in a state of *incipient melting*. One of the modern myths of petrology is that melting can occur only where the mantle is abnormally hot ('hotspots') or where the lithosphere is stretched and thinned, so that mantle can melt upon adiabatic ascent. Usually, a dry mantle is assumed; H_2O and K_2O lower the melting point by hundreds of degrees, making it difficult to avoid melting except in regions that have effectively lost their melts and volatiles (such as the roots of Archean cratons; Polet & Anderson 1995). There is therefore no need to import heat from the core–mantle boundary, or to thin the plate, in order to cause melting. It is necessary to extend or crack the plate in order to allow egress. The lithospheric lid, when under compression, effectively keeps the magma down.

Half of the Earth's upper mantle is hotter than average (hopefully, no reference is needed). Most of the Earth's ridges and active oceanic volcanoes are in this half of the Earth, which also corresponds to that part of the mantle which has not been cooled by the integrated effects of subduction (Ray & Anderson 1994; Scrivner & Anderson 1992; Anderson 1996). It is likely that the lithosphere is under extension in at least some of these regions. The normal variations of mantle temperature, due to plate tectonics (continental insulation, subduction cooling, small-scale flow) are about 100°C (Anderson 1996) and the variations of melting temperature (due to subduction refluxing, melt extraction, density stratification, fertility) are about the same. The magmatic response to extrusion opportunities provided by the LID (the region of high seismic velocity above the low-velocity zone) therefore can vary widely. In addition, lithospheric architecture provides opportunities for magma focusing and ponding (inverse magma lakes) which are ignored in hypotheses that relate all excess magmatism to excess temperature. These hypotheses generally assume a one-dimensional Earth.

The most important controls on locations and extents of giant outpourings of basalt, however, are lithospheric architecture and stress, and the prior history of the underlying mantle. The initial or transient response of magmas in the mantle is quite different from the later steady-state response.

The helium paradoxes

Yes, many things there are, which seem to be
Perplexing, although quite falsely so, because
They have good reasons which we cannot see.

Virgil

G. K. Gilbert, as well as Sherlock Holmes, was an advocate of multiple working hypotheses. Research is an unending process of generating and testing hypotheses. Sometimes, only two hypotheses are necessary. Consider the $^3He/^4He$ ratio which we discussed earlier. Some basalts, such as those from Loihi seamount, on the south flank of Mauna Loa, have ratios 'significantly' higher than the average for MORB. There are only two hypotheses to be tested; Loihi (and other 'hotspot' basalts) has either higher ^3He or lower ^4He than MORB. Of course, some MORBs have higher than average ratios. If the ratios in MORB get too high they are redefined as being under the influence (of plumes) and are not included in the average. This is an example of *immunization.*

Part of the uniformity of MORB is due to the large degree of melting, and the large volume of melting that is required to form tholeiites at the rate needed for spreading ridges. Higher and lower ratios are blended in the melting process, and the small domains with extreme values are lost in the process. Large scale melting is likely to be a better explanation for MORB homogeneity than the 'convecting mantle' explanation usually offered (assuming that convection equals stirring or blending). A MORB source deeper than the dehydration front of subducting slabs is another cause of the depleted, uniform nature of MORB.

Some ocean island basalts and xenoliths have $^3He/^4He$ ratios much higher than the MORB average, some as high as three times those of MORB. Usually the high $^3He/^4He$ materials are small samples (xenoliths, small degree melts) and low $^3He/^4He$ materials occur nearby or in a later eruption. Average values over whole islands or over long periods of time are usually close to MORB values. Sometimes, the only evidence for the existence of a plume is a geochemical ratio that exceeds the average for MORB. This can be called the Eisenhower fallacy.

It is simple to show that the hypothetical 'primordial undegassed reservoir', which in the standard model is most of the Earth (i.e. the lower mantle), must have about the same volatile content as chondritic meteorites.

This is a paradox, since volatile elements in the Earth are depleted by one or two orders of magnitude compared with chondrites (Anderson 1989, 1998*b*) and this depletion is consistent with theories of Earth accretion. High $^3He/^4He$ ratio basalts, in fact, are depleted in helium by about two orders of magnitude compared with MORB (inferred in this model to come from the 'degassed depleted upper mantle reservoir'). This is another helium paradox. The atmosphere contains very little helium but quite a bit of neon and argon. High $^3He/^4He$ basalts (those inferred to have 'excess ^3He') also exhibit extreme atmospheric (or seawater) contamination in Ne and Ar; yet another paradox (Anderson 1998*b*,*c*).

As paradoxes accumulate one should look for another paradigm or at least another hypothesis. In this case, the solution is obvious. High R may imply low ^4He. Low ^4He in turn implies low U and Th. Magmas are high in U and Th and their gases are high in CO_2 and noble gases. Gas/magma separation separates daughters (^4He) from parents (U, Th) and gases can be stored in crystals; i.e. cumulates in magma chambers. Fluid-filled inclusions in refractory lithosphere (harzburgite) contain the gases; the crust contains the U and Th.

Here is where we have paid a terrible price for semantics. By labelling the source of high $^3He/^4He$ magmas as 'undegassed', 'primordial' and 'lower mantle' because of the assumption of excess 3He, we have missed the 'regassed', 'shallow' and 'secondary' reservoir that is right below our feet!

The helium–heat flow paradox implies that substantial helium is stored in the mantle, rather than outgassed with the magma. The carrier of helium is CO_2, and storage of CO_2 in the shallow mantle is consistent with the missing CO_2 in the exosphere and the abundance of carbonatitic metasomatism in the continental and oceanic lithosphere.

The lower mantle appears to be devoid of heat-producing elements (Birch 1965; Patterson & Tatsumoto 1964; Anderson 1989). Those who speak confidently of a 'primordial undegassed lower mantle' as a source for OIB have swept under the rug, or put on the shelf, the data that falsify this hypothesis.

> I mean by 'impenetrability' that we've had enough of that subject, and it would be just as well if you would mention what you mean to do next, as I suppose you don't mean to stop here all the rest of your life.
>
> Humpty Dumpty

Coincidences

Why, sometimes I've believed as many as six impossible things before breakfast.

The White Queen

Sometimes a hypothesis is suspect if one must believe too many coincidences. All of the world's continental flood basalts are on the edges of Archean cratons. Since both CFB and archons occupy a trivial area, the odds that they are accidentally related are enormous. The standard model explanation for CFB is the arrival of a plume head from a thermal boundary layer at the core–mantle boundary.

Consider the Deccan Traps, a prominent much discussed CFB, one of the largest volcanic provinces on Earth. The Narmada-Son lineament marks the suture between two archons, at the ends of which are the Deccan and Rajmahal Traps. The Deccan Traps formed at the intersection of the Narmada, Tapti and Cambay Rifts and the West Coast Fault, near the newly formed continental margin of India. India had rifted from the Madagascar margin some 25 Ma earlier and was moving rapidly across the Indian Ocean at the time of the emplacement of the Deccan basalts. India was just making contact with Asia at the time (Rowley 1996). The whole Indian Ocean is underlain by hot mantle, the result of absence of subduction cooling. There are few active volcanoes ('hotspots') on the Indian plate today, because it is under compression (ridge push from the south and continent–continent collision to the north). When India first contacted Asia, however, an irregular boundary plus plate flexure could have caused tensile stresses at the Narmada suture. Equally complex geological histories occur at other large igneous provinces, usually involving subduction, changes in plate motions, sutures, archons or slab windows. A core–mantle boundary explanation seems more improbable than a near-surface explanation. The edge of an archon represents one of the most profound changes in lithospheric thickness and is a natural place for both stress concentration and magma focusing.

The number of geological structures near Yellowstone and the Columbia River Basalts (CRB) (archon, Rocky Mountains, Basin and Range, Idaho batholith, Cascades, ancestral Cascades) and the number of things happening at the time of emplacement of the CRB (triple junction migration, ridge–trench collision, western North American magmatism, slab-window formation and major extension) would challenge even the White Queen if a plume came up at this time and this place. The CRB is the only large igneous province (LIP) in western North, Central and South America and is near the only Archean craton in these areas. Yellowstone is the only certified 'hotspot' in the western Americas, and is adjacent to the only archon. Any magma in the mantle under the Wyoming craton will certainly drain toward the general vicinity of Yellowstone and the high lava plains. The Pacific Northwest of the USA is probably just now being torn off by the Pacific plate; old sutures and craton boundaries (dotted lines on many maps) are the likely places to tear.

A geological and tectonic prehistory can also be built up for the Siberian, the Keweenawan, the Parana, the Karoo and all other LIPs. The common thread is not the existence of a hotspot track but the emplacement at the edge of an archon at a time when the continent was thrown into extension by processes that are the natural culmination of plate motions (ridge–trench annihilation, slab-window formation, accretion of continental blocks, trench rollback, etc.).

Geologists were slow to recognize the importance of objects falling out of the sky. The early proponents of extraterrestrial (ET) impacts were viewed as Chicken Licken's; 'The sky is falling!' The plume and impact ideas are similar, differing mainly in the source–the deep interior or deep space. Geologists of all persuasions have seized on the plume concept much more readily than on ET invasions.

Summary

The plume hypothesis attempts to explain upper mantle heterogeneities as arising from the deep mantle, ascending through narrow plumes and dispersing radially when they encounter the lithosphere. Plumes serve as point sources of pollution in what is assumed to be an otherwise homogeneous, depleted upper mantle. Although plumes were initially invoked to tap primitive mantle, it is now clear that all of the material attributed to plumes can be found at the surface of the Earth. It was certainly formed there. The various components in plumes include oceanic and continental sediments, altered oceanic crust and seawater. $\delta^{18}O$ values and oxidation state also point toward a near surface origin. Midplate basalts must traverse this kind of material, as they penetrate the plate, and these components are also subducted but stripped off of the slab at relatively shallow depths. It has been proposed that there is a widespread enriched shallow layer (the perisphere) that is tapped by new ridges and rifts and by midplate volcanoes (Anderson 1996, 1998*a*). A widespread enriched shallow layer, renewed by subduction and slab dehydration and depleted by the initial stages of ridge or midplate or backarc volcanism is an alternative to the deep recycling and plume and plume-head return flow hypotheses. Narrow plume-like features are a hypothetical style of convection not likely to occur in an internally heated material with plates and phase boundaries. Thermal boundary layer instabilities, in such a system, are swept into the main flow, and upwellings broaden as they encounter viscosity and phase changes. On the other hand, narrow upwellings are expected at ridges and rifts, leaky transform faults, and lithospheric discontinuities. A plate under extension fails in narrow zones, or at boundaries and sutures, and magmas naturally take advantage of these narrow pathways and regions of extension.

The use of 'multiple working hypotheses' has served the surface Earth scientists well. Deep Earth scientists have had the tendency to hang on to a mesmerizing idea, cutting and stretching to fit the procrustean bed, and ignoring surface features.

We are still far from a theory of the Earth, or even a theory of volcanoes. While we are collecting more data and building bigger computers and mass spectrometers, it would be rewarding to pay attention to Humpty Dumpty and the Holmes (Sherlock, Arthur and Oliver Wendell) so we can extend the foundation of Hutton to even greater depths.

Humankind is in a continuous search for a theory of the Earth. Cave stories and myths evolved to religions and dogmas and then to testable and falsifiable hypotheses and paradigms. Feynman said, 'You must not fool yourself – and you are the easiest person for you to fool.' This is a compact summary of the wisdom of Bacon, Ocm, Popper, Holmes and Humpty Dumpty. Earth scientists ignore it at their peril.

> Like all other arts, the Science of Deduction and Analysis is one which can only be acquired by long and patient study, nor is life long enough to allow any mortal to attain the highest possible perfection in it.
>
> Sherlock Holmes

This work was supported by NSF grant EAR92-18390. Contribution No. 6214, Division of Geological and Planetary Sciences, California Institute of Technology.

References

ANDERSON, D. L. 1989. *Theory of the Earth*. Blackwell Scientific Publications, Boston6.
—— 1996. Enriched asthenosphere and depleted plumes. *International Geology Reviews*, **38**, 1–21.
—— 1998*a*. The scales of mantle convection. *Tectonophysics*, **284**, 1–17.
—— 1998*b*. The helium paradoxes. *Proceedings of the National Academy of Sciences, USA*, **95**, 4822–4827.
—— 1998*c*. A model to explain the various paradoxes associated with mantle noble gas geochemistry. *Proceedings of the National Academy of Sciences, USA*, **95**, 9087–9092.
—— & BASS, J. D. 1984. Mineralogy and composition of the upper mantle. *Geophysical Research Letters*, **11**, 637–640.
—— & SAMMIS, C. G. 1970. Partial melting in the upper mantle. *Physics of the Earth & Planetary Interiors*, **3**, 41–50.
BAILEY, D. K. 1992. Episodic alkaline igneous activity across Africa. *In*: STOREY, B. C., ALABASTER, T. & PANKHURST, R. J. (eds) *Magmatism and the Causes of Continental Breakup*. Geological Society Special Publication, **68**.
BIRCH, F. 1965. Speculations on the Earth's thermal history. *Geological Society of America Bulletin*, **76**, 133–154.
BOLLES, E. B. 1997. *Galileo's commandment*. W. H. Freeman, New York.
BOSTOCK, M. G. & CASSIDY, J. F. 1997. Upper mantle stratigraphy beneath the southern slave craton. *Canadian Journal of Earth Sciences*, **34**, 577–587.
BUTTERFIELD, H. 1957. *The Origins of Modern Science*. G. Bell & Sons.
CHAUVEL, C., MCDONOUGH, W., GUILLE, G., MAURY, R. & DUNCAN, R. 1997. Contrasting old and young volcanism in Rurutu Island, Austral chain. *Chemical Geology*, **139**, 125–143.
DUNCAN, R. A., HOOPER, P. R., REHACEK, J., MARSH, J. S. & DUNCAN, A. R. 1997. The timing and duration of the Karoo igneous event, southern Gondwana. *Journal of Geophysical Research*, **102**, 18 127–18 138.
FARLEY, K. A. & POREDA, R. J. 1992. Mantle neon and atmospheric contamination. *Earth and Planetary Science Letters*, **114**, 325–339.
——, NATLAND, J. H. & CRAIG, H. 1992. Binary mixing of enriched and undegassed (primitive?) mantle components (He, Sr, Nd, Pb) in Samoan lavas. *Earth and Planetary Science Letters*, **111**, 183–199.
HACKER, P. M. S. 1972. *Insight and Illusion: Wittgenstein on Philosophy and the Metaphysics of Experience*. Clarendon Press, Oxford.
HANAN, B. B. & GRAHAM, D. W. 1996. Lead and helium isotope evidence from oceanic basalts for a common deep source of mantle plumes. *Science*, **272**, 991–995.
HART, S. R., BLUSZTAJN, J., LEMASURIER, W. E. & REX, D. C. 1997. Hobbs Coast Cenozoic volcanism: implications for the West Antarctic rift system. *Chemical Geology*, **139**, 223–248.
HOLMES, A. 1916. Radioactivity in the Earth's thermal history. *Geology Magazine*, **3**, 265–274.
JACKSON, E. D. & SHAW, H. R. 1975. Stress fields in central portions of the Pacific plate: delineated in time by linear volcanic chains. *Journal of Geophysical Research*, **80**, 1861–1874.
JACOBSON, S. B. & WASSERBURG, G. U. 1979. The mean age of mantle and crustal reservoirs. *Journal of Geophysical Research*, **84**, 7411–7427.
KAULA, W. 1975. Absolute plate motions by boundary velocity minimizations. *Journal of Geophysical Research*, **80**, 244–248.
KING, S. D. & ANDERSON, D. L. 1995. An alternative mechanism of flood basalt formation. *Earth and Planetary Science Letters*, **136**, 269–279.
MATSUDA, J. & MARTY, B. 1995. The Ar-40/Ar-36 ratio of the undepleted mantle – a reevaluation. *Geophysical Research Letters*, **22**, 1937–1940.
MORGAN, W. J. 1972. Plate motions and deep mantle convection. *In*: SHAGAM, R. ET AL. (eds) *Studies in Earth and Space Sciences*. Geological Society of America Memoirs, **132**, 7–122.
NIU, Y., COLLERSON, K. D., BATIZA, R., WENDT, J. I. & REGELOUS, M. 1996. Evidence for the presence of Hawaii plume material beneath the Northern East Pacific Rise: a trace element and Nd–Pb–Sr isotopic of lavas from the EPR at 11°20′N. *EOS 1996 Fall Meeting Abstracts*, V12B-4, F783.
O'NIONS, R. K. & OXBURGH, E. R. 1983. Heat and helium in the Earth. *Nature*, **306**, 429–431.
OYARZU, R., DOBLAS, M., LÓPEZ-RUIZ, J. & CELERIÁ, J. M. 1997. Opening of the central Atlantic

and asymmetric mantle upwelling phenomena: implications for long-lived magmatism in western North Africa and Europe. *Geology*, **25**, 727–730.

PATTERSON, C. & TATSUMOTO, M. 1964. The significance of lead isotopes in detrital feldspar. *Geochimica et Cosmochimica Acta*, **28**, 1–22.

POLET, J. & ANDERSON, D. L. 1995. Depth extent of cratons as inferred from tomographic studies. *Geology*, **23**, 205–208.

RAY, T. W. & ANDERSON, D. L. 1994. Spherical disharmonics in the Earth sciences and the spatial solution: ridges, hotspots, slabs, geochemistry and tomography correlations. *Journal of Geophysical Res*earch, **99**, 9605–9614.

ROWLEY, D. R. 1996. Age of initiation of collision between India and Asia. *Earth & Planetary Science Letters*, **145**, 1–13.

SANO, Y. & WILLIAMS, S. N. 1996. Fluxes of mantle and subducted carbon along convergent plate boundaries. *Geophysical Research Letters*, **23**, 2749–2752.

SCHUBERT, G., STEVENSON, D. & CASSEN, P. 1980. Whole planet cooling and the radiogenic heat source content of the Earth and Moon. *Journal of Geophysical Research*, **85**, 2531–2538.

SCRIVNER, C. & ANDERSON, D. L. 1992. The effect of post Pangea subduction on global mantle tomography and convection. *Geophysical Research Letters*, **19**, 1053–1056.

SHAW, H. R. 1994. *Craters, Cosmos, and Chronicles: A New Theory of Earth*. Stanford University Press, Stanford.

SKOGSEID, J., PEDERSEN, T., ELDHOLM, O. & LARSEN, B. 1992. Tectonism and magmatism during NE Atlantic continental breakup: the Voring Margin. *In*: STOREY, B. C., ALABASTER, T. & PANKHURST, R J. (eds) *Magmatism and the Causes of Continental Breakup*. Geological Society Special Publications, **68**, 305–320.

SMITH, W. H. F. & SANDWELL, D. T. 1994. Bathymetric prediction from dense satellite aAltimetry and sparse shipboard bathymetry. *Journal of Geophysical Research Solid Earth*, **99**, 21 803–21 824.

SPENCE, D. A. & TURCOTTE, D. L. 1990. Buoyancy-driven magma fracture. *Journal of Geophysical Research,* **95**, 5133–5139.

VERHOOGEN, J. 1973. Possible temperatures in the oceanic upper mantle and the formation of magma. *Geological Society of America Bulletin,* **84**, 515–522.

VOGT, P. R. 1974. Volcano height and plate thickness. *Earth & Planetary Science Letters,* **23**, 337–348.

Hot little crucibles are pressured to reveal and calibrate igneous processes

PETER J. WYLLIE

Division of Geological and Planetary Sciences, California Institute of Technology, Pasadena, CA 91125, USA

Abstract: The fires of Hutton's (1726–1797) Plutonists could not be quenched by the oceans of Werner's (1750–1817) Neptunists. Hall (1761–1832) was convinced that Hutton's theory could be proved by experiments, but he deferred to the fears of his older colleague that failed experiments might discredit the theory (which needed no further proof), and completed the experiments only after Hutton's death. Hutton censured those who 'judge of the great operations of the mineral kingdom, from having kindled a fire, and looked into the bottom of a little crucible'. Hall believed that 'the imitation of the natural process is an object which may be pursued with rational expectation of success'. Following many discussions between Hutton and Hall, three topics were pursued in Hall's experiments: 1790, the magmatic origin of granites, younger than schists; 1798, whinstones/dolerites are as magmatic as known lavas; 1805, powdered calcite is transformed to marble and melted by the effects of compression (and water) in modifying the action of heat. The latter involved the first high-pressure, high-temperature apparatus and earned Hall the title 'Father of Experimental Petrology'. Subsequent development of these topics is outlined, with reference to debates about primary basalts, granitization, and carbonatites.

I was invited to write about James Hutton and experimental igneous petrology, which leads to the work of Sir James Hall. The subject must be considered in the context of the debate between Werner's Neptunists and Hutton's Plutonists. This debate, with its religious overtones, has become ensconsed in textbooks as the classic debate that ushered geology in as a 'real science'. The theories of Werner (1750–1817) and Hutton (1726–1797) involved global philosophies and implications far transcending the disciplines of mineralogy and mining which preceded them.

Werner's theory, 'Neptunism', maintained that all rocks were formed in layers from a primeval ocean, with granite followed by metamorphic rocks, chemical precipitates, and series of strata as water level fell. Basaltic rock stratified with sediments was thought to be quite different from lavas that had flowed from the relatively few, young, anomalous volcanoes. Werner was one of the great teachers of science, with students flocking to his classes when he began to lecture in Freiberg in 1775, and spreading his gospel after they moved on. He published on a variety of topics, but little on his theory, and he travelled little. But his theorizing was fascinating. The Neptunian theory faded rapidly after Werner's death in 1817, as his former students tested his theories in the field and discovered volcanoes, lavas and intrusive granites.

Hutton's *Theory of the Earth* was presented to the Royal Society of Edinburgh in 1785 and printed in 1788, when Neptunism had ruled for about ten years. Hutton adduced evidence from observations in the field that granites and basalts had solidified from a

WYLLIE, P. J. 1999. Hot little crucibles are pressured to reveal and calibrate igneous processes. *In*: CRAIG, G. Y. & HULL, J. H. (eds) *James Hutton – Present and Future*. Geological Society, London, Special Publications, **150**, 37–57.

molten condition, and appealed not only to the weight of overlying strata and ocean to apply pressure which would modify reactions, but also to high temperature at depth. The fiery forces of the Earth's interior, he maintained, had fused the deeper rocks. Furthermore, the granites had intruded overlying schists (in modern terms), and were therefore younger, a reverse of the fundamental time sequence required by Werner. Hutton also discovered and explained unconformities, with the implications for repeated processes, mountainous upheavals, erosion, and millions and millions of years, with no end in sight. My charge, however, is to deal with the igneous rocks.

Hutton's colleagues were not impressed. Distinguished scientists attacked his new theory. His conclusions were so opposed to Werner's theory that few people paid them positive attention. He published an expanded version of his '*Theory of the Earth with Proofs and Illustrations*' in 1795. As late as 1808, Robert Jamieson, appointed Professor of Natural History in Edinburgh, formed a Wernerian Natural History Society with many publications giving Plutonism a hard time. Hutton's poor writing did not help his case. Playfair (1748–1819), Professor of Natural Philosophy at Edinburgh, decided that the theory merited presentation in more attractive form, and his *'Illustrations of the Huttonian Theory'* (1802) was effective in this way.

The publications of Hutton and Hall reveal an interesting scientific relationship between them. After an outline of this relationship, I summarize the novel experiments of Hall on granite, basalt and limestone. Newcomb's (1990) account of experiments contributing to geology during 1780–1820 provides a wealth of detail for this period. An outline review of subsequent experiments on these materials up to the present time refers selectively to those of scientists based in Edinburgh or Scotland, the home of the remarkable developments in Earth sciences that occurred within a couple of decades near 1800, and to experiments from my laboratory. Selection is necessary given space limits and 200 years of experimental literature.

Hutton and Hall

Hutton's young colleague Hall (1761–1832) was slowly converted. He wrote (1805/1812): 'After three years of almost daily warfare with Dr. Hutton, on the subject of his theory ...' and 'I was induced to reject his system entirely, and should probably have continued still to do so, with the great majority of the world, but for my habits of intimacy with the author; the vivacity and perspicuity of whose conversation, formed a striking contrast to the obscurity of his writing.' 'I thus derived from his conversation, the same advantage which the world has lately done from the publications of Mr Playfair's *Illustrations*; and, experienced the same influence which is now exerted by that work, on the minds of our most eminent men of science.'

Hall also explained how he developed his experimental ideas, but did not pursue them through deference to the wishes of his older colleague, until after his death in 1797. He wrote about how he 'conceived that the chemical effects ascribed by him to compression, ought, in the first place, to be investigated ... established in a direct manner by experiment, and I urged him to make the attempt; but he always rejected this proposal, on account of the immensity of the natural agents, whose operations he supposed to lie far beyond the reach of our imitation ... I considered myself bound, in practice, to pay deference to his opinion, in a field which he had so nobly occupied, and abstained, during the remainder of his life, from the prosecution of some experiments with compression, which I had begun in 1790. In 1798, I resumed the subject with eagerness, being still of opinion, that the chemical law which forms the basis of the Huttonian Theory, ought, in the first place, to be investigated experimentally.' The results of this resumption earned Hall the title 'Father of Experimental Geology'.

I am aware of three papers by Hall, in 1790, 1798 and 1805 (printed 1812). Sir James Hall communicated to the Royal Society of Edinburgh in 1790 'the remainder of his paper, *viz.* Observations on the Formation of Granite'. He gave an abstract of Hutton's observations on the junction between granite and schist, which Hutton was preparing along with a variety of proofs and illustrations of his theory (the 1795 publication), followed by a discussion of how granitic minerals would melt together, and how fused granite or granite glass would crystallize. His 1798 paper dealt with 'Experiments on Whinstone and Lava'. His most remarkable paper on 'Accounts of a Series of Experiments, shewing the effects of compression in modifying the action of heat' was read to the Royal Society of Edinburgh in 1805 (printed 1812). These papers dealt in turn with granites, basalts, and limestone/marble.

Observation, theory, experiment and communication

Science advances through a combination of observation, theory and experiment, but the results become informative only if they are communicated. The preceding remarks have referred to Werner, Hutton, Playfair and Hall. When Hutton's *Theory of the Earth with Proofs and Illustrations* was published in 1795, their ages were: Werner 45, Hutton 69, Playfair 47 and Hall 34. Werner had been a young, inspiring theorist and communicator through 20 years; Hutton's challenging *Theory of the Earth*, presented at the end of his career, involved theory supported by observation. Playfair communicated Hutton's theory. Hall did experiments designed to test and prove the theory.

200 years ago in 1797, Hutton died, and Lyell was born. Werner's Neptunism theory lasted through about 50 years, 1775–1825. By the time Lyell wrote *The Principles of Geology* (1830–1833), the situation was like this: 'The contention of the rival factions of the Vulcanists and Neptunists had been carried to such height that these names had become terms of reproach: and the two parties had been less occupied in searching for truth, than for such arguments as might strengthen their own cause, or serve to annoy their antagonists. A new school at last arose, who professed the strictest neutrality, and the utmost indifference to the systems of Werner and Hutton, and who resolved diligently to devote their labours to observation.' '... the reluctance to theorize was carried somewhat to excess ... the time was not yet come for a general system of geology'. The full significance of Hall's experiments appear not to have been recognized by 1830, as Lyell wrote: 'in order to remove the objections started against this theory, his friend, Sir James Hall, instituted a most curious and instructive set of chemical experiments, illustrating the crystalline arrangement and texture assumed by melted matter cooled under high pressure'. Another half century was needed for formulation of Gibbs' phase rule, the next significant advance in theory for the experiments.

Hutton and Hall on granite

In 1790, Hall, an enthusiastic youngster aged 29, summarized the observations of the mature Hutton, aged 64, which replaced Werner's theory that granites were primitive, crystalline precipitates from an ocean: 'wherever the junction of the granite with the schists was visible, veins of the former, from fifty yards, to the tenths of an inch in width, were to be seen running into the latter, and pervading it in all directions, so as to put it beyond all doubt, that the granite in these veins, and consequently of the great body itself, which he observed forming with the veins one connected and uninterrupted mass, must have flowed in a soft or liquid state into its present position.' This observation and interpretation also indicated that the schist was older than the granite, a reversal of Werner's chronology. Lyell gave a detailed account of Hutton's field explorations and observations around granites.

Hall referred to well-known experiments on melting a crushed mixture of quartz and feldspar, with feldspar serving as a flux to the quartz as it runs into 'a kind of glass'. He described a recent accidental experiment at a 'Glass-house' where a mass of glass cooled very slowly 'became white, very hard and refractory', and suggested that if the glass produced by the fusion of granite 'had been allowed to cool with sufficient slowness, it might have crystallized, producing a granite familiar to that which was originally melted'. He continued with an interpretation of what we now call cotectic melting and precipitation, discussing the formation of some perfect crystals included in a confused mass of feldspar, quartz and schorl. He went on to explain the occurrence of large crystals in a mass of small crystals in terms of slow crystallization in the bowels of the Earth, followed by rapid cooling after eruption of the still-liquid solution as a lava. These were novel concepts for the time.

Hutton and Hall on whinstone and basalt

Werner maintained that the rock basalt, in its various forms, was quite distinct from the lava erupted from volcanoes. He believed that his theory was based on observations at every point. In 1787 he examined a hill with a layer of basalt overlying sand, clay and 'wacke', and his observations confirmed to his satisfaction that these layers were all related, and of aqueous origin.

In his 1798 paper 'Experiments on Whinstone and Lava', Hall developed the theme outlined for granites in 1790, and applied them also to basalts (p. 43): 'Granite, porphyry, and basaltes, are supposed by Dr. Hutton to have flowed in a state of perfect fusion into their present position; but their internal structure, being universally rough and stony, appears to contradict this hypothesis; for the result of the fusion of earth substances, hitherto observed in our experiments, either is glass, or possesses, in some degree, the vitreous character.

'This objection, however, loses much of its force, when we attend to the peculiar circumstances under which, according to this theory, the action of heat was exerted. These substances, when in fusion, and long after their congelation, are supposed to have occupied a subterranean position far below what was then the surface of the earth; ... the modification of heat, occasioned by the pressure of the superincumbent mass, ...

'One necessary consequence ... after their fusion, they must have cooled very slowly; ... appeared to me probable, on that account, that, during their congelation, a crystallization had taken place, ... producing the stony and crystallized structure, ... from the large grained granite to the fine grained and almost homogeneous basalt.'

Observation. Hall compared whinstone (various basaltic rocks, considered by Hall to be 'mere varieties of the same class') with lavas from known volcanoes, and found close resemblance in external character, mineralogy, and chemical properties.

Experiment. Hall was able to fuse all specimens to yield glass with rapid cooling, and stony products with slow cooling, the degree of crystallization depending on the rate of cooling and the temperature at which rapid cooling was started.

Conclusion. Whinstone and lavas from volcanoes were identical in form and origin, and undoubtedly solidified from a molten condition.

Hall also recorded the frequent occurrence of calcareous spar (calcite) in whinstone, but never in lava. He noted that 'the compound seems to have entered into fusion, but kept separate, as oil separates from water through which it has been diffused, thus giving rise to the spherical form, which the nodules of calcareous spar generally exhibit with more or less regularity. ... the mutual repulsion of two fluids intermixed, but not disposed to unite'. This observation has connections with his subsequent experiments on calcite at high pressures and temperatures, and suggests the occurrence of silicate–carbonate liquid immiscibility, which figures so strongly in current discussions on the origin of carbonatite magmas – magmas that were unimagined at this time.

Hutton and Hall on the applicability of experiments

The mature Hutton and the young Hall, as outlined above, disagreed on the potential usefulness of experiments, and Hall deferred his experiments out of respect for Hutton. He later (1805, p. 76) wrote that Hutton feared that the experiments would not work: 'and he seemed to imagine, that any such attempt must undoubtedly fail, and thus throw discredit on opinions already sufficiently established, as he conceived, on other principles'. Two quotations establish two schools of thought that still influence experimental petrology and its applications. Hutton (1795) censured those who 'judge of the great operations of the mineral kingdom, from having kindled a fire, and looked into the bottom of a little crucible'. Hall (1812) concluded that 'the imitation of the natural process is an object which may be pursued with rational expectation of success'.

These quotations are reproduced in context below. In the 'Whinstone' paper (1798), Hall provides a detailed account of his enthusiasm to persuade Hutton that experiments would probably prove his theory. Hall had started his experiments on fusion and cooling rock materials in 1790, but they were interrupted until winter 1797–1798, and then resumed. Hutton died in 1797. In 1790, when he presented his interpretation of the fusion and crystallization of granite, Hall (1798, p. 44–45) had 'determined to submit my opinions to the test of experiment. I communicated this intention to all my friends, and in particular to Dr. Hutton; from him, however, I received little encouragement. He was impressed with the idea, that the heat to which the mineral kingdom has been exposed was of such intensity, as to lie far beyond the reach of our imitation, and that the operations of nature were performed on so great a scale, compared to that of our experiments, that no inference could properly be drawn from the one to the other. He has since expressed the same sentiments in one of his late publications (*Theory of the Earth*, vol. 1, p. 251), where he censures those who "judge of the great operations of the mineral kingdom, from having kindled a fire, and looked into the bottom of a little crucible".

'But, notwithstanding my veneration of Dr. Hutton, I could not help differing with him on this occasion: For, granting that these substances, when in fusion, were acted upon by heat of ever so great intensity, it is certain, nevertheless, that many of them must have congealed in moderate temperatures, since many are easily fusible in our furnaces; ... the imitation of the natural process is an object which may be pursued with rational expectation of success; and, could we succeed in a few examples on a small scale, and with easily fusible substances, we should be entitled to extend the theory, by analogy, to such as, by their bulk, or by the refractory nature of their composition, could not be subjected to our experiments. It is thus that the astronomer, by observing the effects of gravitation on a little pendulum, is enabled to estimate the influence of that principle on the heavenly bodies, and thus to extend the range of accurate science to the extreme limits of the solar system.'

Hutton and Hall on limestone and marble

Hall's greatest achievement was to design apparatus permitting the study of reactions under controlled high pressures and temperatures (with somewhat uncertain values and error bars). His objective was to prove Hutton's theory that many rocks were produced through the action of fire rather than of water: 'The essential characteristic principle of his theory is thus comprised in the word *Compression*; and by one bold hypothesis, founded on this principle, he undertook to meet all the objections to the action of fire.' (All quotations in this section are from Hall, 1812.)

The knowledge that limestone was decomposed by fire in kilns, and the discovery of carbonic acid by Black (which 'explained the chemical nature of the carbonate') made it seem 'absurd to ascribe to that same agent the formation of limestone' or of marble. But according to Hutton's radical hypothesis, 'in consequence of the combined action of Heat and Pressure, effects were produced different from those of heat on common occasions; in particular, that the carbonate of lime was reduced to a state of fusion, more or less complete, without any calcination.' Hall considered that 'Of all mineral substances, the *Carbonate of Lime* is unquestionably the most important in a general view.' He reasoned that under pressure the volatility of 'carbonic acid' would be diminished, and its expansion would be opposed, and the carbonate might be 'expected to remain unchanged in a heat, by which, in the open air, it would have been calcined'. Then, the carbonate 'may be as fusible as the muriate'.

Hall completed more than 500 experiments using sealed gun barrels in various experimental designs, with results that demonstrated the decomposition, recrystallization and melting of crushed calcite. Starting materials included chalk, limestone, spar, marble and the 'shells of fish'. The calcite was enclosed in small vessels – tubes of glass, porcelain, iron, and tubes or cups of thin plates of platina. The sample was placed at one end of a gun barrel, which was packed with refractory material, and the other end was sealed. Gun barrels were placed vertically or horizontally into a furnace. He designed the first cold-seal pressure vessel, with the sample end of the barrel in the furnace and the cold end of the barrel outside the furnace being closed by a plug and folder to facilitate shutting and opening the barrel. Water was added to some experiments, to increase the pressure, and, as we know now, this facilitates fusion of calcite (Wyllie & Tuttle 1960).

The experiments confirmed that powdered calcite can be converted into hard, crystalline marble at high temperatures, as long as pressure is applied (representing a stack of overlying rocks). The physical evidence for melting was unambiguous. Powdered samples settled down to form a solid, void-free mass with a surface in the shape of a meniscus. In experiments with periwinkle shells standing upright, the remnants of a shell, with rounded edges, rose from a cup of former liquid, with a meniscus, or disappeared altogether into the melted mass with a concave surface.

Experimental apparatus for high pressures and temperatures: product analysis

Hall (1812) used gun barrels as pressures vessels, and raised the temperature and internal pressure by heating one end of the barrel, with higher pressures achieved if water was added. He calculated pressures attained between 50 and 270 atmospheres, and temperatures varied from numbers 20 to 51 on the scale of Wedgwood's pyrometers (Newcomb 1990). Experimental petrology had its beginnings in these adventurous experiments, but it was not until the beginning of this century that it became a force in Earth sciences, with the systematic determination of high-temperature liquidus phase equilibria in synthetic silicate systems at the Geophysical Laboratory, Washington (reliable temperatures exceeding 1500°C).

High pressures are achieved by pumping a gas into a strong vessel containing the sample, or by squeezing the sample between solid anvils which are driven toward each other by a hydraulic press. High temperatures are achieved either by heating the whole pressure vessel, or with a solid heating device inside the apparatus. This provides essentially four types, externally or internally heated pressure vessels, with the pressure being imparted either by a fluid medium, or by a compressed, solid medium. Only in the 1950s was apparatus designed that made routine the simultaneous maintenance of high temperatures and pressures covering the range of conditions within the continental crust (cold-seal pressure vessel, and internally heated gas pressure vessel). During the 1960s the experimental range was extended to conditions within the mantle, equivalent to about 100 km depth (piston-cylinder). During the 1980s one type of large-volume apparatus (multi-anvil press) reproduced conditions down to 650 km in the Earth. A miniature device using diamond anvils has reproduced conditions corresponding to 2000 km depth, not far short of the mantle–core boundary of the Earth. Because the diamond is transparent, the sample can be studied *in situ* under high-pressure, high-temperature conditions using an optical microscope, spectroscopic techniques, and X-ray diffraction.

Pressures and temperatures corresponding to conditions down to the centre of the Earth's core have been achieved using shock waves. This is a dynamic approach, in contrast with the static apparatus described above. Data are obtained about material properties as the sample is blasted to destruction. The shock wave is delivered by a large cylindrical plastic projectile, with a small metal flyer plate embedded at its front end. The plate strikes the target sample, and the impact generates a shock wave which passes through the sample; properties measured during the last nanoseconds of its existence permit calculation of the pressures and temperatures of phase transitions experienced by the sample. A technique was developed recently to permit the passage of a shock wave through molten silicate. The curve for variation of density as a function of pressure was obtained, and the shock temperatures were calculated.

A sample can be reacted under desired conditions of pressure and temperature, and the phase assemblage produced can commonly be preserved by quenching from the run conditions by rapid cooling and release of pressure. Many silicate liquids quench to glasses which are easily identified by petrographic microscope, but hydrous liquids and carbonate-rich liquids may precipitate complex mineral assemblages on quenching. The microscope was the main tool for identification of phases until X-ray diffraction became available, but in recent years many improved analytical techniques have greatly enhanced the study of fine-grained phase assemblages from experimental runs. The scanning electron microscope has revealed textures previously unseen, and the electron microprobe makes identification of phases unambiguous. The ion microprobe promises a new era for analysis of trace elements in the experimental charges.

Techniques have been developed for some high pressure apparatus to measure the properties of the phases *in situ*, under the conditions of the run. Spectroscopic and X-ray techniques have been used successfully. Synchrotron X-radiation sources have been interfaced, permitting observations on the geometry and distribution of melts among minerals, and the study of kinetics of phase transitions as they occur.

Experimental petrology of basalt

The views of Hutton and Hall prevailed, and through the nineteenth century it was generally recognized that the various occurrences of basalt (whinstone, dolerite, diabase) were magmatic. Several petrologists developed the idea of two primary magmas, one basaltic and one granitic, and others developed the idea that granitic magmas were formed from primary basalts through liquation, or crystallization differentiation perhaps facilitated by assimilation.

From 1907 at the Geophysical Laboratory, the development of furnaces and techniques for the study of liquidus relationships in simple silicate systems defined the possible paths of crystallization in silicate systems and basaltic magmas. Bowen's influential (1928) book marshalled 20 years of experimental data, supported by petrographic observations of rocks, and phase theory (following Gibbs' thermodynamics). Bowen formulated the theory that crystallization differentiation of a primary basaltic magma was a process capable of generating the diversity of igneous rocks, including granites (from magmas of the residua system). From the study of binary and ternary model systems came the concept of the reaction series, with continuous and discontinuous reaction between minerals and liquid as crystallization proceeded, which is still a central tenet in igneous petrogenesis.

Bowen (1928) proposed that basalt was produced by partial melting of peridotite constituting the mantle, and not from some deep layer of basalt, which was a commonly maintained view through the 1940s (peridotite as a magma source received little further attention until the 1950s). He maintained that basalts never contained more than 12–15 per cent olivine in solution, and that olivine-rich basalts and picrites represented basalt liquid plus settled olivine crystals. This position was challenged by the detailed petrographic observations of Drever and Johnston (University of St Andrews) on 'Crystal growth of forsterite in magmas and melts', published in 1957 in the *Transactions of the Royal Society of Edinburgh*, and republished in 1996 as the first in the 'Reprint Series' of forefront Edinburgh papers. They concluded from their interpretation of olivine shapes in their closing sentence that 'What is now beyond reasonable doubt is that large phenocrysts of olivine *can* crystallize *in situ*.' Hall's assignment of large crystals and small crystals in a rock to two different physical environments is not necessarily applicable to olivine.

Drever supervised my PhD thesis, which supported these conclusions (Wyllie & Drever 1963), and he arranged for me to go to Pennsylvania State University in 1956 to work with Tuttle and seek experimental verification. I failed, having access to high-pressure equipment that could reach only granitic (and carbonatite) temperatures. The need for experimental investigation of olivine-rich magmas was reinforced ten years later, when Viljoen and Viljoen (1969) first described the komatiites, characterized by 20–30 per cent MgO, as a new class of volcanic rocks. Nearly 20 years after the 1957 paper, Drever sent another St Andrews student, Donaldson, to Houston in connection with the Lunar Research Program. Donaldson (1976) succeeded in a 'detailed experimental investigation of the shapes of olivine crystals grown from mafic and ultramafic melts, showing that they are systematically influenced by the degree of supersaturation during growth, by the rate of cooling of the melt, and by the olivine content of the melt. Essentially all of the shapes illustrated by them in 1957 were reproduced. It then became possible to estimate magma cooling rate and degree of supercooling during olivine growth in individual rocks.' (Donaldson 1996.)

The Geophysical Laboratory approach, studying progressively more complex model systems, continued to reveal additional details of magmatic paths. When the piston-cylinder apparatus came into widespread use during the 1960s, the systems were re-examined at higher pressures, with the discovery of significant changes in paths of crystallization, and in the nature of reaction relationships. At the same time, attention had shifted to mantle peridotites as the source of basalt magmas, so partial melting processes for model peridotites were also elucidated by these experiments.

The Geophysical Laboratory introduced the systematic study of what became known as 'dirty systems' with the publication by Yoder and Tilley (1962) of an extraordinarily detailed paper: 'Origin of basalt magmas: an experimental study of natural and synthetic rock systems'. They hoped that the 'direct but less rigorous approach to the problem', crystallization of a single bulk composition at various pressures, dry and with H_2O present, would provide 'some insight into the general relations of the various basalts in advance of the field and laboratory studies now under way'. Note the emphasis on parallel studies of natural rocks and the relevant model systems. Among the pioneers in high-pressure phase equilibria studies of peridotites and basalts were A. E. Ringwood, D. H. and T. H. Green, and G. C. Kennedy.

The experimental study of natural rocks expanded with the research rush associated with the Lunar Research Program, when samples were returned from the Moon in 1969, and with the stimulation of the plate tectonics revolution of 1967, which opened up additional source rocks and processes to be considered in petrogenetic theory. At this time, the University of Edinburgh began a new phase as a centre of experimental petrology under the leadership of M. J. O'Hara, who had spent an apprenticeship period at the Geophysical Laboratory. He wrote an imaginative paper in 1965, not in the *Transactions of the Royal Society of Edinburgh*, but in the new *Scottish Journal of Geology*: 'Primary magmas and the origin of basalts'. The realization that the most abundant magmas on Earth were the basalts oozing from the midoceanic ridge system (MORBs), and that these were the best candidates for primary magmas, chemically distinguishable from all other basalts, led to concentration on the mantle–MORB relationship. There have been frustrating experimental problems facing determination of the compositions of melts produced from source peridotite at various depths and temperatures, but with recent developments, the results from model systems and natural rock systems have converged, as shown in Table 1, compiled by Milholland and Presnall (in press).

The depth of formation of MORBs has been debated through more than 20 years, with the two opposing sides adducing experimental results to support their conclusions. According to one view, primitive MORBs were generated or segregated from the mantle source at low pressures of 9–11 kbar, and, according to the other, picritic primary magmas generated at pressures of about 15–30 kbar experienced extensive olivine fractionation during ascent or in a shallow magma chamber, yielding the primitive MORB compositions. The latter view was championed by O'Hara (1965). The debate collapsed when it was realized that the assumption of a primary magma escaping from equilibrium with the mantle at a specific depth and temperature was invalid. The primary magma

Table 1. *Comparison of lherzolite melting reactions for model systems and natural rock compositions (from Milholland & Presnall 1998)*

P(GPa)	Melting interval	System	Melting reaction (wt%)	Reference
1.1	Invariant	CMAS	36 opx + 55 cpx + 9 sp = 77 liq + 23 ol	[1]
1.1	12–22%	CMAS–Na20	34 opx + 56 cpx + 10 sp = 75 liq + 25 ol	[2]
1.0	mg#75–67	Natural	35 opx + 59 cpx + 5 sp = 78 liq + 22 ol	[3]
1.0	~7–18%	Natural	31 opx + 58 cpx + 11 sp = 82 liq + 18 ol	[4]

[1] Gudfinnsson & Presnall (1996); [2] Walter *et al.* (1995); [3] Baker & Stolper (1994); [4] Kinzler & Grove (1992).

concept is now replaced by interpretations that have evolved to dynamic models involving fractional melting during mantle uprise and decompression. Small amounts of melt separate relatively rapidly, and an aggregate of melts collected from a range of depths and temperatures is emplaced into the spreading centre where blending occurs. Some of these ideas were initiated in Edinburgh (O'Hara & Mathews 1981).

The results of experiments with komatiites and picrites have not produced an unambiguous interpretation of their origin. Their very high liquidus temperatures imply long melting columns within the mantle associated with adiabatic decompression, and with fractional melting beginning perhaps deeper than 600 km. Parman *et al.* (1997) concluded from experiments on pyroxenes in the Barberton komatiites that these crystallized from magma with dissolved H_2O. From their measurements of liquidus temperature of the komatiite with H_2O, and using methods developed for fractional MORB models, they calculated that the data fit a model in an island arc environment, with an adiabatic melting column from 68 to 30 km.

Experiments are increasingly concerned with properites of materials. Shock wave compression experiments to determine the pressure–volume–temperature equation of state of a model basalt to 34/36 GPa (Rigden *et al.* 1984) and of komatiite (Miller *et al.* 1991) show that silicate melts can be of density very close to that of mantle minerals and rocks at very high pressures. The same conclusion was reached by Agee and Walker (1988) from olivine flotation experiments in komatitiic liquids at 6 GPa. If silicate melts derived from lherzolite compositions become denser than the residual mantle, this could result in downward segregation of melts and heat-producing elements, which would have significant consequences for the thermal regime of the Earth and the trace element systematics of the upper mantle and erupted lavas.

Mineral and melt thermochemistry and computer programs have advanced sufficiently that calculated phase equilibria now supplement experiments in increasingly persuasive fashion. Asimow's (1997) 'bicentennial' PhD thesis includes thermodynamic models for minerals and melts together with algorithms for seeking equilibrium by potential minimization; he used the MELTS package by Ghiorso and Sack. Among other exercises, he constructed a forward model of MORB genesis. He found that some of the novel aspects of the compositions of melt fractions predicted by MELTS had been anticipated by the experiments of Baker *et al.* (1995).

Interpretation of the origin of basalts has taken several distinct turns through this century (Basaltic Volcanism Study Project 1981). The quantity and quality of analytical data on isotopes and trace elements has improved enormously during the past 40 years, placing constraints on theoretical models. The experimental petrology of model systems and of natural rock systems has placed further constraints, but experimental determination of trace element distribution coefficients under varied conditions has lagged. The pendulum appears to have swung away from the time in the early 1960s when natural rock systems were considered 'dirty' and somewhat suspect, to a situation where many petrologists regard the simple model systems as too 'clean' and inadequate, because they lack important components. The model systems with more than four components suffer from the limits of geometrical representation of the compositional relationships, whereas the studies of natural rock compositions with about ten components do not provide the level of rigorous understanding obtainable from a phase equilibrium diagram (Presnall 1986). Both approaches are needed. They complement each other.

Experimental petrology of granite

Hutton's theory that granites were born of fire prevailed over Werner's theory that they were precipitated from ocean water, but Hall's explanation of granite mineral textures in terms of crystallization of a melt did not remain unchallenged. The ability of water at high temperatures to transform other rocks into granites during metamorphism was soon recognized, and the enduring debate between 'magmatists' and 'granitizers' was underway.

The term 'granitification' was introduced in 1836 by Keilhau. Historical accounts record that 'granitization' was embraced by the French school during the nineteenth century, and by the Fennoscandian school during nineteenth–twentieth centuries. Sederholm (1967, selected papers from 1888 to 1934) described rocks as 'born again' through palingenesis. Anatexis, or refusion, of pre-existing rocks to generate a granitic or granodioritic liquid released granites from the parentage of a basaltic magma. Granitizers referred to granitic juice, or ichor, of uncertain physical and chemical character, which was assumed to be capable of granitizing a large volume of rocks; others referred to colonnes filtrantes, pore films, intergranular films, emanations, acid solutions, and migmatite fronts. The transition from metamorphic rocks through migmatites to massive granitic bodies was described by many petrologists, and a wealth of terms were adopted to describe the observations, and their interpretation (Mehnhert 1968).

During the 1930s and 1940s, the concept of metasomatic fronts was applied to granites and surrounding rocks, and an extreme view developed that large volumes of rocks could be transformed into granites in the solid state, by diffusion of ions on a regional scale. The theories of 'dry granitization' were backed up with thermodynamic theory. The debate became bitter. Magmatists and granitizers or transformists sometimes had trouble maintaining civility during conversation. Edinburgh was home for influential advocates of granitization.

Geochemical arguments were advanced by Reynolds (University of Edinburgh) to explain advancing granitic fronts. Granitization by the 'acid front' introduced ions such as Si, Na and K, converting existing rocks to granite, and the excess of non-granitic components such as Mg, Fe, and Ca were expelled in a wave of emanations, a 'basic front', which became fixed in rocks rich in mafic minerals near the margins of granitic bodies; such marginal rocks are well known. Bowen described this proposal as 'a basic affront to the geologic fraternity'. Reynolds replied, 'This is accusing Nature of an intentional break of politeness.' Others asked if the elements Mg, Fe and Ca are really more mobile than the granitic elements? Perhaps the 'basification' was what remained when the mobile granitophile elements emigrated to generate granites elsewhere. Read

(1951) wrote, 'I suggest for discussion that some basic fronts may be better interpreted as *Basic Behinds'* – a somewhat indelicate term, I admit, but one which expresses the possibility that we may here be dealing with subtraction rocks ... I fly these kites – perhaps a few will still be flying when the experts have finished shooting.'

Critics of the experimental approach to petrology argued that phase equilibria in simple silicate systems at 1 atmosphere failed to provide a sound basis for interpretion of real rocks not only because there were too few components present to represent the rocks, and because many rocks were formed at high pressures, but also because the effects of the volatile components, the 'fugitive' components that disappeared from the magmas during solidification, surely had very important effects which were not taken into account. The ternary residua system, $NaAlSi_3O_8$–$KAlSi_3O_8$–SiO_2 (Ab–Or–Qz), actually makes up 90 per cent or more of the normative components of many granites, but details of the phase relationships at 1 bar had not been worked out because the melts were so viscous, and reactions so sluggish.

There were a few pioneering experiments using H_2O under pressure in the 1930s and 1940s (e.g. Goranson), but the breakthrough that opened up the field for routine experiments was the design by O. F. Tuttle of new experimental equipment, a cold-seal pressure vessel (compare Hall's gun barrels), permitting experimental studies on the melting of granitic minerals and rocks in the presence of H_2O under pressure. Bowen and Tuttle's (1950) paper on the system $NaAlSi_3O_8$–$KAlSi_3O_8$–H_2O at 1–2 kbar demonstrated the enormous kinetic effect of H_2O on reactions in silicate melts, the lowering of liquidus temperatures by hundreds of degrees by dissolved H_2O, and the indication that H_2O under pressure would permit a feldspathic liquid to precipitate both plagioclase and sanidine instead of a single feldspar solid solution.

The granite debate was based largely on observations and their interpretations, without experimental calibration. Field observations, microscopic study of textures, and geochemical analyses of rocks were interpreted by some as evidence for granitization, whereas others with a different conceptual framework interpreted the same observations in terms of magmatic processes. The experimental studies of Tuttle and Bowen (1958) on the melting of granitic minerals in the system $NaAlSi_3O_8$–$KAlSi_3O_8$–SiO_2, and of natural granites in the presence of H_2O under pressure (up to 4 kbar) provided the calibrations that led to the convergence of most interpretations to the view that granites are essentially magmatic rocks. Natural granite compositions cluster around the temperature minimum on the liquidus surface, indicating liquid–crystal control in their formation. The solidus curve marked the beginning of anatexis, and in metamorphic conditions where some transformists argued for ichors or even solid diffusion, it was demonstrated that granitic rocks in the presence of aqueous pore fluid would be partially melted. Associated local granitization was then attributed to aqueous residual melts or solutions. Turner and Verhoogen (1960, Chapters 12 and 15) reviewed the history, and stated that 'If the extreme hypothesis of granitization by solid diffusion ... is excluded, we find surprising unanimity of opinion in recent writings on the origin and general course of evolution of granitic magmas.'

Theoretical application of the phase rule and Schreinemakers' methods for PT diagrams for multicomponent systems were being rigorously applied to experimental phase diagrams by this time, but the thermodynamic basis for the prediction of phase equilibria was still lacking. Smith's (1963) comprehensive book on *Physical Geochemistry*, with many phase diagrams, included calculations and a diagram showing that the solidus for Ab–Or–Qz–H_2O and granite–H_2O would pass through a temperature minimum of about

650°C at pressures near 2.5 Kbar, and then rise to an estimated 830°C at 20 kbar. The calculation was based on the expectation that the molar volume of H_2O in the vapour phase would become less than that dissolved in the silicate liquid at high pressures. It was later demonstrated that the relative changes of molar volumes of H_2O do not change sufficiently to change the slope of the silicate–H_2O solidus curves before another effect takes over, namely polymorphic transitions of the minerals.

Tuttle and Bowen's (1958) melting curves in the Ab–Or–Qz–H_2O and granite–H_2O systems were extended to 35 kbar by my associates, with the results shown in Figs 1 and 2. Huang and Wyllie (1975) determined the dry and hydrothermal melting reactions in Fig. 1. Note the huge temperature decrease in melting temperature caused by saturation of the granitoid liquids in H_2O. Note that the solidus curves with H_2O vapour change slope not at 2.5 kbar, as predicted by Smith, but at 16–17 kbar, where albite is transformed to denser jadeite in both systems. At 20 kbar, the solidus is near 530°C, 300°C lower than predicted by the molar volume calculation.

The solidus curve and melting interval of biotite-granite with excess H_2O in Fig. 2 was determined by Boettcher and Wyllie (1968), who confirmed that the solidus curve followed remarkably closely that in the model system (Fig. 1), and by Stern and Wyllie

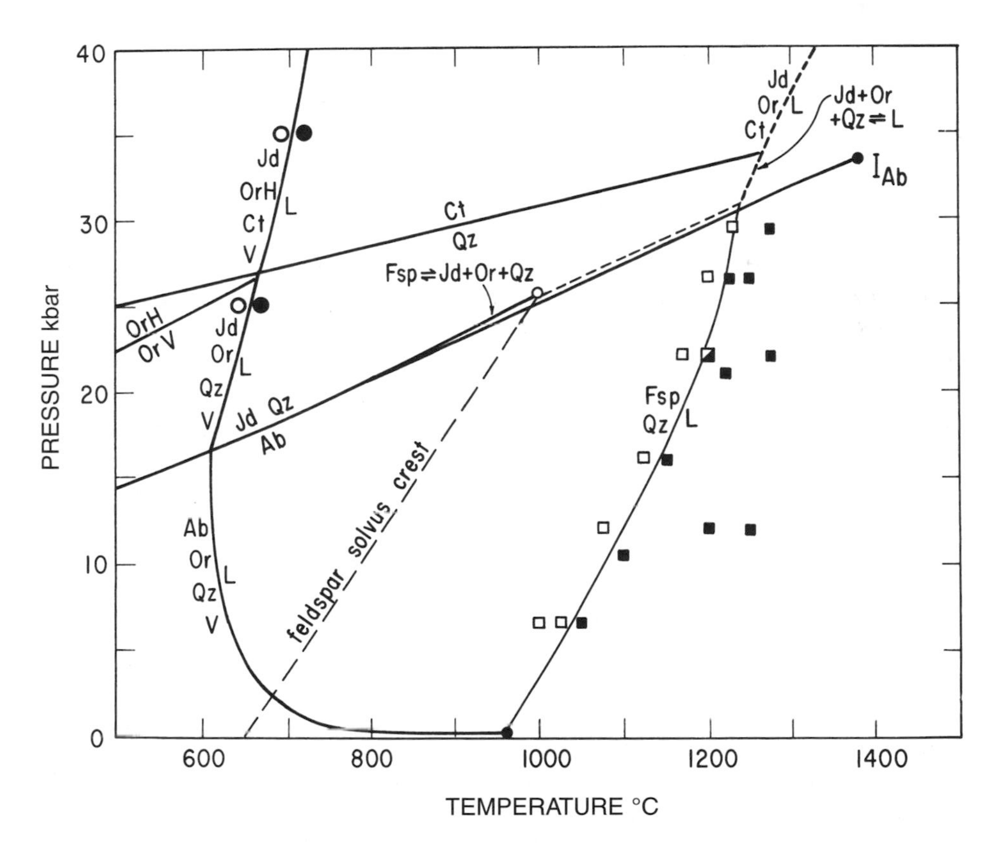

Fig. 1. Univariant reactions in the system $NaAlSi_3O_8$–$KAlSi_3O_8$–SiO_2–H_2O (from Huang & Wyllie 1975). Abbreviations: Fsp = feldspar; Ab = albite; Or = sanidine; Qz = quartz; Ct = coesite; Jd = jadeite; OrH = sanidine hydrate; L =liquid; V = vapour.

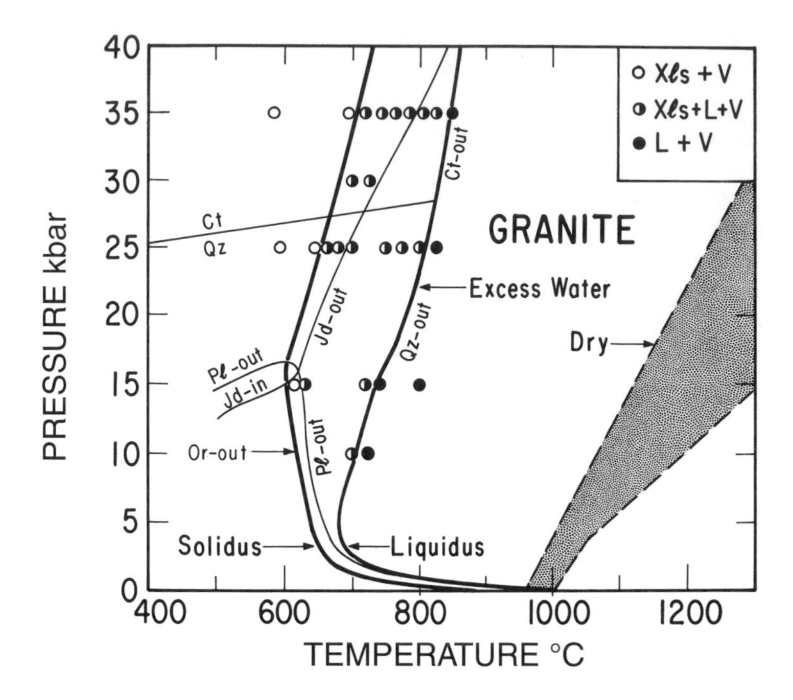

Fig. 2. Melting interval for a natural biotite-granite with excess water, compared with estimated interval for dry granite (from Stern & Wyllie 1973). More detailed phase relationships are given by Boettcher and Wyllie (1968) and Stern and Wyllie (1981), including the biotite reaction curve. Abbreviations: see Fig. 1; and: Pl = plagioclase; Xls = crystals.

(1973, 1981), who showed that eutectic-like melting of granitic rocks was limited to crustal pressures, and to H_2O-saturated conditions. The experimental conditions of H_2O saturation probably obtain only in restricted intervals of magmatic history. Among the many other experimental studies relevant to the origin of granites for which we have no space are those that deal with the vapour-absent melting and crystallization interval of silicate melts with low H_2O contents, initiated by Robertson and Wyllie (1971). Recent experimental studies relevant to granites have been concerned with the compositions of liquids generated by partial melting of other rocks, such as amphibolite, under vapour-absent conditions (Wyllie & Wolf 1993; Johannes & Holtz 1996).

Experimental petrology of limestone and carbonatites

Hall's experiments demonstrating that the combined effect of heat and pressure (with additional water in some experiments) on calcareous material caused melting and the formation of crystalline masses with the properties of marble was taken as confirmation of Hutton's theory. Lyell, in his *Principles of Geology*, proposed the term 'metamorphic' for the stratified primary rocks of Werner, and presented examples where '*secondary* strata have been converted into the *metamorphic*'. In proximity to intruded granite there are examples where '*fossiliferous* strata have been converted into gneiss, mica-schist, clay-slate, or granular marble'; he referred to limestone becoming coarsely crystalline, and 'supposed to have been melted', and to contiguous strata having been reduced to semifusion and, cooling slowly, assuming a crystalline texture. Some time after this (history not known to me), the supposition of partial fusion as a standard process in the formation of metamorphic rocks was dropped, and it was realized that marble was produced by the recrystallization of heated limestone in the solid state. The experimental petrology of limestones and marbles was not pursued further until the 1950s, when Tuttle's cold-seal pressure vessel made possible the study of carbonate–silicate reactions in the presence of CO_2 under pressure.

Two new sets of observations revived the concept of melted sedimentary limestones and brought them back into the realm of fused rocks, but in a magmatic rather than metamorphic context. The first was Daly's (1910) count that carbonate rocks were present in 107 of 155 alkaline igneous rock associations. The second was the discovery of intrusive rocks called carbonatites, by Högböm (1895) and Brögger (1921), which were associated with alkaline igneous rocks.

Daly launched his limestone syntexis hypothesis, in which basalt (later extended to granitic magmas) dissolved limestone, becoming desilicated with loss of some CO_2, forcing the precipitation of nepheline instead of plagioclase, and differentiation to a variety of alkaline magmas. He felt confident that future experimental studies would favour the idea of limestone control on the development of alkaline rock masses. This generated a lively controversy with rather distinct stages. The first, 1910–1935, was occupied mainly by arguments about interpretation of field observations. Between 1936 and 1955 the lines of attack and defence became entrenched, and new experimental data in silicate model systems revealed a thermal barrier on the liquidus between subalkaline and feldspathoidal liquids, denying differentiation from one to the other (at 1 atmosphere without volatile components). During the third period, 1956–1974, the revived study of carbonatites disrupted the field interpretations for limestone assimilation, and additional experimental data at high pressures in systems containing H_2O and CO_2 made it even more difficult to support the hypothesis. The experimental evidence against the limestone assimilation hypothesis was reviewed by Wyllie (1974), and the effects of limestone assimilation are now relegated by most petrologists to some interesting but local phenomena.

Brögger (1921) first used and defined the term 'carbonatite', and the rocks have been defined in various ways since then, including: 'rocks which, though in general mineral composition similar to limestones and marbles of known sedimentary origin, yet appear to behave as intrusive rocks and are closely associated with alkaline igneous rocks'. Brögger and Högböm were convinced that their carbonatites (in Sweden and Norway) were magmatic, probably derived by melting and incorporation into the magma of deep limestones. Bowen argued against the possibility of a carbonatite magma because calcite melts at 1340°C, far higher than that indicated by field evidence for the supposed carbonatite magmas; after petrographic study of the rocks he concluded that the carbonate rocks were products of metasomatic hydrothermal replacement. Petrologists paid little attention to carbonatite magmas, and they are not mentioned in most of the petrology textbooks that appeared during 1930–1950. In 1945, Shand (a Scot working in South Africa) maintained that carbonatites were mobilized or hydrothermally redistributed limestones, because 'imagining a carbonatite magma of unknown origin ... would be a very strange thing'.

Intensive prospecting for radioactive elements, niobium and rare earth elements between 1950 and 1956 resulted in the discovery of many carbonatites, especially in Africa, where numerous limestone hills associated with alkaline volcanic regions, ring

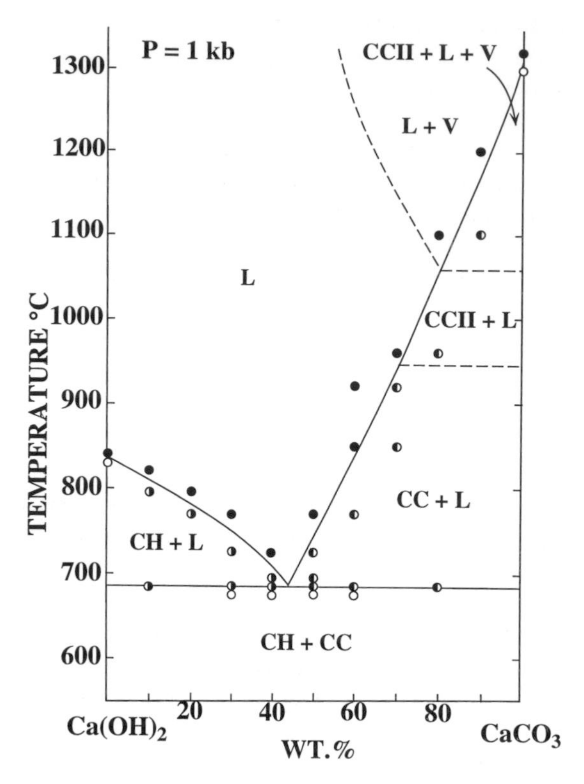

Fig. 3. System $CaCO_3$–$Ca(OH)_2$ at 1 kbar (weight per cent), binary except at highest temperatures where vapour appears (from Wyllie & Tuttle 1960). Abbreviations: CC = calcite; CCII = calcite polymorph; CH = portlandite; L = liquid; V = vapour.

structures and central carbonatite plugs were identified as carbonatites. The revival of interest generated three detailed review articles in 1956. The number of localities listed in 1956 increased from 32 to about 320 by 1966, when two books were published. The 1956 reviews acknowledged the magmatic association, but the high temperature required to melt calcite deterred them from accepting a magmatic origin for the rocks. The 1966 books reported new experimental data confirming the feasibility of carbonatite magmas at suitably low temperatures.

Paterson (1958) and Wyllie and Tuttle (1959), independently and ignorant of Hall's 1805 study (Hall 1812), reported melting calcite at moderate temperatures in the presence of H_2O at moderate pressures. Paterson's experiments were aimed at the deformation of marbles. Wyllie and Tuttle were trying to melt calcite in an investigation of carbonatite magmas; in one experiment, a cleavage rhomb of calcite sealed into a gold capsule with water produced a rounded crystal of calcite, rising from a crystalline mass of calcite with a shiny meniscus-shaped surface, looking like a boiled egg in a shallow egg-cup – an inadvertant reproduction of Hall's experiment with a periwinkle shell. Wyllie and Tuttle (1960) determined the detailed phase relationships in the system CaO–CO_2–H_2O (Figs 3 and 4). They demonstrated that at pressures above a few bars, molten $CaCO_3$ with dissolved H_2O would precipitate calcite through a wide range of temperatures down to about 650°C. The final liquids in this model system would precipitate the mineral portlandite, unknown in carbonatites, but the experiments proved that moderate-temperature magmas could exist, capable of precipitating cumulate rocks composed largely of calcite (sövites). Subsequent experiments investigated the phase relationship linking silicate and carbonate-rich melts.

In dramatic confirmation of the existence in nature of carbonatite magmas, in addition to the crystalline carbonatites, Dawson (1962) observed and collected samples of the 1960 and 1961 eruptions of sodium carbonate lavas on to the floor of the crater of Oldoinyo Lengai ('The Mountain of God'), a cone-shaped volcano rising 6500 feet above the plains in what was then Tanganyika. The erupted magma consists essentially of $(Na,K)_2CO_3$ and $CaCO_3$, in approximately equal proportions, with ~4–5 per cent Cl, and F, and <2 per cent H_2O. This indisputable carbonatite lava (magma) has a composition very different from that of the known carbonatite rocks.

Hall's (1798) description of calcareous spar in whinstone cited above is expressed in terms of liquid immiscibility between silicate and carbonate components. Koster van Groos and Wyllie outlined new experimental results in 1963, reporting their discovery of silicate–carbonate liquid immiscibility in mixtures of plagioclase feldspar and Na_2CO_3, with and without H_2O present. The results indicated that immiscible (Na,Ca)-carbonate-rich melts could exsolve from plagioclase–nepheline-normative silicate parent magmas, and many subsequent experiments have defined the conditions for silicate–carbonate liquid immiscibility as a function of pressure and bulk composition. This process has obvious applications to the Oldoinyo Lengai lavas, now known as natrocarbonatites.

Theories for the origin of carbonatite magmas included a primary source from the mantle. Eggler (1974) demonstrated that in model mantle–basalt systems, the effect of CO_2 under pressure was to deplete the liquid compositions in SiO_2, with liquid compositions becoming larnite normative when they crossed the join forsterite–diopside between 15 and 30 kbar, and with 5 per cent dissolved CO_2 depressing the melting temperature by about 75°C (compare the much larger effect of H_2O on granitic melting

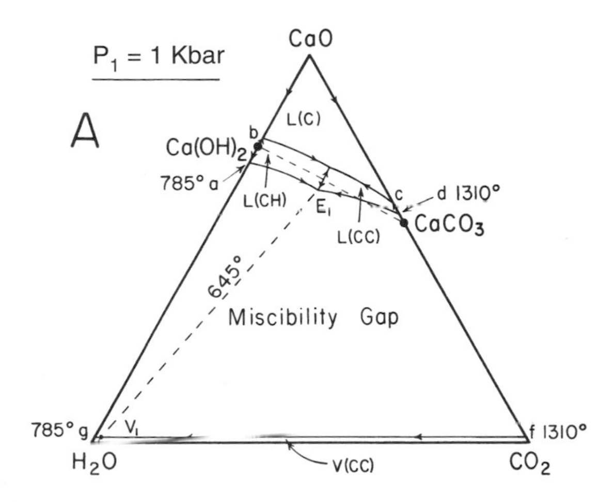

Fig. 4. Liquidus surface in the system $CaO–CO_2–H_2O$ at 1 kbar, according to Wyllie and Tuttle (1960). Figure 3 shows the join $CaCO_3–Ca(OH)_2$ through this system. L(X) is the liquidus surface for C = CaO, CC = calcite, CH = portlandite. V(CC) is the vaporus surface for calcite. a-E_1-d is the vapour-saturated liquidus boundary, coexisting with vapours on the boundary g-V_1-f.

temperatures in Fig. 1). At this time, Wyllie and associates were following subsolidus reactions between model mantle assemblages and carbonates to high pressures and temperatures where melting began, and determining the melting relationships of carbonates and of simple silicate–carbonate systems. At high pressures within the stability fields of carbonates, the eutectic liquids corresponded to synthetic carbonatites, with 50–90 per cent dissolved carbonate (about 25–45 per cent CO_2). In 1975, Wyllie and Huang combined these experimental approaches, and outlined the comprehensive phase relationships in 'Peridotite, kimberlite, and carbonatite explained in the system $CaO–MgO–SiO_2–CO_2$'. Many detailed experimental studies have followed in more complex systems and using natural rocks. Outcrops were found relating carbonate-rich rocks to kimberlites (of undisputed mantle origin). For example, Dawson and Hawthorne (1973) described an intriguing occurrence of coexisting, differentiated kimberlite and carbonatite within individual sills at Benfontein, South Africa.

The key generic conclusions and applications were apparent early in model systems (e.g. Koster van Groos & Wyllie 1963; Wyllie & Huang 1975; and subsequent experimental studies). Later experiments with natural rocks provided more details of compositions and temperatures for specific occurrences, with sometimes complex interpretations facilitated by the known model system phase relationships. The primary carbonatite liquid that can be formed in the mantle contains only a few per cent SiO_2, and is dominated by the composition dolomite (slightly calcic). Continuation of Hall's (1812) pioneering experiments on the effect of pressure and H_2O in permitting calcite to melt has thus defined the conditions for the generation of carbonatite liquids from the effect of CO_2 on upper mantle rocks.

Observation, theory and experiment

Hutton observed, and developed a 'theory of the Earth' which he felt was sufficiently proved by a second round of observations. Hall carried out experiments designed to prove the theory, confident in the power of experiments despite Hutton's fear that experimental failure would discredit the theory. Hall concluded that he had proved Hutton's theory that marble was formed by fusion of shelly material. His experiments were right–limestone was certainly fusible at high pressures–but the application was wrong. We now know that marbles crystallized in the solid state. The experimental data, however, remain valid, and a parallel approach and follow-up about 150 years later proved that carbonatite magmas could exist. Hall could not have made this application, because carbonatites were not known until 1895. The fact that experiments showed that carbonate-rich melts could exist did not prove that carbonatite magmas existed – this conclusion required field observations and interpretations.

Petrology is now firmly based on geophysics, and calibrated at depth by experimental petrology. These experiments also contain an element of exploration which is just as stimulating as marching into an uncharted field area. Good experimental data last for ever. Theories, which are based on some combination of observations and imagination, may be supported, denied or destroyed by experimental data. Experiments may deny the feasibility of some proposed theory or process. The interpretation of both field observations and experimental data is strongly influenced by the current theoretical operating systems which process the signals entering the human brain.

I thank Barry Dawson and the Conference Organizers for the invitation to lecture, and the Earth Sciences section of the US National Science Foundation for Grants EAR-921886 and EAR-950577 and for supporting research in my laboratory on granitic rocks, carbonatites, and kimberlites through many years; and John Gittins for locating the reference source for H. H. Read's famous statement about 'basic behinds'.

References

AGEE, C. B. & WALKER, D. 1988. Static compression of olivine flotation in ultrabasic silicate liquid. *Journal of Geophysical Research*, **93**, 3437–3449.

ASIMOW, P. D. 1997. A thermodynamic model of adiabatic melting of the mantle. PhD thesis, California Institute of Technology, Pasadena.

BAKER, M. B. & STOLPER, E. M. 1994. Determining the composition of high-pressure mantle melts using diamond aggregates. *Geochimica et Cosmochimica Acta*, **58**, 2811–2827.

——, HIRSCHMANN, M. M., GHIORSO, M. S. & STOLPER, E. M. 1995. Compositions of low-degree partial melts of peridotite: results from experiments and thermodynamic calculations. *Nature*, **375**, 308–311.

BASALTIC VOLCANISM STUDY PROJECT 1981. *Basaltic Volcanism on the Terrestrial Planets*. Pergamon Press, New York.

BOETTCHER, A. L. & WYLLIE, P. J. 1968. Melting of granite with excess water to 30 kilobars pressure. *Journal of Geology*, **76**, 235–244.

BOWEN, N. L. 1928. *The Evolution of the Igneous Rocks*. Princeton University Press.

—— & TUTTLE, O. F. 1950. The system $NaAlSi_3O_8$–$KAlSi_3O_8$–H_2O. *Journal of Geology*, **58**, 489–511.

BRÖGGER, W. C. 1921. Die Eruptivgesteine des Kristianiagebietes, IV. Das Fengebiet in Telemark, Norwegen. *Vidensk. selsk. skrift., I. Mat.-naturv. Klasse*, No. 9 (1920), 1–408.

DALY, R. A. 1910. Origin of alkaline rocks. *Bulletin of the Geological Society of America*, **21**, 87–118.

DAWSON, J. B. 1962. The geology of Oldoinyo Lengai. *Bulletin of Volcanology*, **24**, 349–387.

—— & HAWTHORNE, J. B. 1973. Magmatic sedimentation and carbonatite differentiation in kimberlite sills at Benfontein, South Africa. *Journal of the Geological Society of London*, **129**, 61–85.

DONALDSON, C. H. 1976. An experimental investigation of olivine morphology. *Contributions to Mineralogy and Petrol*ogy, **57**, 187–213.

—— 1996. Preface. *In*: DREVER, H. I. & JOHNSTON, R. Crystal growth of forsteritic olivine in magmas and melts. Reprint Series, No. 1, *Transactions of the Royal Society of Edinburgh: Earth Sciences*, **86**, 58–60.

DREVER, H. I. & JOHNSTON, R. 1957. Crystal growth of forsteritic olivine in magmas and melts. *Transactions of the Royal Society of Edinburgh*, **63**, 289–315.

EGGLER, D. H. 1974. Effect of CO_2 on the melting of peridotite. *Carnegie Institute of Washington Yearbook*, **73**, 215–224.

GUDFINNSON, G. H. & PRESNALL, D. C. 1996. Melting relations of model llierzoplite in the system CaO–MgO–Al_2O_3–SiO_2 at 2.4–3.4 GPa and the generation of komatiites. *Journal of Geophysical Research*, **101**, 27 701–27 709.

HALL, J. 1790. Observations on the formation of granite. *Transactions of the Royal Society of Edinburgh*. **3**, 8–12.

—— 1798. Experiments on whinstone and lava. *Transactions of the Royal Society of Edinburgh*, **5**, 43–75.

—— 1812. Account of a series of experiments, shewing the effects of compression in modifying the action of heat. *Transactions of the Royal Society of Edinburgh*, **6**, 71–184.

HÖGBOM, A. G. 1895. Uber das nephelinsyenit auf der Insel Alno. *Geologiska Foreningens Forhandlingar*, **17**, 100–160, 214–256.

HUANG, W. L. & WYLLIE, P. J. 1975. Melting reactions in the system $NaAlSi_3O_8$–$KAlSi_3O_8$–SiO_2 to 35 kilobars, dry and with excess water. *Journal of Geology*, **83**, 737–748.

HUTTON, J. 1788. Theory of the Earth; or an investigation of the laws observable in the composition, dissolution, and restoration of land upon the globe. *Transactions of the Royal Society of Edinburgh*, **1**, 209–304.

—— 1795. *Theory of the Earth, with Proofs and Illustrations*. 2 vols. Edinburgh.

JOHANNES, W. & HOLTZ, F. 1996. Petrogenesis and experimenal petrology of granitic rocks. Springer-Verlag, Berlin.

KINZLER, R. J. & GROVE, T. L. 1992. Primary magmas of mid-ocean ridge basalts 1. Experiments and methods. *Journal of Geophysical Research*, **97**, 6885–6906.

KOSTER VAN GROOS, A. F. & WYLLIE, P. J. 1963. Experimental data bearing on the role of liquid immiscibility in the genesis of carbonatites. *Nature*, **199**, 801–802.

LYELL, C. 1830–1833. *The Principles of Geology*. 3 vols. John Murray, London.

MEHNHERT, K. R. 1968. Migmatites and the origin of granitic rocks. Elsevier, Amsterdam.

MILHOLLAND, C. S. & PRESNALL, D. C. 1998. Liquidus phase relations in the $CaO–MgO–Al_2O_3–SiO_2$ system at 3.0 GPa: the aluminous pyroxene thermal divide and the high pressure fractionation of picritic and komatiitic magmas. *Journal of Petrology*, **39**, 3–27.

MILLER, G., STOLPER, E. & AHRENS, T. J. 1991. The equation of state of a molten komatiite. 1. Shock wave compression to 36 GPa. *Journal of Geophysical Research*, **96**, 11 831–11 848.

NEWCOMB, S. 1990. Contributions of British experimentalists to the discipline of geology: 1780–1820. *Proceedings of the American Philosophical*, **134**, 161–225.

O'HARA, M. J. 1965. Primary magmas and the origin of basalt. *Scottish Journal of Geology*, **1**, 19–40.

—— & MATHEWS, R. E. 1981. Geochemical evolution in an advancing, periodically replenished, periodically tapped, continuously fractionated magma chamber. *Journal of the Geological Society of London*, **138**, 237–277.

PARMAN, S. W., DANN, J. C., GROVE, T. L. & DE WIT, M. J. 1997. Emplacement conditions of komatiite magmas from the 3.49 Ga Komati Formation, Barberton Greenstone Belt, South Africa. *Earth and Planetary Science Letters*, **150**, 303–323.

PATERSON, M. S. 1958. The melting of calcite in the presence of water and carbon dioxide. *American Mineralogy*, **43**, 603–606.

PLAYFAIR, J. 1802. Illustrations of the Huttonian theory of the earth. Cadell and Davies, and William Creech. Edinburgh. Facsimile reprint with an introduction by G. W. White, 1956. University of Illinois Press, Urbana. Reprinted 1964, Dover Publications, New York.

PRESNALL, D. C. 1986. An algebraic method for determining equilibrium crystallization and fusion paths in multicomponent systems. *American Mineralogy*, **71**, 1061–1070.

READ, H. H. 1951. Metamorphism and granitization. *Transactions of the Royal Society of South Africa*, **54**, 1–17.

RIGDEN, S. M., AHRENS, T. J. & STOLPER, E. M. 1984. Densities of liquid silicates at high pressures. *Science*, **226**, 1071–1074.

ROBERTSON, J. K. & WYLLIE, P. J. 1971. Rock–water systems, with special reference to the water-deficient region. *American Journal of Science*, **271**, 252–277.

SEDERHOLM, J. J. 1967. Selected works, granites and migmatites. John Wiley, New York.

SHAND, S. J. 1945. The present status of Daly's hypothesis of the alkaline rocks. *American Journal of Science*, **243-A**, 495–507.

SMITH, F. G. 1963. *Physical Geochemistry*. Addison-Wesley, Palo Alto, CA.

STERN, C. R. & WYLLIE, P. J. 1973. Water-saturated and undersaturated melting relations of granite to 35 kilobars. *Earth and Planetary Science Letters*, **18**, 163–167.

—— & WYLLIE, P. J. 1981. Phase relationships of I-type granite with H_2O to 35 kb: the Dinkey Lakes biotite-granite from the Sierra Nevada batholith. *Journal of Geophysical Research*, **86**, 10 412–10 422.

TURNER, F. J. & VERHOOGEN, J. 1960. *Igneous and Metamorphic Petrology*. McGraw-Hill, New York.

TUTTLE, O. F. & BOWEN, N. L. 1958. Origin of granite in the light of experimental studies in the system $NaAlSi_3O_8–KAlSi_3O_8–SiO_2–H_2O$. *Geological Society of America Memoirs,* **74**.

VILJOEN, M. J. & VILJOEN, R. P. 1969. Evidence for the existence of a mobile extrusive peridotitic magma from the Komati Formation of the Onverwacht Group. *Special Publications of the Geological Society of South Africa*, **2**, 87–112.

WALTER, M. J., SISSON, T.W. & PRESNALL, D. C. 1995. A mass proportion method for calculating melting reactions and application to melting of model upper mantle lherzolite. *Earth and Planetary Science Letters*, **135**, 77–90.

WYLLIE, P. J. 1974. Limestone assimilation. *In*: SØRENSEN, H. (ed.) *Alkaline Rocks*. John Wiley, London, 459–474.

—— & DREVER, H. I. 1963. The petrology of picritic rocks. A picrite sill on the Island of Soay (Hebrides). *Transactions of the Royal Society of Edinburgh*, **65**, 155–177.

—— & HUANG. W. L. 1975. Peridotite, kimberlite, and carbonatite explained in the system CaO–MgO-SiO_2–CO_2. *Geology*, **3**, 621–624.

—— & TUTTLE, O. F. 1959. Melting of calcite in the presence of water. *American Mineralogy*, **44**, 453–459.

—— & —— 1960. The system CaO–CO_2–H_2O and the origin of carbonatites. *Journal of Petrology*, **1**, 1–46.

—— & WOLF, M. B. 1993. Amphibolite-dehydration melting: sorting out the solidus. *In*: PRICHARD, H. M., ALABASTER, T., HARRIS, N. B. W. & NEARY, C. R. (eds) *Magmatic Processes and Plate Tectonics*. Geological Society, London, Special Publications, **76**, 405–416.

YODER, H. S. & TILLEY, C. E. 1962. Origin of basalt magmas: an experimental study of natural and synthetic rock systems. *Journal of Petrology*, **3**, 342–532.

High-pressure experiments and the varying depths of rock metamorphism

WERNER SCHREYER

Research Group of High Pressure Metamorphism, Institut für Mineralogie, Ruhr-Universität, D 44780 Bochum, Germany

Abstract: Hutton's visions of 1785 included burial and metamorphism of rocks and their reincorporation into the continental crust. As a result of changing environmental conditions, mainly of pressure (P) and temperature (T), rocks change their mineral assemblages during metamorphism. High-pressure experimentation has now provided geoscientists with quantitative data on the behaviour of rock systems under varying PT conditions, so that depths of burial or subduction and pathways of exhumation can be reconstructed, and the metamorphic histories of rocks can be used to gauge the internal dynamics of our globe during geological time. An important prerequisite is the knowledge of the states of chemical equilibrium as a function of P, T and rock composition. Several simple chemical model systems are chosen here to demonstrate characteristic mineralogical and petrological behaviour during metamorphism and to identify some important and unusual minerals that typify high- or ultrahigh-pressure metamorphism taking place at depths of up to 150 km, e.g. the dense forms of carbon (diamond) and of SiO_2 (coesite). Low-pressure metamorphism within the normal (~35 km) crust of the Earth, on the other hand, is typified by less dense minerals such as tridymite or cordierite. In this way, deep and very deep subduction of former rocks of the Earth's crust was recognized. This required new geodynamic concepts involving the participation of crustal materials in the overall secular convection processes within the Earth's mantle.

In his 1785 abstract of the *Theory of the Earth* James Hutton gave the world the first hints about the process of metamorphism affecting the rocks of our globe:

> A theory is thus formed, with regard to a mineral system. In this system, hard and solid bodies are to be formed from soft bodies, from loose or incoherent material, collected together at the bottom of the sea; and the bottom of the ocean is to be made to change its place with relation to the centre of the earth.

Although Hutton continued emphasizing the exhumation of rock bodies, his picture also implies their burial. Thus, at the time when Mozart composed his crowning symphonies, James Hutton had understood the essential mechanisms of geodynamics: that loose sediments like the clays of the coastal bays become indurated during burial or, subduction, and that subsequently these materials may be incorporated into mountains by uplift and return to the Earth's surface. What Hutton may not have conceived is that even rocks that are hard from the first, such as pillow lava basalts formed at the bottom of the sea, are metamorphosed to form rocks called eclogites by a complete change in mineralogy despite retaining the old pillow structure, which was formed by flowing lava on the seafloor.

SCHREYER, W. 1999. High-pressure experiments and the varying depths of rock Metamorphism. *In*: CRAIG, G. Y. & HULL, J. H. (eds) *James Hutton – Present and Future*. Geological Society, London, Special Publications, **150**, 59–74.

There is one small detail that I would like to concentrate on in this contribution, and which Hutton surely could not have discussed at his time: *To what extent* do these rocks 'change their place with relation to the centre of the earth'? To what depths are they subducted? Or: what may be the maximum depth of rock metamorphism?

Geoscientists have studied metamorphism of rocks from many different viewpoints. For example, (1) by concentrating on their changing mineral assemblages, or (2) by emphasizing deformational features like the schistosity attained during transport within the Earth. What has emerged more and more in recent years is that these metamorphic rocks are the only reliable and even quantitative gauges for the dynamic processes that have characterized the history of our globe for more than four billion years. As Hutton (1785) envisaged, we can only learn about these processes, which govern the present and the future of our planet as well, 'from things which have already happened; things which have left, in the particular constitution of the bodies, proper traces of the manner of their production'.

Thus, our modern task is to identify these 'proper traces', determine in metamorphic rocks, which ones are characteristic or may even represent quantitative measures for answering questions about depths of burial. There is no doubt that the best and often the only indicators for the varying depths of metamorphism are the *minerals* making up the rock:

(1) Individually, purely by their presence – provided the minerals grew during the metamorphic process. Thus, mineralogy may give crude information on depth.
(2) By their coexistence with other minerals in assemblages by which we can narrow down the metamorphic conditions endured by the rock, at best to invariancy. This is the job of petrology.

Environmental conditions during rock metamorphism

The modern tool by which we can fulfil the task of 'proper trace finding' is the laboratory experiment. The physico-chemical conditions of the environment to which buried rocks are subjected are governed mainly by pressure and temperature, and both these increase with depth. While, as a first approximation, pressure is simply the result of the growing overburden at depth, temperatures may vary considerably, even at constant depth, for example due to the proximity of hot igneous melts. Possible variations of pressure (P in kbar: 1 kbar = 0.1 Gpa) and temperature (T in °C) as a function of depth down to nearly 200 km are summarized in the PT plot of Fig. 1. The values given for selected linearly extrapolated geotherms indicate different possible rates of temperature increase per kilometer of increasing depth. Rates below 5°C km^{-1} may not apply to our globe, or may represent only unusual transitory situations. The PT variations have to be seen in conjunction with the architecture of the outer shells of the Earth, where the crust under the continents has an average thickness of some 35 km, whereas that under the oceans reaches only some 10 km (Fig. 2). Thus, with the exception of in deeper roots of young mountain belts, the pressures governing metamorphism of rocks within the crust of a static Earth do not exceed about 10 kbar (Fig. 1). It is thus understandable that for stationary concepts of global geology, metamorphism of rocks initially formed at the surface was believed to be limited to 10 kar, and the textbooks of metamorphic petrology have followed this scheme until the late 1980s.

The advent of plate tectonics concepts about 30 years ago, involving lateral transport of material and allowing subduction of oceanic plates under continental ones as well as

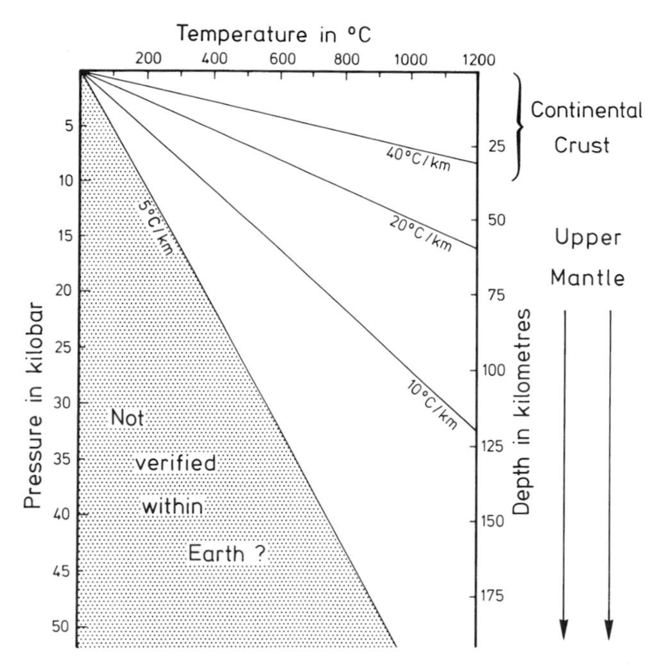

Fig. 1. Pressure (P) – temperature (T) plot showing possible PT conditions within the upper 190 km of the Earth where the metamorphism of rocks is feasible. Those in the shaded field may not exist except under special transient evolutionary stages discussed in the text. Straight lines indicate linearly extrapolated geotherms giving the temperature increase relative to depth. Comparison of the two vertical axes yields the linear increase of pressure (1 kbar = 0.1 GPa) with depth as calculated for an assumed average rock density of 2.8 g cm^{-3}. Note that the depth range includes continental crust and upper mantle (see Fig. 2).

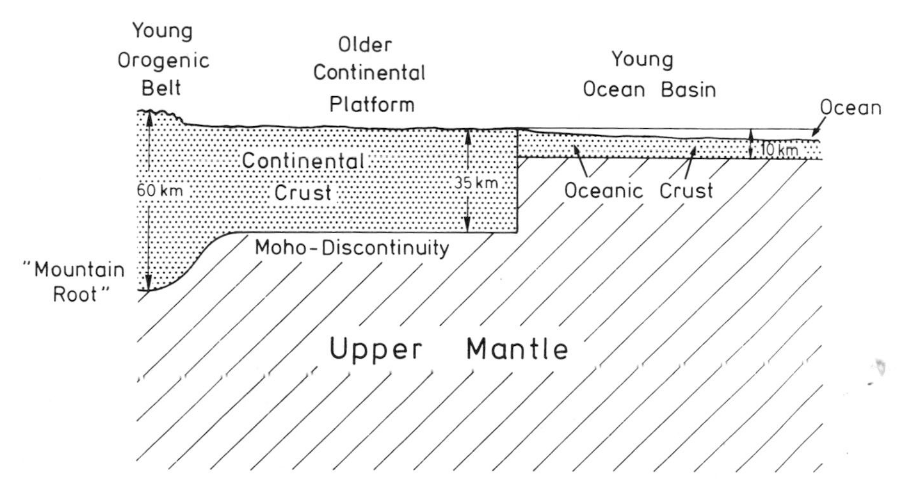

Fig. 2. Schematic cross-section through the outer portions of the Earth distinguishing three different geotectonic areas characterized by different thicknesses of crust overlying the upper mantle.

mutual collisions of continents, has introduced new degrees of freedom for the theory of rock metamorphism. However, only the evidence provided by experiments under controlled conditions of *P* and *T* can determine the possible depths of subduction in this modern geodynamic picture.

Physical chemical background of high-pressure experimentation on rock metamorphism

Rocks of whatever composition or origin represent chemical systems, generally very complicated ones because of the large number of chemical components. These components are mainly the oxides SiO_2, TiO_2, Al_2O_3, Fe_2O_3, FeO, MgO, CaO, Na_2O, K_2O, H_2O and others, which combine to form phases, that is minerals, melts or fluids. All these phases are subject to the rules of chemical equilibrium established by J. Willard Gibbs in 1876. Thus, at equilibrium the number of components determines the maximum number of phases. For rocks the mineralogical phase rule simply says that the equilibrium number of minerals in a specific rock type cannot exceed the number of its chemical components.

All chemical systems eventually strive to attain a state of equilibrium, although many of them never reach it. A prominent and somewhat disturbing example is life on Earth that should not exist if its essential element components, carbon, oxygen, hydrogen, etc., were at chemical equilibrium. However, the low-temperature, low-pressure environmental conditions at the Earth's surface have allowed disequilibrium reactions and products not only to persist, but also to evolve over at least four billion years.

This is generally not true for rock-forming systems at high pressures and temperatures. Many metamorphic rocks obey the mineralogical phase rule with regard to their chemical components and mineral constituents, showing that they have reached a state of equilibrium valid for a particular set of *PT* conditions and thus depth. Others contain too many minerals and are thus not in equilibrium. Microscopic studies often show that minerals formed at a later stage partly replace earlier ones, thus providing the evidence for mineral successions and reactions.

Under these circumstances, the prime goal of high-pressure experimentation has to be to determine the equilibrium phase relations of rock-forming systems as a function of varying pressures and temperatures. The appearance of disequilibria in natural systems and even under experimental conditions cannot distract the laboratory worker from their goal to obtain an equilibrium, that is the state with the lowest Gibbs free energy in the system, because – as N. L. Bowen pointed out in an unpublished letter some sixty years ago – 'the only practical way to study the physical chemistry of geologic processes is to determine the equilibrium relations first and then evaluate those factors which led to non-attainment of equilibrium under natural conditions, together with the magnitude and direction of their effects'.

The nature and quality of chemical equilibrium also invalidates an often heard criticism about experimental studies in mineralogy and petrology, which claims that experiments with durations of days or even months cannot be compared with rock-forming processes lasting millions of years. Chemical equilibrium is independent of time: once a particular equilibrium mineral assemblage has formed, whether during the laboratory run or in a metamorphic rock, it will persist there for ever, provided the environmental conditions remain the same.

Nevertheless, much can be learned about the metamorphism of rocks if the experimentalist also records the time relations during which the system studied approaches its equilibrium destination. Such studies may have direct bearing upon the kinetics of mineral reactions during metamorphism leading from one equilibrium state to another – in other words, on the durations of metamorphic events during geodynamic processes.

In this paper, it is not intended to introduce the various types of apparatus which have been developed for high-pressure experimentation during the last 50 years or so. Let it suffice to state that at present all the *PT* conditions possible within the Earth down to its centre can be reproduced in the laboratory over time periods in which mineral reactions may come to equilibrium.

Experimental results in simplified rock systems containing only few components

In the following, some chemically simple systems will be considered in which individual minerals as well as mineral assemblages occur which, in turn, are characteristic of particular *PT* conditions of metamorphism. Their equilibrium *PT* stability fields as determined by the experimenters allow important first conclusions as to the depths of metamorphism. In fact, because some of the minerals mentioned are spectacular and easy to recognize, their discovery in natural rocks has stimulated the progress of scientific thinking and has recently led to the recognition of Earth processes previously considered impossible.

According to Le Chatelier's principle of 1888, mineral systems at equilibrium react to changes in their physical environment by adaptation of properties such as their volume. Thus, upon increase of temperature, the system tends to expand; it will form minerals of larger specific volume or lower density. Conversely, the system will contract with increasing pressure: high-pressure minerals with higher densities will develop. This simple principle finds its spectacular expression in the internal architecture of minerals, that is in their crystal structures, where the atoms are more loosely arranged in low-pressure solids, but increasingly densely packed in the high-pressure phases that make up the rock materials in the deeper regions of our globe. The crystallography of matter at high and extreme pressures is still one of the most exciting frontiers of science.

The carbon system

Just as life itself is a disequilibrium process on Earth, all its biogenic remains, such as coal, peat or crude oil, often simply summarized as carbonaceous matter, are in a transient, metastable state of equilibrium. Their stable state of equilibrium, which is generally attained during rock metamorphism, simply by the acceleration of reaction kinetics, is attained either by oxidation to fluids like CO_2 and H_2O or – when maintaining the oxidation state, or even through reduction – by the formation of elemental carbon as graphite or diamond.

The equilibrium phase diagram of carbon with these two stable polymorphs is reproduced in Fig. 3. Graphite with a density of 2.27 g cm^{-3} is thus the stable form at relatively low pressures and must certainly develop by metamorphism of carbonaceous matter within continental crust of normal thickness. Diamond, however, with a density of 3.51 g cm^{-3} can be stable only at depths within the Earth's mantle of at least

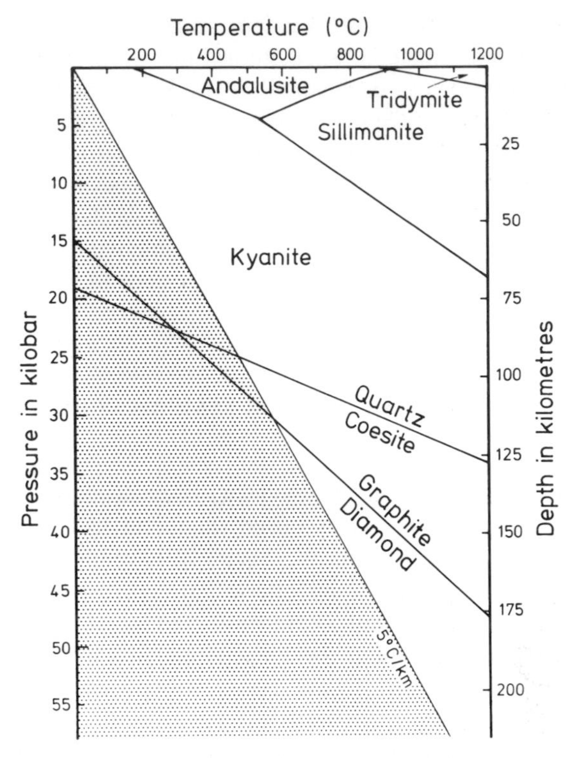

Fig. 3. *PT* plot identical to that in Fig. 1 exhibiting the experimentally determined stability fields of graphite and diamond in the system carbon after Kennedy & Kennedy (1976), of tridymite and coesite in the system SiO_2 (after Tuttle & Bowen 1958 and Mirwald & Massonne 1980, respectively), and of the three polymorphs andalusite, sillimanite and kyanite in the system Al_2SiO_5 (compare Fig. 5) (after Kerrick 1990).

100 – 150 km, depending on the prevailing temperature. There, or even deeper, must lie the source of most natural diamonds that have been transported to the surface by the explosive volcanism of kimberlite pipes. However, this is not the complete story. Why is elemental carbon present at these depths? The sole answer has been, up to very recently, that diamonds represent the carbon that was initially accreted, together with other solid matter, during the primary formation of our planet from the solar nebula. There, carbon was an abundant element and the meteorite group of carbonaceous chondrites presents good evidence for this. However, while this view may be true for some 80 per cent of all natural diamonds known, the isotopic composition of the remaining 20 per cent suggests that they represent the remains of biogenic materials that originated at the surface of the early Earth, and have been carried down and metamorphosed at great depth.

Admittedly, this possibility seemed until recently so remote and fantastic that its long-standing rejection is understandable. Supporting evidence could come only from other affiliated high-pressure metamorphic products that were clearly of crustal provenance and could be proven, by the experimental results, to have formed at *PT* conditions within the diamond stability field. The most convincing examples are the diamond-bearing metamorphic rocks of the Kokchetav Massif in Kazakhstan (Shatsky *et al.* 1995), which were shown to contain minute inclusions of beautiful euhedral diamond crystals (microdiamonds) within the garnet porphyroblasts grown during ultrahigh-pressure metamorphism. Thus, there can no longer be any doubt that these microdiamonds have formed – prior to or simultaneously with the garnet – at mantle depths due to ultradeep subduction of carbonaceous sediments. Many of those were of marine origin. Thus, the 'change of place of the bottom of the ocean with relation to the centre of the earth' (Hutton) may be quite dramatic.

The system SiO_2

The oxide of Si, one of the two most abundant metal elements in the cosmos, is also the most common chemical component of terrestrial rock-forming systems. It is generally linked with other oxides in silicate minerals, often of extremely complex chemistry, but it may also occur as a single phase in rocks of the Earth's crust. Quartz with its density of 2.65 g cm^{-3} is the most abundant SiO_2 mineral, but, as shown in the phase diagram in Fig. 3, it is transformed, for example near active volcanoes, into the less dense mineral tridymite (2.27 g cm^{-3}). Otherwise quartz has an enormously wide stability range, certainly covering the remaining conditions of the continental crust, but also down to some 80–100 km. At these depths it becomes unstable and transforms into the high-pressure phase coesite (density 3.01 g cm^{-3}).

In 1984 the young French petrologist C. Chopin discovered the mineral coesite in a metamorphic rock of the Dora Maira Massif in the Western Alps (Fig. 4). Ever since, the metamorphism of rocks present in the continental crust could no longer be considered a process occurring solely within this thin outermost shell of some 35 km thickness (compare Fig. 2). The coesite-bearing rock of the Alps, although clearly of crustal origin, must have been subducted during its geological history to mantle depths of at least 100 km, that is, not quite as deep as the Kokchetav diamond rocks, because carbonaceous rocks at Dora Maira contain graphite. Conversely, as it should be (compare Fig. 3), coesite has also been discovered at Kokchetav.

At this point, the critical reader may wonder why coesite as a charateristic high-pressure mineral has been discovered so late in metamorphic rocks. Were generations of metamorphic petrologists blindfolded? The answer is that coesite transforms very easily and quickly within hours and days back into quartz once the pressure is lowered. Coesite is, with very few exceptions, only preserved as inclusions within other minerals such as the garnet pyrope in the Alps (Fig. 4). Because of its high strength the host mineral acted like a miniature high-pressure vessel during rock uplift and prevented the necessary volume expansion connected with the transformation of coesite to quartz. Note the radially orientated expansion cracks in the garnet host (Fig. 4) indicating its brittle failure, following which quartz growth began; but the process of total conversion was frozen in, probably because the uplift of the rock unit into regions of low temperatures, where the reaction becomes very slow, was rather fast. In conclusion, many metamorphic rocks containing quartz as the sole SiO_2 mineral could very well have carried coesite during an earlier stage of what is called ultrahigh-pressure metamorphism (Coleman & Wang 1995). For the petrologist, it is thus a detective job to find possible relics of coesite or other ultrahigh-pressure indicators. Meanwhile, coesite relics have been discovered in metamorphic rocks of three more regions in three different continents, in addition to the western Alps and Kazakhstan (Schreyer 1995; Wain 1997), so that ultrahigh-pressure metamorphism cannot be considered a unique or even unusual phenomenon.

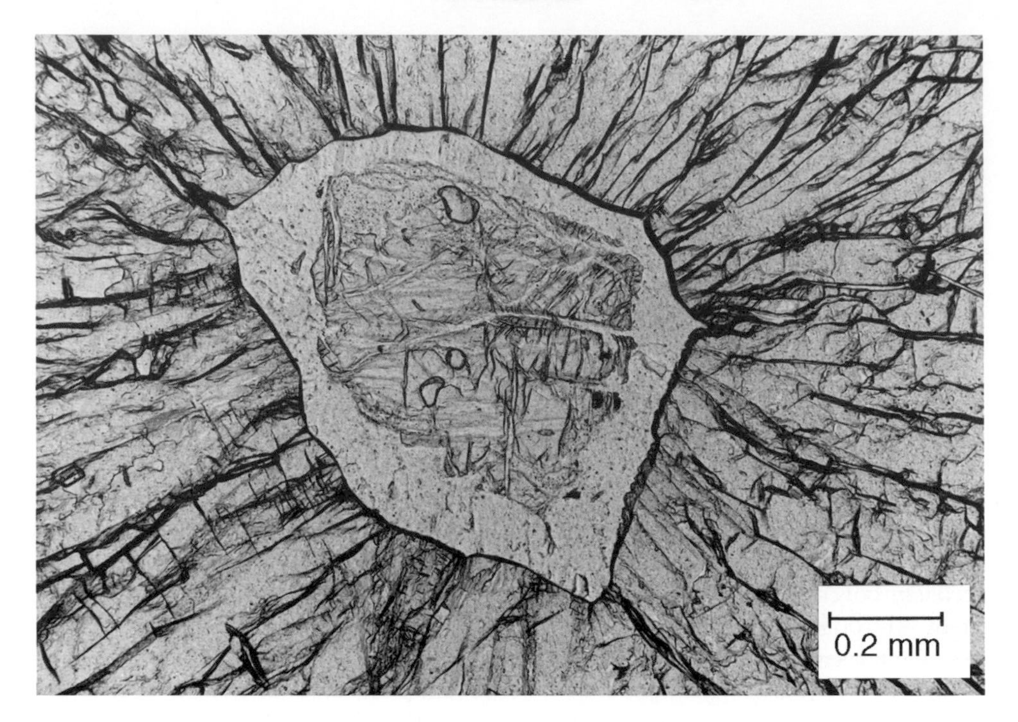

Fig. 4. Thin section photograph of a pyrope–coesite rock from Parigi, Dora Maira Massif, Western Alps, Italy. In the central portion a relic inclusion of the mineral coesite (see Fig. 3) is seen within the garnet mineral pyrope (see Figs 8 and 9). The latter shows radial cracks around the inclusion which are indicative of a volume expansion of this inclusion. Indeed the inclusion itself consists of coesite only in its central portion, which is recognized by the relatively high relief, whereas the peripheries are made up of translucent quartz, the lower-density polymorph of SiO_2. Thus, coesite was partially transformed into quartz during pressure release (see Fig. 3) in the course of rock exhumation.

The system Al_2O_3–SiO_2

With the addition of the component Al_2O_3 (Fig. 5), which is strongly enriched within the Earth's crust because of the process of chemical weathering, additional minerals can be formed: first of all Al_2O_3 itself, the mineral corundum. In nature, the most important compound is Al_2SiO_5, made up of one mole each of Al_2O_3 and SiO_2. Importantly,

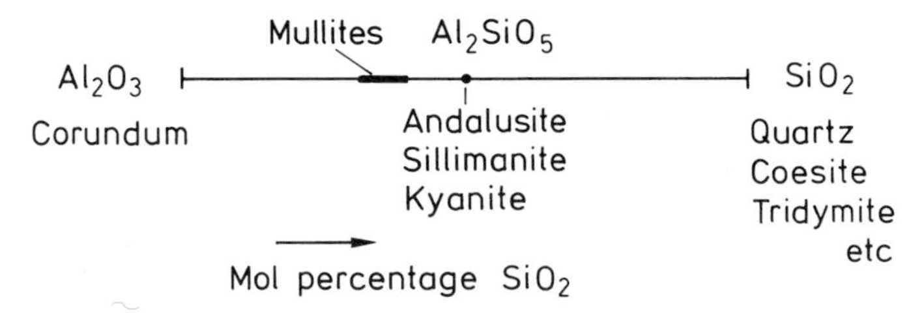

Fig. 5. Compositional plot of the two-component system Al_2O_3–SiO_2 containing the predominant phase Al_2SiO_5, which is treated as single one-component system in Fig. 3. For further discussion see the text.

Al_2SiO_5 also occurs in different modifications, namely the minerals andalusite, sillimanite and kyanite. Their *PT* stability fields, projected in Fig. 3, are determined by their physical properties, which in turn relate to their crystal structures. Kyanite is the densest phase of them (3.67 g cm^{-3}) and thus remains stable up to the highest pressures shown here; it may occur together with coesite and diamond in ultrahigh-pressure metamorphic rocks. All three Al_2SiO_5 minerals can coexist only at one particular *PT* coordinate, the triple point located at about 4.5 kbar, 540°C. It is very significant for the classical studies of metamorphic rocks over the centuries that this triple point lies within continental crustal conditions. Thus, the burial of marine clays, as envisaged by Hutton, may lead to crystalline schists containing either kyanite or andalusite or sillimanite, depending on whether the environment was rather cold or warmer or quite hot. In some cases, two or even three Al_2SiO_5 polymorphs may be found in the same rock. This can, in principle, be explained by conditions of metamorphism lying along the requisite phase boundaries. More likely, however, the Al_2SiO_5 minerals formed consecutively in the course of deeper burial or later heating or the initiation of exhumation. The polymorphism of Al_2SiO_5 and its experimental *PT* calibration stimulated the field of metamorphic petrology enormously and helped to make it a quantitative science which nowadays claims to be able to reconstruct individual pressure–temperature–time paths of specific rock specimens or units, which are the most important witnesses and markers of the dynamic processes within our globe.

The system Al_2O_3–SiO_2–H_2O

Water is the most common volatile component in rock-forming processes. Large amounts of the surface waters that we actually see are involved in what we may call the 'Hutton cycle' of rocks from unconsolidated ocean sediments to solid mountain rocks. H_2O may be present as fluid either in the porous space of the rocks along grain boundaries or – more significantly – within the crystals of the minerals themselves. Here water molecules can occupy voids in the crystal structures, such as in the zeolite minerals or in cordierite, or water may occur in the form of hydroxyl (OH) groups as an essential component of many important rock-forming minerals, such as micas or hornblendes. Needless to say, dissolved water in igneous melts is of paramount importance for magmatic processes discussed in a companion paper (Wyllie 1999).

H_2O in combination with the two previously discussed components, Al_2O_3 and SiO_2, leads to a number of crystalline phases, hydrous minerals, some of which originate under near-surface conditions through the interaction of rocks with the atmosphere (weathering) or hydrosphere (diagenesis of sediments). Kaolinite, $Al_2[Si_2O_5](OH)_4$ (Fig. 6), is a common mineral in many clays and as such becomes unstable at higher temperatures due to partial or complete dehydration. Its *PT* stability field as derived through both experiment and thermodynamic calculation is shown in Fig. 7. Importantly, it is also bounded towards higher pressures where most of the water present in kaolinite is now incorporated in the very dense Al hydrate diaspore, Al OOH. Similar relations hold for the mineral pyrophyllite, $Al_2[Si_4O_{10}](OH)_2$, which is less hydrous than kaolinite and is therefore restricted to somewhat elevated temperatures relative to kaolinite (Fig. 7). One may extract from this behaviour the general rule that progressive metamorphism of rocks at crustal pressures is accompanied by stepwise dehydration, whereby the released water will eventually reach the surface again thus completing the Hutton cycle.

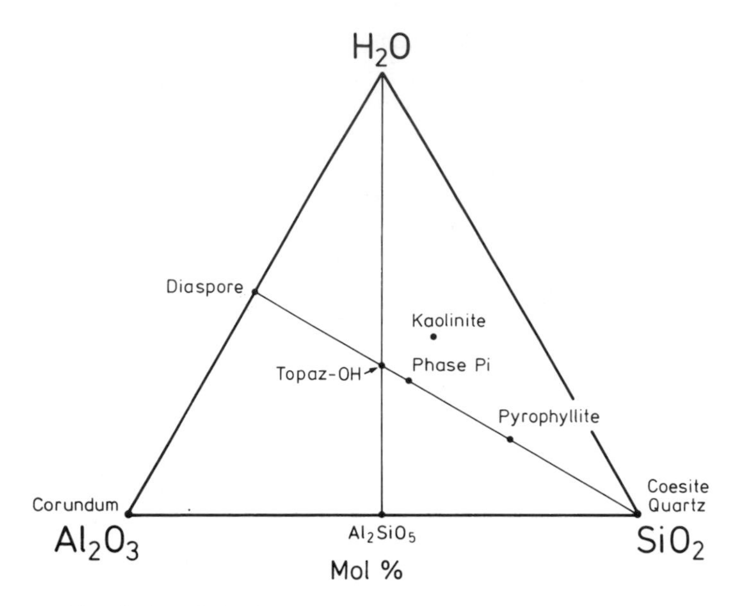

Fig. 6. Compositional plot of the three-component system Al_2O_3–SiO_2–H_2O showing only one anhydrous binary phase, Al_2SiO_5 (see Fig. 5), but numerous binary and ternary water-bearing phases as indicated. Note that nearly all of them plot along the join diaspore–SiO_2, thus indicating that they may enter into reaction relationships with these two minerals and also among each other, without involving the release or consumption of the component H_2O, which may coexist as a fluid phase. For stability fields of phases see Figs 3 and 7.

Surprisingly, experimentation in the system Al_2O_3–SiO_2–H_2O at mantle pressures resulted in the synthesis of two more hydroxyl-bearing phases that have not yet been discovered as minerals and, perhaps, never will be. These are phase Pi, $Al_3Si_2O_7(OH)_3$, and the hydroxyl analogue of topaz, $Al_2SiO_4(OH)_2$, here called 'topaz-OH'. Both are located in the ternary system (Fig. 6) along the compositional join diaspore–SiO_2, which implies that they can form at the expense of those two phases by the incorporation of all the water present in Al OOH. Their *PT* stability fields, outlined in Fig. 7, lead to the conclusion that these two phases can occur as minerals in nature only in very cold and ultrahigh-pressure regions such as may possibly exist in the central portions of old subduction zones. As these are clearly transitory environments in global dynamics, because they are subsequently subjected to heating, the two hydrous high-pressure Al silicates will dehydrate to form kyanite-bearing assemblages (Fig. 7). Thus, their preservation in rocks now exposed at the Earth's surface could be expected only when cold, deep subduction zone materials from depths of at least 90 km (see Fig. 7) return quickly and without later heating into shallow crustal levels – a geodynamically improbable situation. Nevertheless, their possible existence at great depths is by no means of purely theoretical interest. Geophysical research on present-day old and cold subduction zones, such as Izu-Bonin (south of Japan), must take into account their existence in the chemical system as well as their physical properties in order to allow meaningful interpretation of the results of measurements obtained in these zones.

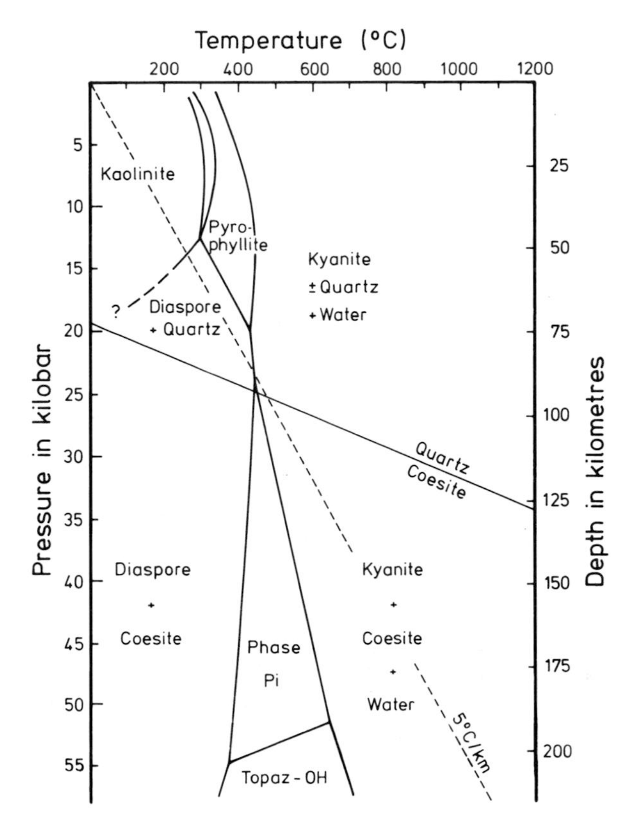

Fig. 7. *PT* plot showing the stability fields of hydrous ternary phases of the system Al_2O_3–SiO_2–H_2O as plotted in Fig. 6. For comparison, the possibly limiting geotherm 5°C km of Fig. 1 is indicated as a dashed line. References: for kaolinite and pyrophyllite, Theye *et al.* (1997); for phase Pi and topaz-OH, Schreyer (1995, simplified). All phases coexist with a fluid phase rich

The System MgO–Al_2O_3–SiO_2–H_2O

In the final model system to be discussed here, MgO is chosen as an additional component, because experimental studies in this system had proven to yield particularly detailed insights into the *PT* dependence of minerals and their assemblages, and because nearly all these mineralogical variations have been found to have counterparts in natural metamorphic rocks. Thus, the close interrelationship between nature and experiment was clearly demonstrated by experience. Petrographic observations from rocks as well as unexpected experimental results were taken as starting points further experimental and petrographical research, respectively. In other words, the usual procedure of applying experimental data in order to explain and delimit the occurrence of particular minerals of natural rocks was complemented by special searches for and the final discoveries in metamorphic terrains of new minerals and mineral assemblages which had previously been obtained only in the laboratory as synthetic products. This type of integrated petrological research has indeed led to important progress especially regarding metamorphism at high pressures.

The quaternary system $MgO–Al_2O_3–SiO_2–H_2O$, shown in a projection in Fig. 8, contains a multitude of phases, of which only the relevant ones to be discussed here are plotted in the triangle. They include some phases of the limiting system $MgO–SiO_2$, with or without H_2O, which carry the most abundant mineral of the Earth's upper mantle, forsterite, Mg_2SiO_4, together with enstatite, $Mg_2Si_2O_6$, and the common hydrous minerals serpentine, $Mg_3[Si_2O_5](OH)_4$, and talc, $Mg_3[Si_4O_{10}](OH)_2$. Of particular interest here are the ternary MgAl silicates with characteristic *PT* stability fields that make them good indicators for the high-pressure versus low-pressure types of metamorphism. In Fig. 9 a selection of stability fields is presented from which it is evident that cordierite, $Mg_2Al_4Si_5O_{18} \cdot xH_2O$, is confined to environments within the continental crust. The Mg endmember of the mineral carpholite, $MgAl_2Si_2O_6(OH)_4$, becomes stable at lower crustal levels and relatively low temperatures but persists up to high pressures near 50 kbar. The minerals pyrope, $Mg_3Al_2Si_3O_{12}$, Mg-chloritoid, $MgAl_2SiO_5(OH)_2$, Mg-staurolite, $\sim Mg_4Al_{18}Si_8O_{46}(OH)_2$, and the synthetic phase $Mg_5Al_5Si_6O_{21}(OH)_7$, provisionally named 'Mg-pumpellyite' here, however, can be formed only at depths in the Earth's mantle. As it turned out, all of these high-pressure phases, except for the pumpellyite phase, were discovered in nature as new minerals, after their syntheses in the laboratory. Significantly, most occur in coesite-bearing continental crustal rocks that had been subducted to depths of about 100 km, so that all mineralogical indicators are consistent in providing evidence for ultrahigh pressures. The reason for the failure to find pumpellyite phase could be the restriction of its stability field to the region below the 5 °C/km geotherm in Fig. 9. Thus, once formed, the phase may not survive exhumation, similarly as has been argued for the hydrous Al-silicates phase Pi and topaz-OH (see Fig. 7 and section on the system $Al_2O_3–SiO_2–H_2O$).

Over the years, experimental research work in the system $MgO–Al_2O_3–SiO_2–H_2O$ has

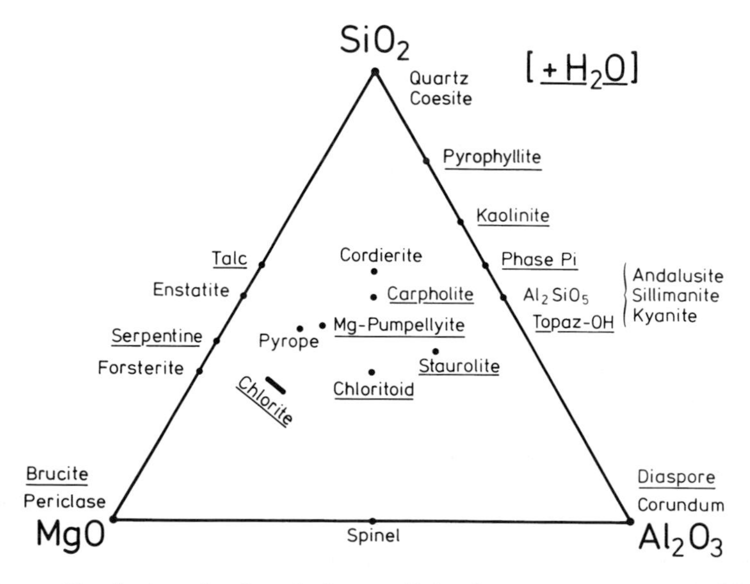

Fig. 8. Compositional plot of selected phases of the four-component system $MgO–Al_2O_3–SiO_2–H_2O$ projected from the H_2O apex on to the base plane. Hydrous phases are underlined.

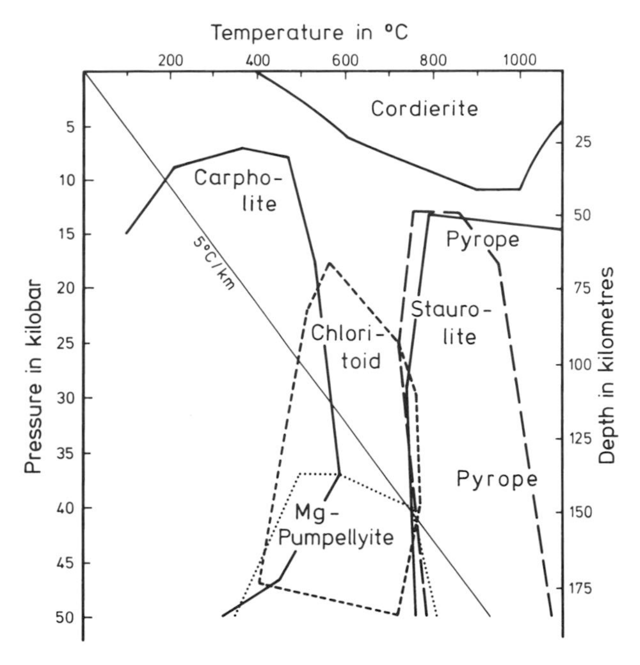

Fig. 9. *PT* plot showing the stability fields of selected phases of the system $MgO–Al_2O_3–SiO_2–H_2O$ in the presence of H_2O fluid. Their compositions are plotted in Fig. 8 and their chemical formulae are given in the text. Note that the five high-pressure phases (Schreyer 1988) do not overlap in their stability fields with that of the low-pressure phase cordierite (Schreyer 1986). The 5°C km^{-1} geotherm of Fig. 1 is for reference.

provided several examples of the importance of the assemblage of two or more minerals as additional petrological indicators of pressure and temperature. Three cases in particular have had considerable impact on the history of research of rock metamorphism, because they lead – for identical bulk rock compositions – to vastly different rock types that may be readily recognized in the field. These three are summarized in Fig. 10, which shows the univariant equilibrium curves of the reactions interconnecting the three characteristic mineral assemblages and their stability fields. At crustal pressures the assemblage chlorite + quarz is stable, which is typical of greenschists, a common type of low-grade metamorphic rock. With increasing pressures and temperatures these two minerals react and form the alternative new pair, talc + kyanite, making conspicuous silvery rocks named whiteschists. This assemblage remains stable up to rather high pressures within the field of coesite but, as shown in Fig. 10, it reacts upon temperature increase to form the pair, pyrope + SiO_2 (coesite or quartz), now leading to a massive garnet rock with much of the free SiO_2 phase. In the field, the latter is quartz, formed during exhumation from coesite, while coesite is only preserved as inclusions within pyrope (see Fig. 4 and the section on the system SiO_2). It should be emphasized once again that an original near-surface chlorite–quartz rock can undergo all these mineralogical changes during its subduction history. Conversely, the ultrahigh-pressure metamorphic pyrope quartzites of the Western Alps were found to exhibit the lower-grade assemblages as retrograde products that were formed during the return trip of these rocks into crustal levels.

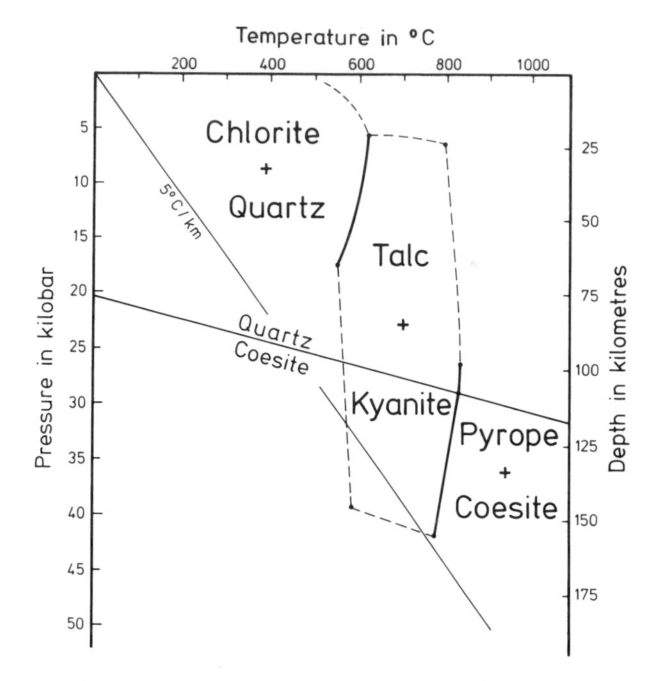

Fig. 10. *PT* plot showing the stability fields of three different two-phase assemblages of the system $MgO–Al_2O_3–SiO_2–H_2O$ in the presence of H_2O. The compositions of all minerals involved are plotted in Fig. 8. The three assemblages may form from a single bulk composition in the system plotting at the intersection of the tie lines talc–kyanite and pyrope–SiO_2 (see Fig. 8). At the highest temperatures of the field pyrope + coesite a melt may be present as well. The solid lines are the specific reaction curves between the requisite assemblages shown, dashed lines limiting the stability fields apply to reactions leading to other phase assemblages not discussed here. (After Schreyer 1988.) The 5°C km^{-1} geotherm of Fig. 1 and quartz–coesite transition of Fig. 3 are shown for reference.

How deep can crustal rocks be buried?

The discovery of characteristic high-pressure minerals and mineral assemblages in metamorphic rocks that had clearly formed initially within continental crust (see Fig. 2) has caused a revolution in the thinking of metamorphic petrologists. Obviously, the metamorphic imprint on these rocks cannot have been attained within the normal thickness of this crust of some 35 km, but burial to depths exceeding this thickness by factors of up to about four must have occurred. This is the realm of the Earth's upper mantle–not even deep 'mountain roots' (see Fig. 2) reach such depths.

The consequence of these petrological discoveries is a complete reconsideration of the geodynamics of our globe. It is now apparent that continental crust can be subducted, during the collision of continents, to mantle depths of at least about 150 km, judging from the beginning of the diamond stability field (Fig. 3). Even more surprisingly, portions of this deeply subducted crust rise again and become incorporated as slices within the complicated architecture of the orogenic belts that develop at the collision sites.

An important aspect is that the kinetics of reconversion of high-pressure phases into lower-pressure analogues increase dramatically with pressure. The experimentalists learned that some of their high-pressure products could not even be pressure -quenched in the laboratory. Thus, the 150 km marker may not be the limit of subduction, because any rocks returned from still greater depths may be completely recrystallized so that not even the best detective work by mineralogists and petrologists could yield evidence of previous super-high-pressure events.

Another open problem is still whether all of the subducted crust returns back into the crust, or whether considerable proportions remain buried, perhaps being conveyed to such great depths that they become incorporated into the chemically quite different material of the Earth's mantle. Geochemists have learned that the isotopic compositions of ocean island basalts such as those from Hawaii are best explained if they assume some contributions from oceanic crust (see Fig. 2). As the melts forming these basalts are believed to be derived from plumes originating near the boundary between the mantle and the core at about 2900 km depth, it must be concluded that the subducted slabs carrying this type of crust have penetrated the total thickness of the mantle to end at the final 'slab graveyard'. It may be very difficult or even impossible to make a distinction between the faint chemical fingerprints of oceanic versus continental crust. Thus the maximum depth of subduction of continental crust may never be really identified. However, returning to Hutton's statement of 1785, it is clear that 'the bottom of the ocean has changed its place with relation to the centre of the earth' by an enormous amount: it went nearly halfway down through our globe!

Crustal materials participate in the enormous secular convection processes that affect the Earth's mantle, although their contribution to the huge volume of mantle material is only small. The present-day crust is not the final sink of all the low-melting and volatile elements where they were believed to have accumulated since the beginning of the Earth's history 4.5 billion years ago. The size and composition of our present crust is due to a recycling equilibrium relative to the convecting mantle. The metamorphism of rocks marks only the beginning or a small portion of such a cycle, but it is impressive to realize how deep its imprint can be followed by the observant geoscientist.

References

CHOPIN, C. 1984. Coesite and pure pyrope in high-grade blueschists of the Western Alps: a first record and some consequences. *Contributions to Mineralogy and Petrology,* **86**, 107–118.

COLEMAN, R. G. & WANG, X. 1995. *Ultrahigh pressure metamorphism*. Cambridge University Press, Cambridge.

KERRICK, D. M. 1990. The Al_2SiO_5 polymorphs. *Reviews in Mineralogy,* **22**.

KENNEDY, C. S. & KENNEDY, G. C. 1976. The equilibrium boundary between graphite and diamond. *Journal of Geophysical Research,* **81**, 2467–2470.

MIRWALD, P. W. & MASSONNE, H.-J. 1980. The low–high quartz and quartz–coesite transition to 4 GPa between 600 and 1600°C and some reconnaissance data on the effect of $NaAlO_2$ component on the low quartz–coesite transition. *Journal of Geophysical Research,* **85**, 6983–6990.

SCHREYER, W. 1986. The mineral cordierite: structure and reactions in the presence of fluid phases. *Berichte der Bunsen-Gesellschaft für physikalische Chemie,* **90**, 748–755.

—— 1988. Subduction of continental crust to mantle depths: petrologic evidence. *Episodes,* **11**, 97–104.

—— 1995. Ultradeep metamorphic rocks: the retrospective view point. *Journal of Geophysical Research,* **100**, 8353–8366.

SHATSKY, V. S., SOBOLEV, N. V. & VAVILOV, M. A. 1995. Diamond-bearing metamorphic rocks of the Koktchetav Massif (Northern Kazakhstan). *In*: COLEMAN, R. G. & WANG, X. (eds) *Ultrahigh Pressure Metamorphism*, Cambridge University Press, Cambridge, 427–455.

THEYE, T., CHOPIN, C., GREVEL, K.-D. & OCKENGA, E. 1997. The assemblage diaspore + quartz in metamorphic rocks: a petrological, experimental and thermodynamic study. *Journal of Metamorphic Geology,* **15**, 17–28.

TUTTLE, O. F. & BOWEN, N. L. 1958. Origin of granite in the light of experimental studies in the system $NaAlSi_3O_8$–$KAlSi_3O_8$–SiO_2–H_2O. *Geological Society of America Memoir,* **74**.

WAIN, A. 1997. New evidence for coesite in eclogite and gneisses: defining a ultrahigh-pressure province in the Western Gneiss region of Norway. *Geology,* **25**, 927–930.

WYLLIE, P. J. 1999. Hot little crucibles are pressured to reveal and calibrate igneous processes. *This volume.*

Coevolution of the Earth's environment and life: Goldilocks, Gaia and the anthropic principle

ANDREW J. WATSON
School of Environmental Science, University of East Anglia, Norwich NR4 7TJ, UK

Abstract: Observation suggests that the Earth's surface environment is maintained by processes in which non-living and living causes are linked inextricably. Once established on Earth, life rapidly became a dominant influence on the evolution of the planetary environment. But life was also shaped by that evolution, constrained and directed by the physical and chemical processes that moulded the planet's surface. Life and the planetary environment form a closely coupled entity, a view of the Earth as a complex system which is prefigured in the writings of James Hutton.

Hutton compared the workings of the Earth's surface to the body of an animal, being both wasted and repaired continually. In modern times, James Lovelock has argued that it is a property of this system that it acts to maintain the planet in a habitable condition. Alternatively, perhaps it is pure chance that the planet has always remained hospitable for life – it could just as easily have followed an infinity of different evolutionary paths, many and perhaps most of which would lead rapidly to global extinction. Consideration of the fates of our near-neighbour planets, Mars and Venus, and the dangerous nature of the inner solar system, leads to the conclusion that there is indeed a substantial element of luck involved in the Earth's biosphere having survived as long as it has. The fact that our own existence is dependent on it having survived makes it nearly impossible to accurately assess *a priori* the probability of survival.

Abstract models such as 'Daisyworld' can capture some of the complex behaviour of the Earth–life system. This may include periods of stasis and sudden changes to new states, the stasis being an example of regulatory behaviour where the system is dominated by negative feedback, and the sudden changes being essentially the opposite – brief but traumatic periods where the dominant feedbacks are positive. GEOCARB, a biogeochemical model for the Phanerozoic which links changes in the long-term carbon cycle to planetary temperature, shows examples of both regulatory and destabilizing behaviour in a less abstract system, and suggests that such responses have indeed characterized Earth history.

I conclude that the properties of the Earth–life system are complex and not easily predictable. The longevity of Hutton's animal (nearly 4 Ga) is no guide to its future life expectancy, and even if the system as a whole lasts many aeons into the future, any given species (such as humans) is most unlikely to.

James Hutton was part of that great debate that in his time set science, and what we can learn by observation with our own eyes, against the tenets of religion as handed to us in the biblical texts. Hutton was steadfastly against those who preferred a literal interpretation of the Bible to the evidence that they could see by their own eyes and discover by the application of intelligence. He came to the conclusion that the cycles of erosion and uplift, of decay and rebuilding, for which he found such compelling evidence, were a part of a system set up by God, but which ran according to laws that the informed

WATSON, A. J. 1999. Coevolution of the Earth's environment and life: Goldilocks, Gaia and the anthropic principle. *In*: CRAIG, G. Y. & HULL, J. H. (eds) *James Hutton – Present and Future*. Geological Society, London, Special Publications, **150**, 75–88.

observer could discern. I am indebted to Donald McIntyre for directing me to the following quotation:

'Was it the work of accident, or effect of occasional transaction, that by which the sea had covered our land? Or, Was it the intention of that Mind which formed the matter of this globe, which endued that matter with its active and its passive powers, and which placed it with so much wisdom among a numberless collection of bodies, all moving in a system? If we admit the first, the consequence of such a supposition would be to attribute to chance the constitution of this world, in which the systems of life and sense, or reason and intellect, are necessarily maintained. If again we shall admit, that there is intention in the cause by which the present Earth had been removed from the bottom of the sea, we may then inquire into the nature of that system in which a habitable Earth, possessed of beauty, arranged in order, and preserved with economy, had been formed by the mixture and combination of the different elements, and made to rise out of the wreck of a former world.' (Hutton, vol. 2, pp. 551–552).

Hutton therefore did consider the explanation of the ordering of the world as a chance sequence of events. However, he rejected this view, preferring instead to retain belief in God, on the basis that it is a more elegant and satisfying theory, which gives to 'reason and intellect' the task of uncovering the nature of the system devised by God for the maintenance of the world. If there is no God, there is no system to discover. In his time, this would have seemed a more reasonable, and certainly less seditious, conclusion than the idea that the constitution of the Earth was attributable to chance.

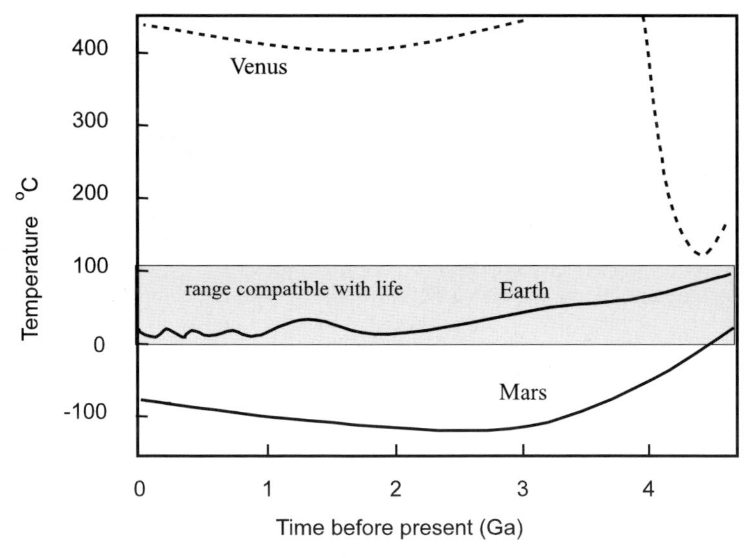

Fig. 1. Schematic to show the possible evolution of the surface temperatures of Earth (solid line), Mars (light line) and Venus (dashed line). Only the present-day temperatures are known with absolute certainty, so much of the graph is speculative. Soon after formation Venus may have undergone a 'runaway greenhouse' in which its outgassed water formed a thick water-vapour atmosphere, leading to very high surface temperatures. Mars once had liquid water at its surface, but has since cooled, probably as the result of the loss of a more infrared-absorbing atmosphere. Earth may similarly have been warmer in its earliest stages. The slowly increasing output of the Sun has probably caused the temperatures of Mars and Venus to increase in more recent times.

In this paper I explore some aspects of this concept of the Earth, the physical and chemical forces acting on it, and the living things which inhabit it, as a system ('a compound system of things, forming together one whole living world', to quote again from Hutton's *Theory of the Earth*). In the 200 years since Hutton's death, God, as an explanation for the apparently ordered nature of the physical world, has suffered a precipitous decline, so that it is no longer considered good form in the scientific literature to debate ultimate causes by reference to the creator. It is nevertheless perfectly proper to ask whether the simultaneous and linked evolution of the planet and the life on it has resulted in a system that is 'like an animal', to use Hutton's simile, in the sense of having some self-regulatory properties that help it to persist. Alternatively, perhaps it has survived simply by blind chance. In recent times, James Lovelock (with due reference to Hutton) has championed the former view and christened the beast 'Gaia' (Lovelock 1987, 1992).

I should perhaps begin by clarifying some terms that have sometimes caused confusion when this subject is discussed. By 'evolution of the Earth's environment', I do not mean 'evolution by natural selection'. Species evolve through time because the offspring of each generation have a diverse genetic make-up on which natural selection can act. Clearly this is not applicable to the Earth's biosphere as a whole, of which there is only one, and which does not reproduce (or to be strictly accurate, has not as yet reproduced as far as we can tell). Thus if the Earth–life system has properties that actively help it to survive, they must be innate; they have not been refined by a process of natural selection acting on the genes of the ancestors of the system, but must be there by chance. This means they are probably rather simple properties, because simple systems are the most likely to have been assembled by chance.

The Goldilocks paradox

Earth's near neighbours in the solar system, Mars and Venus, can serve to give some comparison of possible alternative evolutionary pathways that a planet might take. Figure 1 shows possible histories of their surface temperatures on a common scale. It is notable that all three planets may at one time have been habitable by life, in the sense that liquid water may have existed at their surfaces. However, today only the Earth is habitable by this definition. Evidence (in the form of fluvial channels and outwash plains cut by mud or water) is very strong for an early 'warm and wet' phase for Mars before 3 billion years ago (Donahue 1995; Carr 1996). Today, however, with a mean temperature of –70°C, the surface of Mars is colder than the South Pole and thoroughly inhospitable to life.

There is plenty of evidence too that Venus once had appreciable water, perhaps as much as the Earth. This may or may not have once resided at the surface, but if it did, the planet has long since undergone a 'runaway greenhouse' in which all the water boiled into the atmosphere and was subsequently lost by hydrogen escape and oxygen absorption (Walker 1975; Donahue *et al.* 1981; Watson *et al.* 1984; Kasting 1988; Chassefiere 1996, 1997).

On Mars and Venus, therefore, the large changes in surface temperature to which they were subject preclude the possibility of either planet harbouring life as we know it today, on the surface at least. It is probable that there never was any life at the surface of either of them, but if there was, it was extinguished billions of years ago. Venus is therefore too hot, Mars is too cold, but the Earth is just right for life, and apparently has remained so for nearly four billion years, an observation that has been called the 'Goldilocks paradox' (Rampino & Caldeira 1994).

The surface temperatures of the planets are controlled by the brightness of the Sun, their albedos and the greenhouse effect due to their atmospheres. Most likely Mars and Earth had atmospheres with greater infrared optical thickness in their early histories, and the dissipation of these early greenhouse atmospheres has partially compensated for the steady increase in luminosity of the Sun over time (the so-called 'dim young sun' paradox. In the case of the Earth, this compensation has been just such as to keep the planet habitable. Whether this was by luck, or by biological and geochemical feedbacks, we will examine later.

Changes in surface temperature are not the only threats that life on our planet has survived. Our neighbourhood of the solar system is a dangerous place, with many large bodies in elliptical orbits which cross that of the Earth (150 are known, but many more are thought to exist; the population changes with time because asteroids may be moved into or out of such orbits by close encounters with other planets). In the formation phase of the planets, for 0.6 Ga prior to about 3.9 Ga ago, the accreting planets were subject to intense bombardment, but even after this phase, collisions with large meteorites have continued to be common.

Figure 2 illustrates the approximate relationship that holds today for the frequency of impact events on the Earth. The largest event of which there is a geological record was that which caused the Chicxulub Formation, which has been associated with the Cretaceous–Tertiary extinction (Hildebrand *et al.* 1991). This is believed to be a once-in-

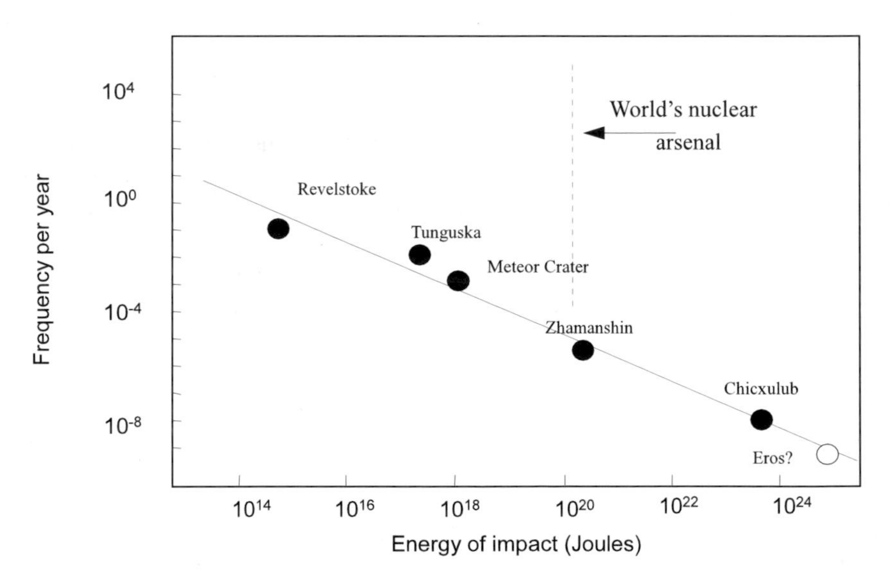

Fig. 2. Relationship between expected frequency and energy for various impact events on the Earth. The Chicxulub event, associated with the K–T extinction, is the most energetic known impact feature and is thought to be roughly a one-in-10^8 years event. If the Earth-crossing asteroid Eros were to strike, as suggested by Michel *et al.* (1996), this would be a one-in-10^9 year event. The approximate energy that would be liberated by explosion of the world's nuclear arsenal is shown for comparison. (Figure courtesy of Richard A. F. Grieve, Geological Survey of Canada, redrawn with additions.)

100-million-years event, a timescale that at least suggests that extraterrestrial cataclysms of even greater destructive power, perhaps big enough to sterilize the planet, might be expected to have occurred over the period since life began. It is presumably just luck that no such sterilizing event has in fact occurred. One of the largest of the Earth-crossing asteroids, Eros, has recently been shown to have about a 50 per cent chance of colliding with the Earth in the next 100 Ma (Michel *et al.* 1996). Eros would produce an impact about an order of magnitude more powerful than the Chicxulub event.

The anthropic principle

Hutton's explanation for the persistence of the Earth and the life on it, and the seemingly integrated nature of the 'one whole living world', was that it was God's creation and designed to be so. It would have been difficult in his age to come to any other conclusion; the revolution in our ideas about the origin of living things which Darwin's work ushered in was still a half-century in the future at the time of Hutton's death.

As I have explained above, one cannot apply evolution by natural selection to the Earth as a whole, but there is one insight central to Darwin's vision which is just as applicable to the whole system as to the parts of it. This is the idea that the history of the Earth is a 'survivor's tale' – life is as we see it because that is what has survived. Life may be a commonplace in the universe, such that there are planets with thriving biospheres circling round every other star, or it could be a one-in-10^{100} coincidence, in which case there is, with a high degree of certainty, no other life in the universe. With the evidence we have today, there is unfortunately no way to tell which of these two possibilities is closer to the truth.

The reason that we are unable to pin down the probability of life beginning and surviving is tied up with an axiom called the 'anthropic principle' which is important in modern cosmology. The anthropic principle in its general form states that the observed universe must be compatible with the presence of the observers (in our case, human beings). Thus, for example, if the fundamental constants of nature were such that carbon did not form organic compounds, living things such as ourselves could not have come into existence in that universe. In principle such a universe might exist, but creatures like us would be unable to observe it.

At a number of points in the history of life on Earth we can identify circumstances or events that, had they not happened, 'intelligent observers' such as ourselves could not have evolved. Some of these are astronomical events or non-events. Examples are the existence of a planet within the 'habitable zone' around the sun (Kasting *et al.* 1993), the fact that the Earth possesses a moon which stabilises the obliquity of the planet (Laskar *et al.* 1993), or the fact that no very large, Earth-sterilizing impact has occurred since the origin of life. Some are biological: the origin of life itself, the evolution of the genetic code, the origin of oxygenic photosynthesis (without which the amount of energy available to the biosphere would be many orders of magnitude smaller) and the origin of the eukaryotic cell. We may also name social circumstances, such as the origin of language. If we knew the probabilities of occurrence of all these events, we could evaluate the overall probability that intelligent observers would arise around a given star. We can make some progress on the astronomical phenomena, because we have other planets and suns to study, but evaluation of the probabilities inherent in the biological phenomena is much more difficult because we know only our own biosphere. The anthropic principle tells us that it is inherently impossible to calculate these probabilities by studying only the sequence of events on our own planet, because our very existence depends on that sequence having a particular outcome.

Our dependence on a particular Earth history thus introduces a bias to our observation of the past. Because our ability to observe depends on a particular string of events, we cannot evaluate without bias the probability of those events; simply by being here, we have already predetermined the outcome. This, on a grand scale, is the well-known problem of the observer affecting the observation, consideration of which was central to the development of quantum physics in the early part of this century. In the present case the existence of the observers today has in some sense predetermined the outcome of events that occurred deep in the past. This is a hard concept to grasp – our everyday experience is that cause comes before effect, not after it – but there are precedents. Experiments can be designed (in the mind if not in practice) in which the actions of an observer determine the outcome of an event, even though the event occurs before the observation is made (Wheeler 1980).

Many palaeontologists conclude that the path by which life has developed on Earth is a sequence of accidents, so that if the 'tape were played twice' the biosphere that developed would not remotely resemble the one that we know (Gould 1989). Nevertheless, we often naively overestimate the probability that life, *a priori*, would turn out the way it actually has. This is an understandable human tendency, given the difficulty of imagining the countless other possible outcomes, most of them much less interesting to us than what actually happened on this Earth. This tendency is readily apparent in modern culture, in which we populate the universe of our imagination with aliens who usually have hominid-like features and frequently even speak English. It is, I believe, an important component of religious belief. We find it difficult to live with the idea that our own existence (both as a species and as individuals) is attributable to a series of events having a vanishingly low probability and no cosmically preordained meaning. It is natural instead to postulate a God, who is the repository of meaning and who has preordained the unfolding of events. This was essentially Hutton's position, as set forth in the earlier quote.

The bias that the anthropic principle applies to our observations of our own past would not apply if we were able to observe other planets which had evolved independently of Earth, to determine whether they had life on them. One of the most exciting and important projects for the early part of the next century must be to look for evidence of life on planets around other stars, a programme that now seems technically feasible and to which I shall return in my conclusion.

Stability and longevity of the Earth's biosphere: lessons from Daisyworld

From the above discussion it follows that there is no absolute need to invoke special processes to explain the fact that the Earth's biosphere has survived for around 4 Ga; this could be a chance outcome of a system that *a priori* would not have been expected to last so long. Thus, for example, when faced with the 'dim young sun' problem already alluded to, the geochemist may shrug and say that the survival of the Earth's biota through time was just luck. While this must always be considered, it would not be too surprising if the biosphere has some simple properties that tend to enhance its stability and longevity. Such a biosphere would be more likely to survive longer, so if we imagine that many different kinds of biospheres are possible, it would be those that have such properties to promote their long-term survival which would be most likely to last long enough to produce complex, highly evolved observers like ourselves.

The possibility that the biosphere is self-stabilizing was raised by Lovelock and Margulis when they first put forward the Gaia hypothesis, without at the time having a firm view of the mechanisms that might bring it about (Lovelock & Margulis 1972). A decade later, studies of a model system which Lovelock christened 'Daisyworld' shed light on at least one possible 'systems' mechanism that might contribute to stability (Watson & Lovelock 1983). Daisyworld repays considerable study, elaborated on by various authors over the years (Lovelock 1992; Degregorio *et al.* 1992; Saunders 1994; Harding & Lovelock 1996), but the essence of the argument is as follows.

(1) Suppose that life on Earth is able to substantially alter the Earth environment, including changing the surface temperature. In Daisyworld, this tendency is modelled by a biosphere that consists of coloured daisies; white daisies tend to cool themselves and the planet by reflecting sunlight away, while black daisies tend to warm things up by absorbing more radiation.

(2) Suppose equally that life is constrained by that same Earth environment. In the case of planetary temperature, it thrives best at a comfortable mean of, say, 20°C, but its productivity (and therefore ability to change the environment) falls off rapidly at higher or lower temperatures.

Using simple equations from population ecology and the energy balance of the planet, the behaviour of such a system can be modelled. Even the simplest systems are found to have a quite complex behaviour, typical of non-linear systems with feedback. The steady-state behaviour of the simplest possible system (one species of white daisy) is shown in Fig. 3. Surface temperatures, and daisy populations, are shown as a function of increasing solar luminosity, such as is thought to have occurred over time with the Sun. The temperature of the planet in the 'no life' condition is also shown for comparison. The figure illustrates a number of instructive points.

(1) Over substantial regions of luminosity the daisies act as a negative feedback on external forcing of temperature. The reason for this is that the normal steady-state solution is one in which the daisies are self-limiting, so that any increase in their number tends to drive the temperature in a direction that limits further growth. Conversely, a decrease in their numbers moves the conditions to be more favourable for growth.

Why should the solution be self-regulating? It does not have to be. There is, in general, another steady-state solution, a positive-feedback condition in which the daisies tend to reinforce changes in planetary temperature and destabilise the system. This solution is, by definition, less stable than the negative-feedback solution and has a smaller locus of attraction. This means that, when the model is initialized at some arbitrary point and allowed to run forward, it is more likely to be attracted to the negative-feedback condition than the positive-feedback one. If we imagine increasing from zero the potential of the daisies to alter planetary temperature (i.e. by changing their albedo away from that of the bare ground that they cover), the positive feedback solution becomes less and less stable. At some point its locus of attraction becomes infinitely small so that it can no longer be observed. Such metastable and unstable states may exist in the real Earth system, but they will tend to be transited more rapidly than the stable, negative-feedback conditions, and may therefore be difficult to observe in the geological record.

(2) Another stable state is the 'dead planet' solution in which there are no daisies. At

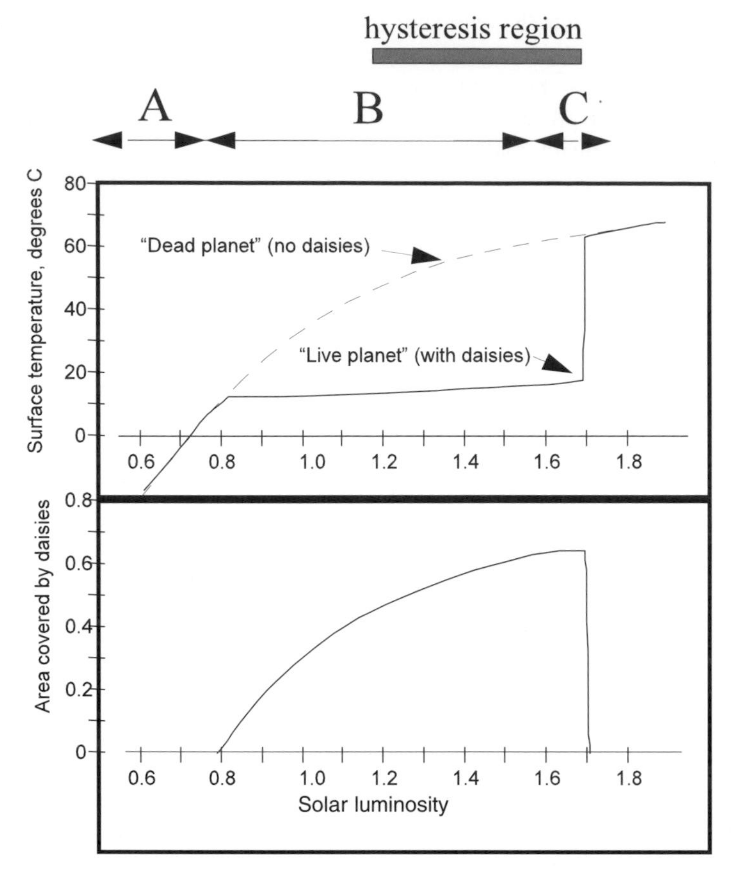

Fig. 3. Responses of a simple Daisyworld, with one type of daisy which is white in colour and so tends to cool the planet. The ordinate is the luminosity of the Sun, in arbitrary units. The upper panel shows surface temperatures, both when the daisies are allowed to grow (solid line) and for the barren planet (dashed line), while the lower panel shows the fraction of the planet's surface covered by daisies. At low luminosities (region A) the planet is too cold for life. Through a wide range of intermediate luminosities (region B) the daisy population tends to regulate surface temperature at 'comfortable' values. If the luminosity becomes too high the system becomes unstable (region C); the daisy population goes extinct and the temperature jumps to a high value. At temperatures higher than about 45°C the daisies are unable to grow, thus, while the daisies thrive if they are initially present in the zone marked 'hysteresis region', if they go extinct here, they cannot re-establish because the 'dead planet' temperature is too high for them.

the extremes, a long way from a 'comfortable' solar luminosity, this solution is the only possible one. There is a region of solar luminosity where the 'dead planet' solution is too hot to allow daisies to grow, but where the environment can remain perfectly habitable provided daisies are there to begin with. In this region the solutions exhibit hysteresis, and which solution is followed depends on the history of the system. If this region is entered by means of a slow increase in luminosity then the daisies continue to thrive and the 'living planet' solution is followed, but if the numbers of daisies are suddenly greatly reduced (for example because of the impact of a large meteorite, or equally because an animal with a voracious appetite for daisies suddenly evolves on their planet) then the solution switches to that of the 'dead planet'.

(3) As the solar luminosity is increased further a point is reached where, even in the absence of any sudden shock, the 'living planet' solution becomes unstable. The daisy population then crashes to extinction, and the temperature simultaneously changes to a much higher value. In this region, and in contrast to its influence in the 'comfortable' region, the effect of the biota is dramatically to *destabilize* the environment, for the change in temperature in the presence of daisies is much greater than that without them.

What is the essential difference between the behaviour of the system with life and that without it? It is not increased stability, for though this is apparent in some regions, the opposite occurs in others. Rather, it is a change in the character of the system due to the non-linearity that is introduced by the equations governing the population of daisies. Linear and nearly linear systems such as simple climate and geochemical models generally have few and simple steady-state solutions. By contrast, non-linear systems with feedbacks may exhibit multiple steady states, periodic solutions, and/or chaotic behaviour. They may transit between these solutions under suitable external forcing, exhibiting altogether a much richer behaviour than linear systems. The ultra-simple Daisyworld described above exhibits rather simple behaviour, but as soon as time delays (for example), are introduced, chaotic and periodic behaviour becomes a possibility.

The real Daisyworld: controls on atmospheric CO_2 and temperature through time?

Does anything like Daisyworld operate to affect the temperature of the real Earth? In practice it seems that the biota does not hugely affect the albedo of the planet (though its influence on cloud albedo may be important (Charlson *et al.* 1987). However, the biota does strongly influence the concentrations of greenhouse gases in the atmosphere and by this means has a substantial influence on planetary temperature. Thus the basic requirements for a Daisyworld-like system are satisfied, i.e. the biota affects the environment and the environment affects the biota. We might therefore expect to see in the history of the Earth, its biota and temperature, some interesting 'systems' behaviour of the kind that Daisyworld exhibits.

Walker *et al.* (1981) were the first to seriously consider how negative feedback processes might stabilize the temperature of the Earth in the face of changes in the Sun's luminosity. They pointed out that one of the most important sinks for carbon dioxide in the atmosphere/ocean system was the weathering of silicate minerals via the Urey reactions, which can be schematically written

$$XSiO_3 + CO_2 \rightleftharpoons XCO_3 + SiO_2$$

where X is either Ca or Mg. Uptake of CO_2 by weathering of rocks (the forward reaction) is balanced by the inverse reaction occurring as a result of metamorphic transformation of rocks after subduction. The lifetime of carbon in the atmosphere/ocean system against the weathering reaction is less than a million years, so it follows that there must be a mechanism for adjusting the weathering sink to match the metamorphic/tectonic source over longer time intervals. Walker *et al.* (1981) proposed that this mechanism was the temperature dependence of the reaction, coupled with the greenhouse effect of CO_2. For example if the source exceeded the sink for a long enough period, CO_2 would build up in the atmosphere, leading to higher planetary temperature, and thence to a faster weathering of silicate rock until source and sink balanced again.

Walker *et al.*'s purely inorganic mechanism was elaborated on substantially by others. Lovelock and Watson (1982) showed that biological processes had the capability to enhance silicate weathering rates substantially. Berner *et al.* (1983) developed in more detail a model of atmospheric CO_2 through the last 100 Ma. This was forced by variation in the tectonic source of CO_2 deduced from rates of tectonic spreading, variation in chemical weathering due to run-off and temperature, and rates of carbonate and organic matter burial deduced from carbon isotopic measurements. Volk (1987) and Schwartzman and Volk (1989) examined the effects of biological enhancement of weathering in models, and included the important role of organic carbon burial and weathering. Most recently, Berner (1990, 1994) has extended this approach to the whole of the Phanerozoic, and has included a more in-depth investigation of the extent to which CO_2 weathering may be enhanced by land vegetation (Berner 1997). Berner's model thus covers a long enough period that the evolution of solar output may be expected to be important, and also that the evolution of the Earth's biosphere may be expected to have influenced planetary temperature.

Land plants originated in the Ordovician, and vascular plants radiated widely in the Devonian (Edwards 1998). We expect that the rise of land plants had a very substantial effect on the rate of chemical weathering. Berner (1995) estimates that present-day vegetation may have increased the rate over that which is appropriate to bare rock by a factor of 60. How much the rate of weathering actually increased when vascular plants appeared depends on what is assumed to have covered the land surfaces before that time; it seems unlikely that the rock surfaces were entirely bare, and so the increase was probably less than this factor. Figure 4, redrawn from (Berner 1992), shows the predicted levels of CO_2 in the atmosphere over the Phanerozoic, for various assumptions about how much the weathering rate increased at the time that vascular plants originated. The amount

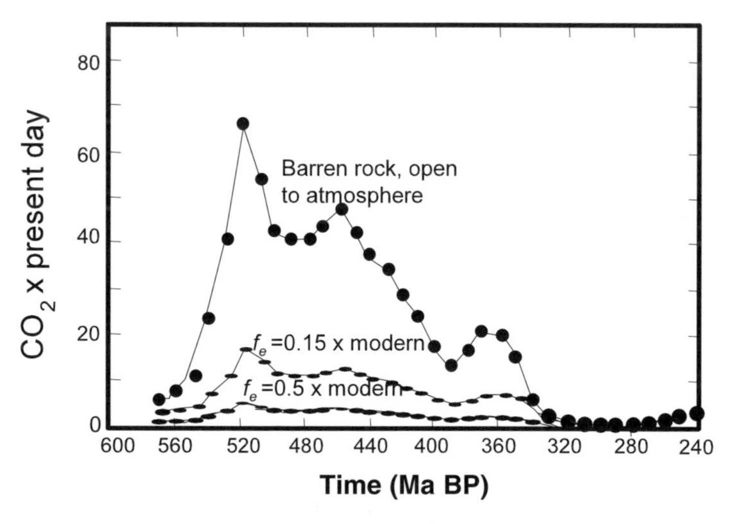

Fig. 4. Carbon dioxide in the atmosphere (expressed as multiples of the present-day value) for Phanerozoic time, predicted from the GEOCARB model (Berner 1994). The predicted concentrations are shown for three possible rates of weathering enhancement occurring due to the rise of vascular plants. The upper curve corresponds to a 60-fold increase, possibly appropriate if the continents were barren rock before the first appearance of land plants. Other curves correspond to 6–7-fold increase, and a two-fold increase. Redrawn from Figs 2 and 3 of Berner (1992).

of CO_2 predicted in the atmosphere prior to the rise of land plants is seen to be very dependent on the value chosen; Berner's 'best estimate' is the middle curve, corresponding to a 6–7-fold increase in the rate of weathering due to the evolution of vascular plants.

Figure 5 shows the temperature evolution in Berner's model which goes with this best estimate of atmospheric CO_2 concentration. Overall, temperatures are rather constant, exhibiting a slow decline from the mid-Mesozoic to the present, in broad agreement with a variety of palaeotemperature proxies (Frakes 1979). As the second curve shows, if the model is run with constant CO_2, a substantial warming is inferred because of the increase of the solar constant with time. Thus the model is doing what our discussion above would lead us to expect it to; it is providing a feedback that stabilizes the Earth's temperature against changes externally forced on it. However, much of that stabilization is in fact non-biological, due mostly to the increase of weathering rate with temperature because of increased continental run-off in a warmer, wetter climate.

The direct effect of the biota can, however, be seen in the most interesting feature of the temperature curve, which is the substantial cooling predicted for the Permo-Carboniferous. This also is in agreement with the presence of extensive glaciations in the southern hemisphere during this time (Frakes 1979), though it is deeper and longer lasting in the GEOCARB model than might be inferred from proxy records. In the model, the cooling is a direct result of the rise of vascular plants, which increases weathering and carbon burial and thus causes a strong reduction in atmospheric CO_2. Thus in this model at least, the chief effect of the biota is not to regulate, but to produce a major perturbation in the climate as a consequence of an evolutionary change.

In the model, the decrease in temperature is eventually halted by a combination of effects tending to reduce weathering. Rates of continental run-off decline in the colder

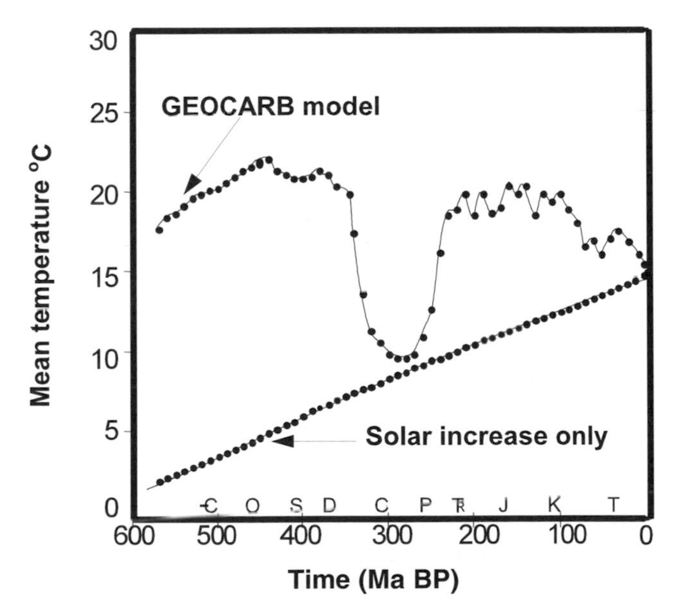

Fig. 5. Surface temperatures from the GEOCARB model. The values correspond to the middle curve of Fig. 4. Also shown are values that are obtained if carbon dioxide levels are held constant, and only solar luminosity is allowed to vary. Redrawn from Fig. 20 of Berner (1994).

climate, chemical weathering is (weakly) dependent on atmospheric CO_2 concentration, and lower CO_2 concentration has a direct effect on biological weathering because productivity is assumed to be related to CO_2 concentrations. The model does not in fact contain the main 'Daisyworld' interaction that would give a negative feedback; that is, a direct effect of temperature (and run-off) on vegetation. However, it is clear that a biologically induced decrease in temperature as large as the model infers during the Devonian would be self-limiting. Cooling and drying of the climate would tend to restrict the vegetation, and therefore their effect on temperature. In fact, recent simulations of the Carboniferous climate do indicate that dense vegetation was restricted to the equatorial regions, where temperatures were high enough and sufficient water was available (Beerling *et al.* 1998). Presumably the inclusion of such feedbacks would reduce the size of the perturbation predicted by the model for this period.

Conclusion

Hutton's view of the Earth and the life on it as 'one whole living world' continues to excite and inspire scientists. However, the revolution in human thought which was ushered in by Darwin challenges us to explain how this complex system has come to be and to survive for so long. It cannot have evolved in the sense that species evolve, because natural selection acts on populations of organisms which inherit characteristics from their forebears, but there is only one Earth. We must presume therefore, that it has arisen essentially by chance. The effect of life on the Earth environment has often been to stabilize and regulate, but equally at times has been to disturb and destabilize. Though the system has survived for about 4 Ga, a consideration of the potential catastrophes that *might* have befallen suggests that this may have been just astonishingly good luck. Our perspective, biased by the fact that, had life not survived, we would not be here, makes it nearly impossible to evaluate the *a priori* probability of survival.

This would not be the case if we were able to observe many other solar systems and make measurements that would reveal the presence or absence of life on their planets. Such a possibility is not as far in the future as it might at first seem. As Lovelock first pointed out, an infrared spectroscopic analysis of a planetary atmosphere has the potential to show whether there is an active biosphere on the surface. If such a biosphere is vigorously interacting with the atmosphere in the way that life on Earth does, it will inevitably drive the composition away from near equilibrium. We might expect to see exotic gases such as methane and oxygen coexisting in the atmosphere of a planet having life at its surface. Such a coexistence would be a clear signal that life was present, for detectable concentrations of both gases would mean they were wildly out of thermodynamic equilibrium. Their simultaneous presence would indicate therefore that some process was putting substantial amounts of energy into their production – almost certainly, life.

It is not a trivial matter to design and build an infrared spectrometer/telescope that would be capable of detecting planets orbiting nearby stars and analysing their atmospheres. It is, however, technically feasible, and there are two designs for such instruments now being drawn up for consideration by NASA and ESA. These instruments would be space-based telescopes having sufficient resolution to detect ozone in the atmospheres of stars within about 10 parsecs of the solar system (Angel & Woolf 1996, 1997). There are more than 100 stars like the Sun within this distance, so these instruments have the potential to answer the question of whether life is common, or rare, in our part of the universe.

I am grateful to Graham Shimmield, for inviting me to give the lecture on which this paper is based, and to Donald McIntyre for assisting me with his in-depth knowledge of James Hutton. I am also grateful to Tim Lenton, Jim Lovelock and Jackie Watson for much lively discussion of the topics covered here.

References

ANGEL, J. R. P. & WOOLF, N. J. 1996. Searching for life on other Planets. *Scientific American,* **274**, 60–66.

—— & —— 1997. An imaging nulling interferometer to study extrasolar planets. *Astrophysical Journal,* **475**, 373.

BEERLING, D. J. *ET AL.* 1998. The influence of Carboniferous palaeo-atmopsheres on plant function: and experimental and modelling assessment. *Philosophical Transactions of the Royal Society, Series B,* **353**, 131–140.

BERNER, R. A. 1990. Atmospheric carbon-dioxide levels over phanerozoic time. *Science,* **249**, 1382–1386.

—— 1992. Weathering, plants and the long term carbon cycle. *Geochimica et Cosmochimica Acta,* **56**, 3225–3231.

—— 1994. GEOCARB-II - a revised model of atmospheric CO_2 over phanerozoic time. *American Journal of Science,* **294**, 56–91.

—— 1995. Chemical-weathering and its effect on atmospheric CO_2 and climate. *Reviews in Mineralogy,* **31**, 565–583.

—— 1997. Paleoclimate – the rise of plants and their effect on weathering and atmospheric CO_2. *Science,* **276**, 544–546.

—— *ET AL.* 1983. The carbonate–silicate geochemical cycle and its effect on atmospheric carbon dioxide over the past 100 million years. *American Journal of Science,* **283**(7), 641–683.

CARR, M. H. 1996. Water on early Mars. *Ciba Foundation Symposia,* **202**, 249–267.

CHARLSON, R. J. *ET AL.* 1987. Oceanic phytoplankton, atmospheric sulfur, cloud albedo and climate. *Nature,* **326**, 655–661.

CHASSEFIERE, E. 1996. Hydrodynamic escape of hydrogen from a hot water-rich atmosphere - the case of Venus. *Journal of Geophysical Research – Planets,* **101**, 26 039–26 056.

—— 1997. Loss of water on the young Venus: the effect of a strong primitive solar wind. *Icarus,* **126**, 229–232.

DEGREGORIO, S. *ET AL.* 1992. Feedback between a simple biosystem and the temperature of the Earth. *Journal Of Nonlinear Science,* **2**, 263–292.

DONAHUE, T. M. 1995. Evolution of water reservoirs on Mars from D/H ratios in the atmosphere and crust. *Nature,* **374**, 432–434.

—— *ET AL.* 1 981. Venus was wet: a measurement of the ratio of deuterium to hydrogen. *Science,* **216**, 630–633.

EDWARDS, D. 1998. Climate signals in Palaeozoic land plants. *Philosophical Transactions of the Royal Society, Series B,* **353**, 141–157.

FRAKES, L. A. 1979. *Climates through geologic time*. Elsevier, Amsterdam.

GOULD, S. J. 1989. *This Wonderful Life*. Norton, New York, 347.

HARDING, S. P. & LOVELOCK, J. E. 1996. Exploiter-mediated coexistence and frequency-dependent selection in a numerical-model of biodiversity. *Journal of Theoretical Biology,* **182**, 109–116.

HILDEBRAND, A. R. *ET AL.* 1991. Chicxulub crater – a possible Cretaceous Tertiary boundary impact crater on the Yucatan Peninsula, Mexico *Geology*, **19**, 867–871.

HUTTON, J. 1975. *Theory of the Earth, with proofs and illustrations.* Creech, Edinburgh.

KASTING, J. F. 1988. Runaway and moist greenhouse atmospheres and the evolution of Earth and Venus. *Icarus*, **74**, 472–494.

—— *ET AL.* 1993. Habitable zones around main-sequence stars. *Icarus*, **101**, 108–128.

LASKAR, J. F. *ET AL.* 1993. Stabilization of the Earth's obliquity by the moon. *Nature,* **361**, 615–617.

LOVELOCK, J. E. 1987. *The Ages of Gaia: A Biography of Our Living Earth.* Oxford University Press, Oxford.

—— 1992. A numerical-model for biodiversity. *Philosophical Transactions of the Royal Society of London, Series B,* **338**, 383–391.

—— & MARGULIS, L. 1972. Atmospheric homeostasis by and for the biosphere: the Gaia hypothesis. *Tellus,* **26**, 2–14.

—— & WATSON, A. J. 1982. The regulation of carbon-dioxide and climate – Gaia or geochemistry. *Planetary and Space Science,* **30**(8), 795–802.

MICHEL, P. ET AL. 1996. The orbital evolution of the asteroid Eros and implications for collision with the Earth. *Nature*, **380**, 689–691.

RAMPINO, M. R. & CALDEIRA, K. 1994. The Goldilocks problem – climatic evolution and long-term habitability of terrestrial planets. *Annual Review of Astronomy and Astrophysics,* **32**, 83–114.

SAUNDERS, P. T. 1994. Evolution without natural-selection – further implications of the Daisyworld parable. *Journal of Theoretical Biology,* **166**, 365–373.

SCHWARTZMAN, D. W. & VOLK, T. 1989. Biotic enhancement of weathering and the habitability of Earth. *Nature,* **340**, 457–460.

VOLK, T. 1987. Feedbacks between weathering and atmospheric CO_2 over the last 100 million years. *American Journal of Science,* **287**, 763–779.

WALKER, J. C. G. 1975. Evolution of the atmosphere of Venus. *Journal of Atmospheric Science*, **32**, 1248–1256.

—— ET AL. 1981. A negative feedback mechanism for the long-term stabilization of Earth's surface-temperature. *Journal of Geophysical Research – Oceans and Atmospheres,* **86**, 9776–9782.

WATSON, A. J. & LOVELOCK, J. E. 1983. Biological homeostasis of the global environment – the parable of Daisyworld. *Tellus B*, **35**(4), 284–289.

—— ET AL. 1984. Temperatures: a runaway greenhouse of the prehistoric Venus: implications for water loss. *Earth and Planetary Science Letters*, **68**, 1–6.

WHEELER, J. A. (ed.) 1980. *Beyond the Black Hole*. Some Strangeness in the Proportion: a centennial symposium to celebrate the achievements of Albert Einstein. Addison-Wesley, Reading, MA.

Impacts from space: the implications for uniformitarian geology

URSULA B. MARVIN
Harvard-Smithsonian Center for Astrophysics, 60 Garden Street, Cambridge, MA 02138, USA

Abstract: The geological implications of the Earth's collisions with other bodies in space have become fully evident only since the opening of the Space Age. In the early eighteenth century, most western natural philosophers accepted the view, inherited from Aristotle and confirmed on mechanistic grounds by Isaac Newton, that interplanetary space is empty of solid matter. In the final decade of that century, two books, one by Ernst F. F. Chladni of Wittenberg and one by James Hutton of Edinburgh, contributed to the rise of meteorite studies and uniformitarian geology, respectively. Although they arose almost simultaneously, these two branches of science, one of which postulated the fall to Earth of solid bodies from space while the other endorsed only strictly endogenous processes acting upon the Earth, evolved separately over the next 200 years. This paper traces the long estrangement between mainstream geology and the science of meteorites. The two disciplines collided head-on in 1980 when a team of scientists headed by the physicist, Luis Alvarez, of the University of California, hypothesized that the massive extinctions at the end of the Cretaceous were triggered by the hypervelocity impact of a large body from space. Many geologists rejected outright such an exotic cause. More recently, as evidence has accumulated for the K–T impact as well as for many other crater-forming impacts, we are beginning to realize that unpredictable collisions have played a role of fundamental importance throughout the history of the solar system.

Our battered solar system

Seventeenth-century speculations on comet Impacts

Comets first were shown to be members of the solar system by Isaac Newton (1642–1727), who determined that the comets of 1680 and 1681 were the same body following an elongated elliptical orbit around the Sun. Newton (1687) declared that, far from being omens of God's wrath, as was popularly supposed, comets fulfil a benign purpose by continually resupplying the Sun and planets with fresh moisture and vital spirits. Only in private did he speak of the destruction of worlds that could ensue from collisions of comets with planets.

Working with Newton, Edmond Halley (1656–1743) calculated comet orbits from historical accounts, concluded that several of them were periodic, and in 1705 he predicted the return of a comet which was named for him posthumously when it appeared on schedule in 1758. Halley appreciated the benefits Newton ascribed to the apparitions of comets but he also clearly envisaged the disastrous results of collisions, or even of close encounters, between comets and the Earth: a tilting of the Earth's axis, shifting of its poles and its rate of rotation, a flooding of oceans over the lands, and the possible destruction

MARVIN, U. B. 1999. Impacts from space: the implications for uniformitarian geology.
In: CRAIG, G. Y. & HULL, J. H. (eds) *James Hutton – Present and Future*. Geological Society, London, Special Publications, **150**, 89–117.

of all living things. Halley (1694) surmised that such an event had reduced a pre-Adamic world to utter chaos, from which our present world arose, and he expected another collision with a comet to end this world in preparation for a future one, and so on indefinitely. Halley's line of thought spawned a speculative literature on the dire consequences of comet impacts that continued from the late seventeenth to the twentieth century.

Newton (1704, p. 368), having constructed his clockwork solar system governed by universal gravitation, declared that 'to make way for the regular and lasting Motions of the Planets and Comets, it's necessary to empty the Heavens of all Matter, except ... an exceedingly rare Æthereal Medium.' Thus, Newton included comets among members of the solar system and at the same time granted the Earth safe passage from bombardment by stray bodies as it orbits the Sun.

The idea of the emptiness of space was inherited from Aristotle (384–322 BC), who envisioned the heavenly bodies as consisting of shining ether in a universe of unchanging perfection, except within the mundane region between the Earth and the Moon. By Newton's time, observations of supernovae and the realization that comets occur beyond the Moon had shown that the heavens do change, but space still was deemed to be empty. Robert Hooke (1635–1703) acknowledged this belief when he duplicated the rimmed circular depressions he saw on the Moon by dropping weights into damp clay. But Hooke (1665, p. 243) conceded that the lunar craters could not have formed by such a process because 'it would be difficult to imagine whence those bodies should come'. Turning to experiments with pots of boiling alabaster, Hooke duplicated the pockmarked lunar surface sufficiently well to postulate a volcanic origin for the craters.

Collisions in space

Today, we realize that the presence of solid bodies in interplanetary space has been the single most fundamental factor influencing the origin and evolution of the Earth and, indeed, of all the bodies of the solar system. This is a recent conclusion, arrived at since images and data transmitted to us by spacecraft have shown us that every planet and every satellite is different from every other; and they all display clear evidence of heavy battering in collisions that have tilted axes, altered bulk compositions, and cratered those bodies with rocky surfaces.

We envisage the planets forming about 4600 million years ago in the primeval solar nebula, where dust grains accreted to pebbles and thence to cobbles, to boulders, to planetesimals, to planets – with much fragmentation and recombination all along the way. As the planets approached their present mass, they swept up all the large bodies in their neighbourhoods with results that are visible today. Mercury, a planet that is less than half the diameter of the Earth, is almost equal to it in density. A late collision appears to have stripped away much of Mercury's silicate mantle, leaving its iron core occupying three-quarters of its interior. In a system of bodies rotating counterclockwise, Venus, our 'sister planet', rotates slowly clockwise, and evidently has done so since a massive impact reversed its original sense of rotation. Mars shows striking bilateral symmetry with its southern hemisphere cratered by impacts and its northern displaying the largest volcanoes in the solar system. Farther out, Uranus rolls over and over on its side with its equator tilted 97° to the plane of its orbit – tipped over by an impact. These are only few examples in a solar system ruled by chance events, in which not a single planet or satellite has 'normal' characteristics that would be predicted by any theory of origin (Taylor 1992, p. 294).

The Earth is unique in having the Moon. Other planets have moons but no other has so huge a moon – one-quarter the diameter of the Earth itself – making the Earth–Moon system, in effect, a double planet. By today's favoured scenario, the Moon formed after a giant collision occurred between the early Earth, which already possessed its iron core, and another cored body at least three times the size of Mars. The force of the collision tilted the Earth's axis by ~23° – providing us with our seasons – and reduced the impacting body to a hot disc of liquid and vapour. The metal droplets from the impactor's core rained down through the Earth's molten mantle and fused with our core. The remaining material of the impactor recondensed and some of it coalesced to form the Moon (e.g. Shigeru *et al.* 1997; Cameron 1997). By the loss of its core we account for the Moon's low density (3.3 g cm^3 compared to the Earth's 5.5 g/cm^3); by the hot disc we account for the Moon's lack of water and volatile elements; to the force of the collision, the steep tilt of the Moon's orbit and its high angular momentum.

Radiometric dating of lunar samples shows that the Earth–Moon system formed ~4450 million years ago (Allègre *et al.* 1995). During the first few hundred million years, both bodies may have been largely molten, but by about 4200 million years ago the Moon was sufficiently solid to sustain the great lunar basins excavated by giant impacts. At the same time the Earth must have been struck again and again by impactors that destroyed its earliest patches of crust and boiled away its waters and atmosphere. We have no extant record of this early period on the Earth, but the Moon's face shows us that large impacts began to decline in frequency about 3900 million years ago, shortly after the oldest surviving rocks formed on the Earth.

Hypervelocity impacts continued to scar the Earth and Moon, but the Earth, with its active processes of erosion, deposition and tectonism, preserves a very incomplete record of them. The oldest and largest currently recognized impact scar is the ~2000 million year old Vredefort structure of South Africa, 300 km in diameter. This great scar is younger by ~2000 million years than the great basins of the Moon. More than 150 other impact scars have been identified on the Earth's landmasses, and two or three new ones are recognized nearly every year. The smallest well-preserved one known today is the 20 m, 27 000 year old Dalgaranga crater of Western Australia (Grieve *et al.* 1997).

Crater-forming impacts continue. On 17 May 1990, a witnessed meteorite fall blasted a crater 10 m across and 5 m deep in loamy soil at Sterlitamak, Bashkir Territory, Russia. About two dozen fragments of an iron meteorite, ranging in weight from a few grams to several hundred grams, were collected in the vicinity of the crater. Subsequently, using heavy equipment to excavate the floor, investigators recovered two large fragments of the iron, weighing 6.60 and 3.06 kg, at a depth of 8 m. While digging, they struck water and the crater walls began to slump. Today, the crater is largely filled with damp soil, which must conceal many fragments because the total weight of the impacting mass is estimated at 1 to 1.5 tonnes (Petaev 1992).

Space Age technology has revealed that the Earth orbits amid a swarm of so-called near Earth objects (NEOs) – asteroids and inactive cometary bodies variously called Apollos, Amors and Atens. More than 2000 of these bodies are at least 1 km in diameter, and there are many more thousands of smaller ones. The presence of these bodies leads us, realistically, to expect more cratering impacts in the future, and several tracking programmes are in operation or planned, including Spacewatch, which made its first discovery in 1989 from the Kitt Peak National Observatory in Arizona (Carusi *et al.*

1994). Impacting bodies also originate in the asteroid belt between Mars and Jupiter, and in two main reservoirs of comets: long-period comets from the Oort cloud, which extends half way to the nearest star, and short-period comets from the Edgeworth–Kuiper–Whipple (EKW) disc just beyond Neptune. Incidentally, many astronomers now regard Neptune, with its almost perfectly circular orbit despite its weak gravitational link with the Sun, as the outermost planet of the solar system. This relegates Pluto and its companion, Charon, to membership in the EKW comet belt where, given their physical and orbital characteristics, they make a much better match (e.g. Marsden 1997).

Although comets are icy bodies, their spectra show that they contain frozen-in solid matter with the bulk composition of primitive stony meteorites, plus a large array of hydrocarbon molecules including amino acids. Today, some scientists (e.g. Chyba *et al.* 1994) credit comets with supplying the Earth with its waters and seeding it with the organic building blocks of life. Others dispute this idea (e.g. Holland 1997). Each time a comet rounds the Sun, it loses some of its ice and adds dust and gas to its coma and its streaming tails. Many of the NEOs are believed to be 'dead' comets which have lost all their ice and are physically and spectroscopically indistinguishable from asteroids (Wetherill & Shoemaker 1982, p. 2).

Today, the Earth gains, on average, about 10 000 tonnes of meteoritic and cometary dust each year, and ~52 meteorites weighing more than 85 g fall to Earth every day. Of these, 11 are estimated to weigh at least 900 g and two of them weigh at least 10 kg (Halliday *et al.* 1984). Add to this steady influx the occasional impacts of large bodies and we can no longer speak of the elegant clockwork solar system of Isaac Newton; the one we live in is ruled by unpredictable collisions in space.

Despite all the early pandemonium and our present daily increment from the skies, few people seem to notice. The Earth is so large and so watery that it is easy for most of us to spend our entire lives totally unaware of bodies falling from space. And thus it was in the eighteenth century, when the sceptical spirit of the Enlightenment persuaded scholars that all the old reports of stones and fragments of iron falling from the sky simply could not be true: they said that the idea violates common sense (which, in fact, it does) and Newton's laws of physics.

Early books on geology and meteorites

In the final decade of the eighteenth century, two books appeared, each of which ultimately would wield a powerful influence on the course of science. In 1794, Ernst Florens Friedrich Chladni (1756–1827) of Wittenberg in Germany, wrote a 63-page book titled (in translation) *On the Origin of the Mass of Iron found by Pallas and of Other Similar Ironmasses, and on a Few Natural Phenomena Connected Therewith.* One year later, in 1795, James Hutton (1726–1797) of Edinburgh published his two-volume *Theory of the Earth with Proof and Illustrations.*

James Hutton and geology

James Hutton is honoured today for lengthening, immeasurably, the span of geological time and for his insights that basalts, traps, and granites are intrusive rocks, that valleys are cut by the rivers flowing through them, and that to interpret past changes in the Earth we must look to the processes observed in operation today. He theorized that the Earth undergoes a continuous succession of cycles of erosion, deposition and the uplift of new lands, always maintaining itself as an abode favourable for life. Inasmuch as each of his cycles was indistinguishable from all of the others, Hutton denied the Earth a narrative history of unrepeatable events. He wrote that he saw no vestige of a beginning and perceived no prospect of an end of the world; leaving both to the will of the Creator. In Hutton's view, each cycle was self-generating and inevitable – part of an Earth machine as mechanistically determined as Newton's system of planetary motions.

In the context of our study, the views for which Hutton is most remembered are expressed in two passages in which he cautions geologists against calling upon destructive accidents or extraordinary events:

> ... in discovering the nature and constitution of this earth ... there is no occasion for having recourse ... to any destructive accident in nature, or to the agency of preternatural cause, in explaining what actually appears. (Hutton 1788, p. 285)

> ... no powers are to be employed that are not natural to the globe, no action to be admitted of except those of which we know the principle, and no extraordinary events to be alleged in order to explain a common appearance. (Hutton 1795, vol. 2, p. 547)

Hutton's views were well suited to his time, when collisions from space were unknown. Thus, he bequeathed to geologists an Earth that was a safely closed and benign system shielded by Newton's umbrella.

Hutton's book quickly fell into quasi-oblivion, partly because it challenged the Mosaic timescale and partly because its brief flashes of brilliance were all but lost among long, repetitive passages and page after page of quotations from French and Swiss sources. In 1802, his friend John Playfair (1748–1819) rescued Hutton's theory from oblivion by casting his ideas – minus their teleology, plus some sense of history—into the more felicitous prose of his own book *Illustrations of Hutton's Theory of the Earth*. It was through Playfair's book that Charles Lyell (1797–1875) learned of Hutton's principles and then marshalled an abundance of evidence showing that the present is the key to the past. In 1897, Archibald Geikie (1835–1924) remarked that Lyell went on to become 'the great high priest of Uniformitarianism'. Incidentally, Hutton was not lost in the glare of his famous successor. In 1947, on the 150th anniversary of his death, the title 'The Father of Modern Geology', was inscribed on Hutton's tombstone in Greyfriars Churchyard, Edinburgh.

In his own three-volume masterwork, *Principles of Geology*, published from 1830 to 1833, Lyell described a steady-state, continuously recycling Earth modified solely by processes that always remain uniform in intensity and may be observed in operation. Like Hutton, he acknowledged no progressive development in Earth history. One reader who greatly admired Lyell's work was John Herschel (1792–1871), who wrote to Lyell in 1836 that he had read the *Principles of Geology* not once but three times, and every time with increased interest. Herschel added, 'it appears to me one of those productions which work a complete revolution in their subject by altering entirely the point of view in which it must thenceforward be contemplated'.

This letter was first published in 1961 in an article with the very apt title 'The impact of uniformitarianism' by Walter F. Cannon, of the University of California at Berkeley. Cannon (1961, p. 305) pointed out that such a response from Herschel, who was arguably the most famous and admired scientist in England, clearly demonstrates the immediate impact of Lyell's new geology. Presently, although it gained little acceptance on the continent, Lyellian uniformitarianism came to dominate geological thinking throughout the English-speaking world,

One natural philosopher, William Whewell (1794–1866), was less enthusiastic than John Herschel. In an anonymous review of Volume 2 of Lyell's *Principles*, Whewell (1832, p. 126) asked,

> Have the changes which lead us from one geological state to another been, on a long average, uniform in their intensity, or have they consisted of epochs of paroxysmal and catastrophic action, interspersed between periods of comparative tranquillity? These two opinions will probably ... divide the geologic world into two sects ... the *Uniformitarians* and the *Catastrophists*.'

Whewell declared that to him it seemed somewhat rash to suppose, as the uniformitarian does, that with our limited experience we have learned all the laws and causes that influence the natural history of the globe. He asked the question (which resonates today) of whether we may not be ignorant of important agents that may, one day, manifest themselves in great and distant catastrophes.

Whewell's two terms swiftly were adopted into geological thinking but with meanings rather different from those he gave them. From his time to ours, a majority of English-speaking geologists have declared themselves to be uniformitarians, although few of them ever accepted Lyell's vision of a recycling, ahistorical Earth or his notion of uniform rates of change. Clearly, most of these 'uniformitarians' would fit more closely with Whewell's definition of 'catastrophists'. However, catastrophism retained an unwelcome taint of divinely willed calamities which caused geologists to reject it in favour of a modified uniformitarianism. Ultimately, the usage of 'uniformitarianism' became so diffuse that the term was rendered essentially meaningless (e.g. Gould 1965, 1987; Albritton 1967, 1989; Shea 1982). In recent years, some scientists (e.g. Berggren & van Couvering 1984) have referred to catastrophes in Earth history, including meteorite impacts, as 'the new uniformitarianism'. However, rather than to willfully reverse the meaning of an historical term, we might better serve geology by following the advice of Claude C. Albritton (1989, p. 180) by saying farewell to both of these old 'isms' and describe the ever-changing Earth without reference to such outmoded concepts.

Ernst Chladni and meteorites

Ernst Chladni's research on the physics of sound waves, published in 1787, won for him the title 'Father of Acoustics'. Subsequently, Chladni began puzzling over meteors and fireballs, which originate at great heights and streak across the sky in all directions at velocities far exceeding those attributable to bodies originating, as was then supposed, within the Earth's atmosphere.

During three weeks in the library at Göttingen, Chladni compiled historical reports of 24 great fireballs and 18 falls of masses of stone and iron dating from antiquity to 1785. To his astonishment, he found strikingly similar reports of falling bodies accompanied by brilliant fireballs, thunderous explosions, prolonged rumblings, and/or horrid hissing sounds. After considering the physics of the problem, Chladni put forward the following three main hypotheses.

(1) Stones and masses of iron do, in fact, fall from the skies.

(2) They form fireballs from frictional deceleration as they plunge through the Earth's atmosphere.
(3) They originate in space as either (a) primordial masses in interstellar space which never aggregated into planets, or (b) debris of planets disrupted by explosions from within or collisions from without.

Chladni made some errors regarding the temperatures and the extent of melting to be expected, but after two centuries of additional investigations his postulates numbered (1), (2), and (3b) above are universally accepted. Needless to say, Chladni did not accept Newton's dictum that outer space is empty of small bodies. He saw no physical basis for it. Chladni (1794, p. 56) wrote that to declare space between the great bodies to be empty – aside from some species of elastic fluid or ether – is as arbitrary as to assert the presence of small bodies. Neither could be proved a priori, and the issue must be settled on observations, not speculation. Chladni thought he had the evidence (Marvin 1996).

Chladni's German readers were shocked by his reliance on reports they equated with folk tales, and by his infamous flouting of the Aristotelian–Newtonian views of the cosmos. He might well have watched his book lapse into oblivion, but Chladni's reputation was rescued when stones began to fall from the skies.

Witnessed falls of stones: 1794–1798

Siena, Tuscany, 1794. On 16 June 1794, about 60 days after Chladni's book appeared in Germany (and two years before it would reach England), a shower of stones fell at Siena in Tuscany. Witnesses were startled by the rapid approach from the north of an unusually high, grey cloud, laced with bolts of red lightning. Suddenly, after violent explosions, stones rained down a few kilometres southeast of the city.

In September 1794, the Abbé Ambrogio Soldani (1736–1808), Professor of Mathematics at the University in Siena, issued a 288-page book on the circumstances of the fall and character of the stones. Soldani concluded that the stones accreted from stony and metallic dust in the high, igneous cloud.

In December 1794, the Abbé Domenico Tata (1723–1800), Professor of Mathematics and Physics at Naples, published a 74-page *Memoire* on the fall at Siena and also on an earlier fall of a stone that was witnessed at Calabria in 1755. Tata had not previously reported that event for a (well-founded) fear of ridicule. In their texts, both Soldani and Tata included mineralogical descriptions of the Siena stones by Guiglielmo (William) Thomson (1761–1806), the English expatriate physician–chemist–mineralogist residing in Naples (Thomson 1794*a*, *b*). Tata and Thomson agreed with Soldani that the stones formed in the high, dusty cloud through the action of lightning.

The Siena fall occurred 18 hours after Mt Vesuvius sprang into full eruption. Many felt that such timing must have been more than coincidental. Sir William Hamilton (1730–1803), the British Ambassador to the Kingdom of Naples, who was monitoring the day-to-day activity of Mt Vesuvius, thought, at first, that he had seen similar stones on the slopes of the volcano. However, when he failed to find any, Hamilton (1795, p. 105) speculated that the stones may have accreted from vesuvian ash that had been expelled to great heights and wafted northwestward for some 250 miles until it met an opposing draft and, mixing with a stormy cloud, precipitated stones over Siena. He ascribed the exterior vitrification (fusion crust) on the stones to the action of the electric fluid on them. The idea of some sort of link between volcanic activity and fallen stones continued to attract supporters until about 1860. As early as 1802, however, some leading natural philosophers had begun to regard lunar volcanoes as more likely sources of fallen stones than terrestrial ones.

The fall at Siena was of special significance in the founding of the science of meteorites because it occurred in the vicinity of a university city where it was observed by so many people that its authenticity could not be denied and it prompted investigations that raised the subject of falls of stones to the level of scholarly discourse.

Wold Cottage, Yorkshire, 1795. In December, 1795, a large, 56-pound stone burst out of an overcast sky and plunged into a field at Wold Cottage in Yorkshire. The landowner, Captain Edward Topham (1751–1820), exhibited the stone in Piccadilly, London, and published an account of the event (Topham 1797). Wold Cottage is the second largest stone to fall in Europe; the larger one was the 280-pound stone that fell at Ensisheim in Alsace in 1492 (Marvin 1992). Fragments of both stones are on display today; one in the museum in the Hôtel de la Régence in Ensisheim and the other in the British Museum of Natural History in London.

Evora, Portugal, 1796 and Benares, India, 1798. On 19 February 1796, a stone fell near Evora in Portugal. News of it reached England in 1797 in a volume of letters on his travels written by Robert Southey (1774–1843), the admired 'Lake Poet' (and future Poet Laureate of England). Unfortunately, that stone is long lost to science. In December 1798, a spectacular fireball heralded a large shower of stones near Benares in India. John Lloyd Williams (*c.* 1765–1838), a Fellow of the Royal Society residing in India, immediately sent a detailed description of the event to Sir Joseph Banks (1743–1820), the President of the Royal Society in London.

Chemical and mineralogical analyses, 1802

When Sir Joseph Banks received Williams' letter in 1799, he decided it was time for scientific study of this phenomenon. He gave his own samples from the Siena and Wold Cottage falls to the distinguished young chemist Edward C. Howard (1774–1816), and asked him to analyse them to test the theory that they were the bodies of fiery meteors. Howard sought out samples of two more allegedly fallen stones and of four erratic irons, including two that Chladni had reasoned must have fallen from the sky. Howard and the French mineralogist Jacques-Louis de Bournon (1751–1825) performed the first series of chemical and mineralogical analyses of meteorites.

The two scientists observed that each of the stones was coated with a shiny dark crust and had several other features in common, including the tiny, spherical bodies we call chondrules, which differed from anything observed in terrestrial rocks. Their crucial discovery, however, was the presence of nickel; Howard found several per cent of Ni in all four irons and in metal grains in the four stones. That discovery linked the stones with the irons and set both apart from rocks of the Earth's crust. Howard published the results in a paper, which included sections authored separately by de Bournon and Williams, in the *Philosophical Transactions of the Royal Society* of February 1802. The following October, their findings were presented to the National Institute in Paris, whereupon the debate in France immediately began to switch from whether stones fall from the skies to how and where they originate.

All lingering doubts about the reality of falls vanished after one o'clock on the afternoon of 26 April 1803, when nearly 3000 stones pelted down at L'Aigle in Normandy. The young Jean-Baptiste Biot (1774–1862), who was sent out from Paris to investigate the event, returned with samples for analysis and the first map of a typically elliptical meteorite strewn field. In concluding his detailed account, Biot (1803, p. 405) wrote, 'I shall consider myself happy if they [the philosophers] find that I have succeeded in placing beyond a doubt the most astonishing phenomenon ever observed by man'.

Geology and meteoritics

We have seen that uniformitarian geology and the study of meteorites both emerged as new sciences in 1802. John Playfair saw to it that James Hutton received posthumous credit for his contributions to geology, and new meteorite falls and laboratory analyses secured Ernst Chladni full credit for his brilliant insights during his lifetime. The two sciences were born separately and over the next two centuries they evolved separately, with geologists viewing meteorites as natural curiosities of no serious consequence to the science of the Earth.

Meteorite origins. Debates on meteorite origins continued into the Space Age. Two hypotheses–that they form as concretions in the Earth's upper atmosphere or as ejecta from lunar volcanoes–were abandoned in about 1860. Chladni's two hypotheses – that they are masses of matter from interstellar space or the debris of disrupted planets – were disputed until the late 1950s, when calculations of their elliptical orbits decisively ruled out an interstellar origin (e.g. Marvin 1996, p. 581). Scientists then agreed that most meteorites originate as fragments of collided asteroids. However, since 1982, 13 meteorites from the Moon and 12 from Mars have been found on the Earth. Each of them is a sample of crustal material that was accelerated to escape velocity by the impact of an asteroid or a comet. Today, after some 160 years, Chladni's second choice of origin is universally accepted.

Lyell and comet impacts. Meteorites continued to fall all through Charles Lyell's lifetime. All of them were small bodies that made only minor pits in the soil, so Lyell never had to consider meteorites as playing a role of any geological importance. Indeed, in 1830 he specifically dismissed comet impact as a possible cause of global climate changes. Comet impact had been invoked by several earlier writers to account for major disruptions in the Earth's history. For example, in 1696 William Whiston (1667–1742) had called upon a grazing collision with a comet to account for the Earth's spheroidal shape, its tilted axis, its daily rotation, and the cracking of its crust to release the waters of the deluge – in tides eight miles high. In 1749, the Comte de Buffon (1707–1788) theorized that successive shocks of a comet on the Sun had split off the planets and sent each of them into heliocentric orbit. A year later, Pierre Maupertuis (1698–1749), Newton's most enthusiastic disciple in France, wrote in his *Essay de Cosmologie* (1750, p. 35) that a comet striking the Earth would cause vast disruptions with the greater part of the animals perishing due to heat, poisoned air and acid waters – a premature hypothesis that could not be incorporated into the cannons of Earth science for more than 200 years. But Lyell would have none of this. In 1830, after puzzling over the problem of drastic climate changes, he wrote to a friend (in Lyell, 1881, p. 261),

> ... without help from a comet, or any astronomical change ... or any change of inclination of axis or central heat, or volcanic hot vapours and waters and other nostrums, but all easily and naturally. I will give you a recipe for growing tree ferns at the pole, or if it suits me, pines at the equator; walruses under the line, and crocodiles in the arctic circle.

Lyell's recipe involved a redistribution of land and sea by the erosion of old landmasses and the exposure of new ones.

Impact craters and structures

In 1873, two years before Lyell's death, the British astronomer, Richard A. Proctor (1837–1888) put forward the first hypothesis in modern times that the great basins and many of the craters of the Moon may have been formed by falling meteorites. Proctor referred to the distinctive forms of these features, which, unlike most volcanic craters, are bowls in the land surface surrounded by raised rims similar to raindrop impressions in mud. Proctor did not vigorously press his idea, and he gained no following for it.

Over the next few decades a number of others proposed variations of a meteoritic origin for lunar craters, but, as noted in a review by A. C. Gifford (1930, p. 74), geologists posed the following three major objections – all of which seemed valid at the time.

(1) It would require a terrific bombardment by innumerable meteorites, many of vast dimensions, to produce the formations that we see on the Moon. (i.e. The bombardment is too catastrophic to contemplate.)
(2) If lunar craters are due to meteoric bombardment, the Earth should show similar scars. (But none is known to us.)
(3) The circularity of lunar forms implies that all the impacts were direct, whereas it is certain that most meteorites would strike the surface obliquely.

The Arizona Crater, 1891

The first crater on the Earth to be suspected of having an impact origin was a rimmed bowl, nearly a mile across, excavated in flat-lying limestone and sandstone in northern Arizona, with iron meteorite fragments strewn on the surrounding plains.

In 1891, when Grove Karl Gilbert (1843–1918), chief geologist of the US Geological Survey, learned of this crater, his imagination soared. 'I am going to hunt a star', he wrote to a friend (in Davis 1926, p. 183). Gilbert surmised that, long after the Earth had accreted from planetesimals, a late-falling body had struck the surface and excavated the crater. His main problem would be to find persuasive evidence of impact, a previously unrecognized crater-forming process. Gilbert assumed that a single cause had produced the crater, the iron meteorites and the association of the two. He estimated the probability of coincidence as being only one chance in 800. 'This', wrote Gilbert (1896, p. 11), 'legitimately inclines the mind toward causality.'

Gilbert made the following three assumptions about the physical effects of an impact by an iron meteorite on the Earth.

(1) The main mass of the iron would bury itself in the crater floor.
(2) The crater would be elliptical because most meteorites strike the Earth at oblique angles.
(3) The volume of the bowl would be less than that of the ejected rim material because of the extra mass of iron in the floor.

Gilbert's plane table map showed the crater to be essentially circular; he detected no magnetic anomaly, and he calculated the volumes of the bowl and rim as 82 million cubic yards each. Gilbert could not have known that in a hypervelocity collision the impacting body would largely destroy itself and create a circular crater regardless of its trajectory; this knowledge awaited the early twentieth century. Neither could he have known that the bedrock of the crater rim was tilted upward and partially overturned beneath the ejecta blanket, which, itself, had been lowered an unknown amount by erosion. Nor would anyone learn until drilling was done in the first decade of the twentieth century that the crater is underlain by 21 meters of lake sediments.

How should a scientist respond when all his tests fail? Rather than clinging to his pet theory, Gilbert yielded with good grace. Although he found no ash, lava, or hot spring deposits in or near the crater, he settled for a hypothesis that the crater was blasted open by a deep-seated steam explosion consequent on migration of magma from a nearby volcanic field. He also had to concede that the irons were coincidental to the presence of the crater.

Five years after he examined the crater, Gilbert (1896) recounted this story in a beautifully written paper, *The Origin of Hypotheses: Illustrated by the Discussion of a Topographic Problem*, which makes instructive reading on how the proper application of the scientific method may lead to the wrong answer – if basic assumptions are flawed. Had he been able to satisfy himself of the crater's impact origin, Gilbert, with his towering prestige among geologists, might well have established meteorite impact as a geological process 100 years ago. In his paper, Gilbert left open the possibility that his verdict could be overturned if new information favourable to impact were to come to light. However, his readers took his conclusion as final, and it led many American geologists, particularly members of the US Geological Survey, to steadfastly reject meteorite impact as a crater-forming process. Some continued to do so into the 1960s. However, Gilbert, himself, favoured an impact origin for lunar craters. In 1893 he published '*The Moon's face, a study of the origin of its surface features*', in which he attributed such features to impacts by bodies from a ring of moonlets, each of which struck the Moon directly and created a circular crater. He argued that the impacts tilted the Moon this way and that, exposing the whole body to direct impacts.

By 1906, Daniel Moreau Barringer (1860–1929), a mining entrepreneur, had staked claims on the crater and developed abundant evidence of impact which is wholly acceptable today – including overturned bedrock of the rim, large tonnages of shattered quartz, and a meteorite fragment mixed into the rubble of the rim. But with Gilbert's volcanic explanation in the literature, only a small minority of geologists listened to Barringer. The last major papers opposing an impact origin were published by D. Hager in 1953 and W. H. Bucher in 1963. Hager ascribed the crater to structural collapse consequent on the dissolution of salt deposits at depth. We will meet again with W. H. Bucher. Today, we recognize the 50 000 year-old Meteor Crater, also called the Barringer Meteorite Crater, as the best preserved and the most readily accessible of the world's impact craters.

Additional meteorite craters

A flurry of new discoveries began with the finding of a crater associated with iron meteorites at Odessa, Texas, in 1929; a group of 13 craters with hundreds of iron fragments at Henbury Station, Australia, in 1931; and two craters with irons at Wabar, in the Empty Quarter of Arabia, in 1932 (e.g. Marvin 1986). Meanwhile, in 1929, Leonidas A. Kulik (1883–1942) returned from the Tunguska region of Siberia with impressive pictures of a flattened forest with trees fanning outward from the site of an enormous fireball explosion in 1908. Kulik's party found no meteorites there, but he assumed (mistakenly) that lakes in the area were impact craters. Later research showed that the incoming fireball, seen for great distances over Siberia, had exploded in the air above the site (Krinov 1952). A debate continues today on whether the body, which completely destroyed itself, was a fragment of an asteroid or a comet.

In 1933, Leonard J. Spencer (1870–1959), Keeper of Minerals at the British Museum of Natural History, became the first impartial scientist to declare that new evidence positively established meteorite impact as a geological process. Spencer had examined iron meteorite fragments and masses of slaggy black silica glass collected by Harry St John Philby (1885–1960) at the Wabar craters in Arabia. Embedded in the glass he found millions of minute Ni–Fe spherules and concluded (Spencer 1933, p. 401) that the quartz sand had boiled and droplets of Ni-Fe had condensed from a vapour cloud and rained down into the bubbling silica. He estimated that the temperatures involved had exceeded 3500°C – far above those of known igneous processes.

Spencer listed seven additional examples of probable impact craters, and new discoveries quickly began to accumulate. For a long time, however, geologists tended to accept as genuine only those few craters with associated meteorites and to reject an impact origin of rounded depressions or lake basins lacking associated meteorites, regardless of how dramatically they might interrupt geological terranes.

Cryptovolcanic structures

The name 'cryptovolcanic' structure, denoting an origin by volcanism of some unfamiliar (hidden) type, was applied to the Steinheim Basin in Bavaria by Branco and Fraas (1905), who described striated conical features they called *stralenkalk* in the limestones. In 1936, Walter H. Bucher (1888–1965), then at the University of Cincinnati, applied the name 'cryptovolcanic' to three structures he had mapped in Indiana, Kentucky and Tennessee. Such structures are roughly circular, from 1 to 25 km in diameter, with radial or bilateral symmetry and elevated central portions consisting of a jumble of severely faulted rocks forced up from below. They contained the striated conical features found at Steinheim, which Bucher called 'shatter cones'. Clearly, the structures were loci of violent explosions, but none of them contained volcanic lava or ash or showed any signs of hydrothermal alteration, contact metamorphism, or mineralization. Bucher ascribed them to deep-seated explosions of gases from subsurface igneous intrusions.

A few years later, John D. Boon, Sr (1874–1950), a physicist, and Claude C. Albritton, Jr (1913–1988), a geologist, argued (1936, 1937) that these structures are deeply eroded impact scars with central uplifts. They extended this hypothesis to the Vredefort Dome of South Africa. Many geologists expressed shock at the suggestion of an impact origin for cryptovolcanic structures. These were geological features, not just holes in the ground, and geologists felt confident that, in time, they would learn how the Earth produces them with no assistance from the skies.

The impact of the Space Age

The Space Age emerged from the rocket technology of World War II, which engineers and visionaries quickly recognized would enable missions to the Moon and planets. Until then only a few scientists, usually working alone, had begun to take a serious interest in the meteoritic hazard in space and the frequency and magnitude of impacts on the Earth and Moon. In their efforts to be heard, they faced great difficulties. In 1933, a small, diverse group had founded at Chicago a Society for Research on Meteorites (subsequently named the Meteoritical Society), but, riven by internal disputes, it had failed to exert a decisive influence on the field (Marvin 1993). In 1941, Ralph B. Baldwin, a young instructor in astronomy at Northwestern University, wrote a paper titled 'The meteoritic origin of lunar craters', which was rejected by three astronomical journals before appearing in *Popular Astronomy* in 1942. Baldwin's senior colleagues warned him that the Moon was not an acceptable subject for astronomical research – particularly since the volcanic origin of lunar craters was well established. Nevertheless, he persevered in his studies of the Moon.

In 1946, a paper titled 'The meteoritic impact origin of the Moon's surface features' by Robert S. Dietz (1915–1995), at the University of Illinois, appeared in the *Journal of Geology*–the first mainstream journal to publish on such a subject. Dietz argued that the sizes, shapes and distribution of the lunar craters make them unlikely to be volcanic craters and calderas, particularly since the Moon, which lacks a hydrosphere and atmosphere, seems to be too small a body to support the internal temperatures and pressures required for volcanism. Dietz proposed (1946, p. 373) that explosive impacts had generated sufficient heat to cause melting and the eruptions of the dark lava plains of the maria.

Shatter cones and cryptoexplosion structures

In 1947, Dietz proposed that shatter cones at the 'cryptovolcanic' structure at Kentland, Indiana, resulted from impact shock. Shatter cones are conical features with flaring striae that converge towards their apexes. They often have small half-cones clustered on the surfaces of the master cones, with all apexes pointing towards the locus of a high-energy explosion. Similar features have since been produced in shock-wave experiments, but none is known at volcanoes or along fault planes. Dietz argued that shatter cones are diagnostic of impact structures, and in 1959 he proposed that the genetic name 'cryptovolcanic' for them be replaced by the descriptive term 'cryptoexplosion'. This suggestion was widely adopted. Indeed, it outlived the use of 'astrobleme' (star wound), which Dietz coined for impact scars in 1959.

In 1963, in response to writings by Dietz and others, Walter Bucher, by then a Professor Emeritus at Columbia University, wrote a powerful paper in which he presented evidence for an endogenous origin involving deep-seated volcanism and/or structural collapse of the best known purported impact structures and craters in Europe and America – including the Barringer Meteorite Crater. Bucher (1963, p. 643) wrote,

> Before we look to the sky to solve our problems miraculously in one blow, we should consider the possibility that cryptoexplosion structures and explosion craters may hold important clues to processes going on at great depth below our feet ... Doing so will

probably yield more useful results than computing possible velocities of imagined meteorites.

The following year, Bucher visited the Barringer Crater with three guides: his former student, Wolfgang Elston, and Eugene Shoemaker and Jack McCauley of the US Geological Survey. Afterward, he wrote to Elston that he had had few days in his life so thoroughly crammed with new insights into geological matters (Mark 1987, p. 153). Bucher died soon afterwards personally persuaded of the impact origin of that particular crater but holding fast to a terrestrial origin for others, including the Ries Kessel in Bavaria.

Depth–diameter ratios of explosion craters

In 1949, Ralph Baldwin published a 239-page book, *The Face of the Moon.* It did not sell very well but it wielded enormous influence because Harold C. Urey (1893–1981), the Nobel prize winner in chemistry and one of the leading planetary scientists of the early Space Age, read a pre-publication copy. Among much new data, Baldwin had put forward a persuasive kind of evidence for the impact origin of lunar and terrestrial craters. While performing ordinance research for the US Army, Baldwin compiled depth–diameter ratios of craters produced by bomb and shell explosions and plotted them on a log–log diagram along with those of lunar craters and the four terrestrial craters then known to be associated with iron meteorites. All these craters, large and small, plotted close to a smooth curve suggestive of a common mode of origin–namely, point-source explosions. By that time, it was well known that explosions of military projectiles will yield essentially circular craters regardless of their trajectories. Baldwin assumed the same would be true of explosive meteorite impacts. Urey visited Baldwin and became totally convinced of the impact origin of the lunar basins and craters. Subsequently, Urey was instrumental in making a trip to the Moon America's primary goal in space (Wilhelms 1993, p. 19).

Although he left academia to direct a family-owned machine-tool company, Baldwin authored a second book, *The Measure of the Moon,* in 1963, in which he further discussed lunar basins and craters and listed proved and possible terrestrial impact structures. He received several honours for his contributions. In 1993, Don E. Wilhelms dedicated his definitive history of the Apollo missions to 'the amazing Ralph Baldwin, who got so much so right so early'.

Crater research in Canada

In the 1950s, Carlyle S. Beals (1899–1979), director of the Dominion Observatory at Ottawa, instituted the first national research programme on impact structures. Searches of air photographs for circular features were followed by gravity and magnetic surveys, and core drilling of the most promising sites. This project revealed that, unlike volcanoes, impact structures are underlain by deep lenses of megabreccia with angular blocks of bedrock up to many metres across. In a review, Beals *et al.* (1963) reported conclusive evidence of the impact origin of three Canadian craters that fitted perfectly on Baldwin's depth–diameter curve, and listed several more that were under study.

The Sudbury Basin, Ontario. Despite all of this systematic research, peals of derisive laughter greeted Robert Dietz in 1962 when he proposed an impact origin for the Sudbury

Basin in Ontario. That structure exhibits numerous puzzling features that had eluded explanation by the generations of geologists who had worked there on the great Sudbury nickel irruptive. However, they closed ranks in rejecting an impact origin. Within two years, however, Dietz had found dramatic displays of shatter cones along the southern margin of the basin. When the rocks were remapped in their predeformation positions, the apexes of the cones pointed towards the centre (Dietz & Butler 1964). In subsequent field work J. Guy Bray *et al.* (1966), a geologist employed at Sudbury, reported finding shatter cones in pre-intrusive bedrock in a zone about 18 km wide entirely surrounding the nickel ore body. However, shatter cones were still so novel that the authors, themselves, were not yet convinced that they were unique to impact sites.

The following year, Bevan French (1967) reported petrographic evidence at Sudbury of shock deformation in quartz and feldspar, and the presence of impact glass in a megabreccia he interpreted as fall-back ejecta. Today, the Sudbury Basin is one of the 26 – and counting – well-established impact structures in Canada.

Crater research at the US Geological Survey

In 1948, Eugene M. Shoemaker (1928–1997), a youthful member of the US Geological Survey, heard stirrings of future space exploration and decided, in a flash, that he wished to be a geologist-astronaut. He read G. K. Gilbert's paper (1893) on the Moon and Ralph Baldwin's book (1949). They convinced him of the importance of impact cratering and sparked in him a consuming interest in the Moon. Shoemaker tried to persuade the Geological Survey to establish a programme of lunar studies. He failed, at first; but, after much effort and a lot of good luck, he succeeded in 1960, as will be noted below. Meanwhile, Shoemaker examined diatreme volcanoes and nuclear bomb-test sites and then arranged in 1957 to examine the Barringer Meteorite Crater in Arizona. He was the first member of the Survey to do so since G. K. Gilbert in 1891. In a detailed study, he documented the abundant evidence of the crater's impact origin – which still was opposed by many – and analysed the magnitude of the blast (Shoemaker 1960).

Sputnik IV, 1957, to Project Apollo, 1960–1972

Few were aware of living in the Space Age until the world woke up on the morning of 4 October 1957 to the beep-beep-beep of the Soviet Union's satellite, Sputnik IV, orbiting overhead. In the United States, space flight, which already was in planning stages, suddenly assumed prime importance. On 1 October 1958, a civilian agency, the National Aeronautics and Space Administration (NASA) was created, with lavish funding. The following year seven astronauts were selected from a nationwide pool of jet pilot volunteers. In July 1960, NASA announced Project Apollo, a mission to put men in orbit around the Earth and, possibly on the Moon. In August 1960, NASA agreed to fund a programme of lunar research to be directed by Eugene Shoemaker at the US Geological Survey. After working in scattered offices for two years, the Astrogeology Branch of the Survey opened its headquarters at Flagstaff, Arizona, in 1962. Shoemaker instituted a programme of mapping the Moon using the geological principles of superposition, cross-cutting relationships, and states of preservation. The maps enabled the construction of a relative geological timescale keyed to four major lunar events. The Astrogeology Branch also trained the astronauts in geological field work (with an obligatory visit to the Barringer Meteorite Crater), and sent some of its members to study far-flung terrestrial impact craters. In later years, the Branch progressed to mapping Mars and other geologically interesting planets and satellites.

In 1961, President John F. Kennedy announced the national purpose to fly men to the Moon and return them safely to Earth within the decade. With its mission redefined, Project Apollo mounted six field expeditions to the Moon between July 1969 and December 1972. Much to his regret, Shoemaker himself had been disqualified as an astronaut for health reasons. However, the one geologist-astronaut, Harrison Schmitt, walked on the Moon as a team member of Apollo 17, the final mission.

The participation of geologists in lunar and planetary programmes was an extremely promising development. At first, heated debates took place on whether geological terminology, including rock names, could be extended to the Moon. Should not lunar basalts be given a strictly lunar name – particularly when we learned that they contain no water and are more calcic than terrestrial basalts? Should not lunar geophysics be called selenophysics? Such questions echoed a uniformitarian belief that geology is strictly a science of the Earth. Despite these objections, irrepressible lunar investigators persisted in using terrestrial terminology in their talks, classrooms and publications, thereby successfully integrating lunar with terrestrial geology.

Shock metamorphism. In 1968, the year Apollo 8 orbited the Moon, a 644-page book, *Shock Metamorphism of Natural Materials* (French & Short 1968), launched a new discipline. The book reported on a decade of comparative studies of rocks and minerals at nuclear bomb-test sites and those subject to shock-wave experiments in laboratories in efforts to develop criteria for the identification of impact sites. These criteria included shatter cones, coesite, stishovite, shock lamellae in quartz, kink banding in micas, sintered or fused impact glass, meteorite fragments, vapour-condensed Ni–Fe spherules, decomposed or disordered minerals with anomalous extinction, and *in situ* replacement of quartz by lechatelierite or feldspar by maskelynite due to lattice destruction by shock waves rather than fusion.

In the book's preface, the editors (French & Short 1968, p. 7) wrote that, along with the increasingly wide acceptance of impacts, some geologists continued to argue against meteorite impact on the basis of: (1) the undesirably catastrophic character of large impacts, (2) a suggested association of proposed impact sites with geological structures, and (3) the assumption that some sort of deep-seated (but heretofore unrecognized) volcanic pressures could produce the observed shock-metamorphic effects. They were correct in their judgement: many geologists the world over continued to dispute the authenticity of impact structures, in part because impacts of meteorites or comets seemed to be an affront to geology itself. B. B. Brock (1965, p. 1049) spoke for many colleagues when he wrote, 'To call upon astronomy to solve our tectonic problems would be to minimize the usefulness of geology.'

Plate tectonics

We must, however, remember what else was going on at the time. The late 1960s saw the advent of plate tectonics. Geology itself was undergoing what seemed at the time to be a revolutionary shift from the classic fixist to mobilist views. Geologists everywhere were applying new insights to their field and laboratory data and fitting them into the grand new global scheme. Perhaps we can accommodate only one 'revolution' at a time.

In retrospect, we can view plate tectonics not as truly revolutionary but, in fact, as a great triumph for uniformitarianism (Marvin 1990, p. 153). The plates split, slide and suture at rates of a few centimetres per year. The ocean floors recycle continuously; we see no vestige of a beginning and no prospect of an end. And plate motion is ascribed to forces intrinsic to the Earth (although today a vocal contingent is arguing for impacts as the driving force). We may speculate that both James Hutton and Charles Lyell might have found it possible to reconcile themselves to plate tectonics. But, without seriously compromising his basic principles, neither of these two founders of uniformitarian geology could have reconciled himself to meteorite impact – a process of random violence, originating outside the Earth, that can wreak sudden destruction on a global scale. Many of the intellectual heirs of Hutton and Lyell kept the faith and made it possible for geologists and the planetary science community to continue on their separate ways. This is evident in the virtually complete lack of articles and discussions of meteorites and impacts published in geological journals and textbooks throughout the 1970s.

The Cretaceous–Tertiary boundary event

The Alvarez hypothesis

Mainstream geology and meteoritics collided head-on on 6 June 1980, when a research team headed by the Nobel laureate in physics, Luis Alvarez (1911–1988), published an article in *Science* that caught everybody's attention. It was titled 'Extraterrestrial cause for the Cretaceous–Tertiary extinction: experimental results and theoretical interpretation'.

The Alvarez group had analysed a thin layer of unfossiliferous clay separating Cretaceous from Tertiary limestones in Italy, Denmark and New Zealand, and found that values of iridium were enhanced above background by 30, 160 and 20 times, respectively. Iridium is virtually absent in the Earth's much-reworked crustal rocks but is present in cosmic abundance in meteorites and comets. The authors proposed that an asteroid, about 10 km in diameter, had struck the Earth and injected about 60 times the object's mass into the stratosphere as pulverized impactor mixed with target rock; the dust spread worldwide, screened out sunlight, suppressed photosynthesis and caused the collapse of food chains that led to the extinctions, including that of the dinosaurs, observed at that horizon in the palaeontological record. They pointed out that if the K–T extinction was triggered by the impact of an asteroid, the same might be true of all of the five major extinctions that have occurred since the end of the Precambrian, 570 million years ago.

The response: total uproar

The Alvarez paper generated its own shock waves and aroused acrimonious criticism from geologists and palaeontologists, most of whom were unaware of the research being performed on impact processes and sensed this as a bolt from the blue hurled at Earth scientists by physicists and geochemists. Critics took scant comfort from the fact that Walter Alvarez, Luis' son, is a geologist. Virtually overnight, responses poured into journals, meetings and workshops were called, and the literature on impacts and extinctions began to expand exponentially. The popular press revelled in the story of the fiery impact–extinction of the dinosaurs. Without attempting a step-by-step, fully referenced account, we will briefly trace some of the highlights of the ensuing debate as they were presented at the three multidisciplinary 'Snowbird' conferences of 1981, 1988 and 1991, and then bring the evidence and argument up to date.

Snowbird I

In October 1981, geologists, micropalaeontologists, vertebrate palaeontologists, palaeobotanists, atmospheric scientists, meteoriticists, planetary scientists, physicists, geophysicists and cosmochemists met at Snowbird, Utah, at a conference titled 'Large Body Impacts and Terrestrial Evolution: Geological, Climatological, and Biological Implications'. Reportedly, arguments were so intense that few participants found time to appreciate the spectacular scenery. While geologists and palaeontologists were introduced to the flux and dynamics of impacting bodies and their potentially catastrophic disruptions of the Earth's oceans, atmosphere and biosphere, meteoriticists and planetary scientists learned that the very concept of mass extinctions is a much debated issue. One speaker questioned whether mass (i.e. worldwide) extinctions are illusions or realities. His answer: a few have been severe and worldwide but each one stretched on for millions of years instead of being sudden and catastrophic. Another lauded Georges Cuvier (1769–1832), 'the Father of Biological Catastrophism', for reporting extinctions without invoking miracles. He and others cited the many sources of error inherent in framing hypotheses of catastrophic extinctions. A lively discussion ensued on the fate of the dinosaurs. One speaker pointed out that dinosaur species had been declining in numbers and range for several million years before they finally succumbed – most likely from the effects of a 150–200 m drop in sea level. Some argued that the dinosaurs died out before the end of the Cretaceous; others that they survived into the Tertiary. Many participants believed that the massive eruptions of the Deccan Traps of India, which occurred ~65 million years ago, caused the extinctions, and some opined that they also supplied the iridium to the boundary clay.

By the time of Snowbird I, however, the iridium-bearing boundary clay had been discovered at numerous sites around the world in continental as well as marine strata. This countered a hypothesis that the iridium came from the daily increment of extraterrestrial dust and had been concentrated in the clay by dissolution of pelagic limestones. In addition to iridium, other platinum group and related elements, including Pt, Os, Rh, Re and Au, had been found in the clay in approximately cosmic proportions (e.g. those observed in spectra of the solar photosphere and in bulk analyses of chondritic meteorites). The isotopic ratio of $^{187}Os/^{186}Os$ in the boundary clay was proving to be a particularly sensitive indicator of extraterrestrial material in sedimentary strata.

After contentious discussions of impacts and extinctions, some participants left the Snowbird I conference inspired to undertake new research projects while others continued to reject the reality of cataclysmic impacts, or extinctions, or both. Many were impressed by the evidence for a powerful K–T impact without accepting the killing scenario of the Alvarez group. The papers presented at Snowbird I may be found in Silver & Schultz (1982).

Periodic extinctions

The first palaeontologists to report evidence of periodic extinctions were Alfred G. Fischer, a professor at Princeton, and his graduate student, Michael A. Arthur (1977). They asserted that major extinctions have occurred approximately every 32 million years since the greatest extinction of all wiped out ~90 per cent of species at the end of the Palaeozoic era, 250 million years ago. As a possible cause, the authors suggested a cyclic pattern of convection within the Earth. 'This was anathema!' wrote David M. Raup (1986, p. 107). Biological communities do not keep time locally so how could they do so globally over such a time span? For the most part, he said, palaeontologists and geologists met Fischer's periodic extinctions with an embarrassed silence.

The issue of periodicity arose again in 1984 when Raup himself and J. J. Sepkoski, Jr, palaeontologists at the University of Chicago, reported that their analysis of a vast computerized compendium of data Sepkoski had compiled on fossil marine families showed that 12 extinctions had occurred at 26 million year intervals during the past 250 million years. They suggested that the cause might be astronomical, hoping, wrote Raup (1986, p. 126), 'that the astronomers and astrophysicists would pick up the challenge. They picked it up with a vengeance.'

Within two months after Raup and Sepkoski's paper was published in February 1984, the 19 April issue of *Nature* contained five letters suggesting astronomical causes of the periodicity. Two of the letters related the extinctions to the Sun's regular oscillation through the plane of the Milky Way Galaxy, which it crosses every 33 million years or so. They postulated either a lethally enhanced radiation flux at peak sites above and below the plane (Schwartz & James 1984), or that showers of comets are perturbed from the Oort cloud into the inner solar system by the gravitational force of interstellar molecular clouds clustered at the galactic plane (Rampino & Stothers 1984). A third letter posited that an unseen companion star (Nemesis), in a moderately eccentric orbit about the Sun regularly perturbs comets Earthward as it passes through the Oort cloud at perihelion (Davis *et al.* (1984). A fourth, ascribed the same effect to an unnamed companion star that precesses through the Oort cloud (Whitmire & Jackson 1984). A year later this companion evolved into Planet X, in orbit beyond Neptune, where it perturbs comets from the EKG belt (Whitmire & Matese 1985). In the fifth letter Walter Alvarez and Richard Muller (1984) reported finding a periodicity of 28.4 million years in the excavation of 11 large impact craters during the past 250 million years. They calculated the probability as only one in 1000 that the agreement in the periodicity of extinctions and cratering is accidental.

In an editorial, Anthony Hallam, a palaeontologist at the University of Birmingham, who places his faith in terrestrial causes of extinctions, wrote that any claim of periodicity depends on which geological timescale it is based on. Hallam (1984) pointed out that, using the K–T event as the reference point, only five of the 12 events listed by Raup and Sepkoski fall within a million years of the dates given for them on a newly revised and more accurate timescale than the one they used. He saw no clear evidence of extra-terrestrial causes and felt no need for them – he reminded his readers that there is an abundance of terrestrial ones, including sea-level changes, that have exhibited cyclicity throughout the Phanerozoic.

This issue of *Nature* marked a dramatic about-face in thinking within the palaeontological community. Appropriately, the cover featured a coloured photograph of Meteor Crater and the title 'Mass Extinctions'. Although several astronomers and planetary scientists (e.g. Nininger 1942; Öpik 1958; Urey 1973, Napier & Clube 1979) had ascribed extinctions to astronomical causes, very few palaeontologists had done so. These included: M. W. de Laubenfels (1956), who suggested that a giant impact killed the dinosaurs; Otto Schindewolf (1962), who postulated that a supernova explosion had caused the mass extinction that ended the Palaeozoic era, and Digby Mclaren (1970), who suggested that the Frasnian (late Devonian) mass extinctions were triggered by impacts.

Lacking tangible evidence, these speculations had been greeted by a stony silence. In 1980, the Alvarez group presented the first testable hypothesis, based on analytical results, that an impact had produced a global geochemical anomaly and contributed to the extinctions at the K–T boundary.

Snowbird II

Needless to say, periodicity of impacts and extinctions was a major topic of discussion at the second Snowbird conference, 'Global Catastrophes in Earth History: An Interdisciplinary Conference on Impacts, Volcanism, and Mass Mortality', convened in October 1988. This conference was dedicated to Luis W. Alvarez, who had died earlier that year.

The two most favored causes of periodic extinctions were comet showers and eruptions of continental flood basalts. Comet showers, a concept introduced by Hills (1981), were swarms of bodies perturbed from the Oort cloud, several of which might hit the Earth over a period of a million years or so. Most participants who preferred volcanism viewed it as a strictly terrestrial process. However, one speaker described a 33 million year quasi-periodicity in eruptions of flood basalts, mass extinctions, and impacts caused by comet showers.

Impact products discovered in the K–T boundary clay since Snowbird I included grains of shocked quartz, stishovite, abundances of glassy microspherules, magnesioferrite (a high-temperature Ni-rich spinel not known in terrestrial rocks), and deposits of fossil charcoal and soot which were ascribed to wildfires of continental proportions, set by the heat of the explosion and fall-back of hot ejecta. The group that reported the fossil carbon compiled a list, gleaned from the literature, of 12 environmental stresses expected from a K–T-magnitude impact: tsunamis and winds to 500 km hr^{-1} lasting for hours; darkness, cold, wildfires, and an H_2O greenhouse effect lasting for months; pyrotoxins and acid rains continuing for years; a CO_2 greenhouse effect and destruction of the ozone layer lasting for decades; impact-triggered volcanism and mutagens continuing for millennia. They argued that the seemingly inexplicable selectivity of K–T extinctions, in which some species succumbed while similar ones survived, may be explained by local or regional variations in intensities of these stresses. The following year, Raup (1991) addressed the question of selectivity in Extinction – Bad Genes or Bad Luck? He concluded that both apply: most species go extinct when they cannot adapt to stressful environmental changes, but some have the luck to survive, for a while.

At Snowbird II, one group reported that the normally positive values of carbon-13 in surface sea water had crashed to zero, and temporarily to negative values at the boundary, reflecting an interval of severely suppressed biomass production in a so-called 'strangelove' ocean which may have continued for thousands of years.

Another group reported a search for iridium and 40 other elements in thousands of samples taken from across bio-event boundaries ranging in age from the Precambrian–Cambrian boundary to the late Eocene. They found only meagre showings of iridium in low to medium values of 0.002–0.2 ppb at a few sites. None of these anomalies extended worldwide or was clearly attributable to an impact. None approached the values of ~10–20 ppb of iridium found in the K–T boundary clay. This study suggested that the K–T boundary clay is unique as a global time–stratigraphic marker. The papers of the Snowbird II conference were compiled and edited by Sharpton and Ward (1990).

Snowbird III

In February 1994, the third Snowbird conference convened in Houston, Texas. Three years earlier the 'smoking gun'–the K–T impact crater–had been discovered at Chicxulub in Yucatán. The size, dating, and wall-rock composition of that crater and the thick blanket of impact ejecta and tsunami deposits on its periphery were principal topics of discussion. Newly discovered impact products in the boundary clay included two varieties of minute diamonds: nanometre-sized diamonds bearing the isotopic signature of an interstellar origin (as do diamonds in carbonaceous chondrites), and somewhat larger diamonds formed by impact on the target rock. Some of the clay samples with interstellar diamonds also contained 51 amino acids of inorganic origin, including 18 known only in carbonaceous chondrites. These findings indicated that the Chicxulub impactor was either a comet or an asteroidal fragment of carbonaceous chondrite composition. Also found in the clay were glassy droplets containing crystals of magnesiowüstite, a high-temperature Ni–Fe magnesium oxide that sometimes forms in meteorite fusion crusts but not in the Earth's crustal rocks.

Reports of anomalous iridium in volcanic aerosols, ash and lavas gave heart to those who believed in a volcanic source of the iridium. However, abundances of the accompanying trace elements proved to be far from cosmic values. At the Kilauéa volcano in Hawaii, for example, the Ir/Au ratios were eight to several hundred times lower than in meteorites and the K–T boundary clay. Numerous other topics are covered in the Snowbird III volume *New Developments in the Cretaceous–Tertiary Event and Other Catastrophes in Earth History,* compiled and edited by Ryder *et al.* (1996).

Current overview of the K–T event

Two enormously powerful forces occurred almost simultaneously 65 million years ago: the hypervelocity impact in Yucatán and the massive outpouring of the Deccan basalts in India. The volcanism began first.

The Deccan Traps: with boundary clay and dinosaur fossils. The eruptions of the Deccan Traps, which are up to 2 km thick and cover ~1.5 million km^{-2} of land and seafloor, are most often cited by geologists (but not by volcanologists, according to Glen (1996, p. 45)) as the factor that triggered the K–T extinctions by dimming sunlight and poisoning the air and waters. They argue that it furnished the iridium in the boundary clay by mantle outgassing. Recent dating and palaeomagnetic determinations indicate that the eruptions began ~67 million years ago and continued for up to 3 million years (Chatterjee & Rudra 1996, p. 511). Although each eruptive pulse seriously degraded the environment, vegetation luxuriated in the sedimentary layers between the flows – only to be overwhelmed by the ash, lava and noxious fumes of the next eruption.

At Anjar, in Kutch, the thin 65 million year old boundary clay, with its iridium anomaly and meteoritic ratio of iridium to osmium, has been identified among the sediments that accumulated in the third interval between basalt flows (Bhandari *et al.* 1996). No such anomaly has been found at other levels in the intertrappean sediments or in the lavas. Also at Anjar, dinosaur bones have been collected from immediately beneath the boundary clay. Neither the bones nor the cross-bedded limestone in which they occur contain values of iridum above background (~82 parts per trillion (ppt)), but the clay contains 348 ppt of iridium (Chatterjee & Rudra 1996, p. 520). These authors argue that, in addition to

Chicxulub, a second, much larger 65 million year old impact crater was excavated in the floor of the Indian Ocean and has since been split apart by seafloor spreading. However, in the absence of shocked rocks or other compelling evidence, this hypothetical crater has received little acceptance. Meanwhile many investigators agree that the Chicxulub impact alone can account for the global distribution of ejecta and stratospheric fallout (e.g. Hildebrand 1997).

The Chicxulub crater. The gigantic Chicxulub crater lies buried beneath 1 km of post-Cretaceous sediments on the Yucatán Peninsula (Hildebrand *et al.* 1991). The impacting meteorite penetrated about 3 km of Cretaceous limestone, dolomite and anhydrite and excavated the crater in andesitic bedrock. Seismic reflection surveys by Morgan *et al.* (1997) have revealed that Chicxulub is a multi-ringed crater about 180 km in diameter. Multi-ringed structures are well known on the Moon and Venus but Chicxulub is the first to be identified on the Earth. Although the two larger Precambrian impact structures, Sudbury and Vredefort, may have formed as multi-ringed features, no evidence of rings remains visible today. The most surprising results of the seismic surveys show that the outermost of the three rings at Chicxulub is an inward-dipping fault scarp that plunges beneath the crater and offsets the Mohorovicic discontinuity at a depth of *c.* 35 km. No trace of a soft, yielding asthenosphere is present at this section of the crust–mantle boundary. These observations show that Chicxulub is smaller in diameter than estimated by some scientists (e.g. Sharpton *et al.* 1996), but its effects penetrate much deeper than anyone suspected. Calculations show the Chicxulub impact to have been approximately a 100 million megatonne event (e.g. Kring 1993, p. 70).

Impact glasses recovered from drill cores that penetrated a deep lens of megabreccia beneath the crater floor yield $^{40}Ar/^{39}Ar$ ages of 64.98 ± 0.05 million years (Swisher *et al.* 1992). Samples of melt rocks in the centre of the structure show enhanced values of Ir, Re and Os in meteoritic proportions (Sharpton *et al.* 1996). Coarse crater ejecta, mixed with tsunami deposits and overlain by the layer of boundary clay, are thickest around the Gulf of Mexico, where a number of outcrops show a basal bed of tektites and shocked quartz. At nearby Beloc, in Haiti, a tektite deposit, 0.5 m thick, consists of aerodynamically shaped spherules, teardrops, rods, discs and dumbbells up to 8 mm across. Most of these tektites are altered to clay but a few retain cores of dark glass similar in composition to the basement crystallines at the crater (Sigurdsson *et al.* 1991). The tektite glasses match the crater glass in age: 65.07 ± 0.10 million years (Swisher *et al.* 1992). Some of the dark glass is streaked with yellow, Ca-rich glass from melted limestone, and all of it is very different from volcanic glass in oxygen isotopic composition (Blum & Chamberlain 1992).

The deposits of microtektites and fragmental ejecta thin out in North America and in Pacific cores at distances approaching 4000 km from the crater (Kring 1993, p. 69). Beyond the ejecta, which must have been deposited within minutes of the impact, the overlying clay layer, fallout from a dust–vapour cloud, continues around the world. Today, few scientists doubt that a gigantic impact took place 65 million years ago at the end of the Cretaceous period.

A revised extinction scenario. In their paper of 1980, the Alvarez group postulated that years of post-impact darkness and cold triggered the extinctions. Shortly thereafter, this model was adopted as a potential cause of a 'nuclear winter'. More recently, Walter Alvarez (1997) outlined a more complicated scenario in which the impact produced a short impact winter followed by a long impact summer due to the greenhouse effect of the volumes of CO_2 in the stratosphere. A key assumption of his new model was that the impact blasted away a column of the atmosphere, making way for the lofting into space of two successive fireballs, the first consisting mainly of vaporized impactor and target rock, the second, cooler fireball, consisting of a great cloud of CO_2 and SO_2 released from the limestones and anhydrite penetrated by the projectile. This second fireball also distributed shocked quartz. Rains of sulphuric and nitric acids followed, due to the hydration of the SO_2 released from the anhydrite and NO released by shock heating of the atmosphere itself. The acids devastated the lands and contributed to the poisoning of the surface waters of the oceans.

Questioning periodicities

Is there persuasive evidence for periodicity of either large impact craters or major extinctions? Extinctions are notoriously difficult to characterize and date, and the record gets worse as one goes further back in time. It is particularly hard to measure rates of extinction. At present, palaeontologists appear to agree that there have been five major extinctions plus a (debated) number of minor ones since the end of the Precambrian. Arguments continue on whether they are periodic.

Despite persistent claims of periodicity in large cratering events, R. A. F. Grieve of the Geological Survey of Canada, who maintains a list of impact craters and their most recent age determinations, finds no compelling evidence for it. Grieve (1997, p. 333) explains that biases in the cratering record are too strong and uncertainties in crater age estimates are too large to yield a periodicity by means of time-series analysis. Also, the assumption of a zero background for any million-year interval lacking a known crater may lead to a false impression of periodicity. In any case, whatever massively destructive impacts may occur, at random or periodically, they take place against the steady infall of fragments derived from the asteroid belt which have provided us with meteorites and excavated a large proportion of the craters on the Earth and Moon.

Grieve (1997, p. 338) reviewed the 20 reported occurrences of impact debris–tektites, microtektites, shocked minerals, anomalous iridium and/or siderophile elements–in the stratigraphic column. They range in age from the 3400 million year old early Archaen spherule beds (of disputed origin) in South Africa and Australia to the 700 000 year old Australasian microtektites. Nine of the occurrences of impact products can be attributed to specific impacts, but only three of them, (late Devonian, K–T and late Eocene) correlate with extinctions. Although the record is far from complete, this finding suggests that not all, or even most, extinctions are due to impacts.

A much closer correlation is found between extinctions and eruptions of continental flood basalts. More than 75 per cent of the major and minor extinctions of the past 400 million years are approximately coeval with outpourings of flood basalt. Why should flood basalts erupt periodically? This question has led to hypotheses that planetwide upheavals occur, marked by flood basalts, extinctions, episodes of mountain building, magnetic pole reversals, and abrupt changes in plate motion, climate and sea level (e.g. Rampino & Caldeira 1993). These authors argue that such all-encompassing events occur with a periodicity of ~30 million years, and attribute them to impacts possibly resulting from the passage of the solar system through the galactic plane.

However, if the Earth undergoes such convulsions every 26–30 million years, they are totally out of phase with the Sun's crossings of the plane. Today, the Sun is close to the galactic plane, where, theoretically, maximal disturbances of the Oort cloud should be taking place. Yet the most recent extinction occurred in the mid-Miocene, about 13 million years ago, when the Sun was nearly at its maximum distance from the plane. Should the Sun's crossing of the plane pose any special danger? Thaddeus and Chanan (1985) addressed this question and decided that it does not. They calculated that giant molecular clouds are not sufficiently concentrated in the galactic plane to seriously perturb the comet reservoirs of the solar system. Other writers disagree (e.g. Napier 1987).

The Sun's hypothetical companion, Nemesis, remains unseen despite diligent searches for it. In any case, the orbit of such a small companion would seem unlikely to remain stable long enough to periodically perturb comets to Earth during the past 250 million years. Orbital technicalities also cast doubt on the existence of Planet X.

Could the Earth itself capture swarms of small asteroidal and cometary bodies into geocentric orbits from where they periodically pummel the planet with impacts? In *Craters, Cosmos, and Chronicles: A New Theory of the Earth,* Herbert Shaw (1994) postulated that it can, and does. He argued that the asymmetrical distribution of mass within the Earth, inherited from the giant collision that gave rise to the Moon, serves to capture the bodies and at times of crisis – perhaps due to a periodic galactic tide – it gravitationally focuses them into trajectories that impact the Earth along certain swaths. The resulting non-random bursts of impact activity influence plate motion, volcanism, extinctions, magnetic reversals and the other major events recorded in the stratigraphic column. Aside from a few favourable reviews, Shaw's ideas are under heavy attack by geophysicists and astronomers, whose many objections include the observations that comets, asteroids and near Earth objects all orbit the Sun, not the Earth. However, as we have seen in these pages, unorthodox ideas often open up fruitful new lines of research.

As we celebrate the Hutton–Lyell bicentennial, we may ponder whether the Earth, which shows abundant evidence of its long history of collisions in space, may be coupled in a rhythmic interplay with forces external to the planet. We cannot depart farther than this from the uniformitarian geology of Hutton and Lyell.

Conclusion

Newton's umbrella is closed. Today we understand that we must incorporate sudden, unpredictable, cataclysmic impacts from space into our inventories of geologic processes. Indeed, we have witnessed such an event in operation. In July 1994, we watched spellbound as 21 fragments of a comet bombarded Jupiter, one after another, producing Earth-sized spots in the atmosphere that generated rising plumes of dark vapour with surface temperatures, measured by infrared, of ~10 000°. The spots still were visible a year later.

Afterward, Robert Dietz (1995) wrote, 'Of course, Shoemaker-Levy 9's impact of Jupiter makes impact an actualistic process now.' Actualistic, yes; uniformitarian, no! Efforts to incorporate multi-megatonne impacts into 'uniformitariansm', when for the past 160 years that term has denoted gradual change by processes intrinsic to the Earth, is an Orwellian reversal in meaning of the 'Freedom is Slavery' type. We have learned from Space Age research that we live in a universe in which, by sheer happenstance, the Earth has its Moon, Venus rotates backward, and a giant impact blasted away the Mesozoic era. Today we realize that collisions in space are the most fundamental process that has operated throughout the history of the solar system. This is a truly revolutionary insight that requires a fresh vision of the basic tenets of geology.

I wish to thank Brian G. Marsden and S. Ross Taylor for many interesting discussions on the small bodies of the solar system, and two referees who made helpful suggestions for revising my manuscript. I appreciate the support I received for participation in the Hutton–Lyell Conference from the Royal Society of Edinburgh and the Smithsonian Institution.

References

ALBRITTON, C. C., JR 1967. Uniformity, the ambiguous principle. *In*: ALBRITTON, C. C., JR (ed.) *Uniformity and Simplicity: A Symposium on the principle of Uniformity of Nature*. Geological Society of America Special Paper, **89**, 1–2.

—— 1989. *Catastrophic Episodes in Earth History*. Chapman & Hall, New York.

ALLÈGRE, C. J., MANHÈS, G. & GÖPEL, C. 1995. The age of the Earth. *Geochimica et Cosmochimica Acta*, **59**, 1445–1456.

ALVAREZ, L. W., ALVAREZ, W., ASARO F. & MICHEL, H. V. 1980. Extraterrestrial cause for the Cretaceous–Tertiary extinction: experiment results and theoretical interpretation. *Science*, **208**, 1095–1108

ALVAREZ, W. 1997. *T. rex and the Crater of Doom*. Princeton University Press, Princeton, NJ.

—— & MULLER, R. A. 1984. Evidence from crater ages of periodic impacts on the Earth. *Nature*, **308**, 718–720.

BALDWIN, R. B. 1942. The meteoritic origin of lunar craters. *Popular Astronomy*, **50**, 365–359.

—— 1949. *The Face of the Moon*. University of Chicago Press, Chicago.

—— 1963. *The Measure of the Moon*. University of Chicago Press, Chicago.

BARRINGER, D. M. 1906. Coon Mt. and its crater. *Proceedings of the Academy of Natural Sciences of Philadelphia*, **57**, 861–886.

BEALS, C. S., INNES, M. J. S. & ROTTENBERG, J. A. 1963. Fossil meteorite craters. *In*: MIDDLEHURST, B. M. & KUIPER, G. P. (eds) *The Moon, Meteorites, and Comets*, 235–284. University of Chicago Press, Chicago.

BERGGREN, W. A. & VAN COUVERING, J. A. (eds) 1984. *Catastrophes and Earth History: The New Uniformitarianism*. Princeton University Press, Princeton, NJ.

BHANDARI, N., SHUKLA, P. N. GHEVARIYA, Z. G. & SUNDARAM, S. M. 1996. K/T boundary layer in Deccan Intertrappeans at Anjar, Kutch. *In*: RYDER, G., FASTOVSKY, D. & GARTNER, S. (eds) *The Cretaceous–Tertiary Event and Other Catastrophes in Earth History*, Geological Society of America Special Paper, **307**, 417–424.

BIOT, J. -B. 1803. Lettre à M. Picket. *Bibliottèque Britannique*, **23**, 394–405.

BLUM, J. D. & CHAMBERLAIN, C. P. 1992. Oxygen isotope contraints on the origin of impact glasses from the Cretaceous–Tertiary boundary. *Science*, **257**, 1104–1107.

BOON, J. D. & ALBRITTON, C. C., JR 1936. Meteorite craters and their possible relationship to 'cryptovolcanic structures'. *Field and Laboratory*, **5**, 1–9.

—— & —— 1937. Meteorite scars in ancient rocks. *Field and Laboratory*, **6**, 53–64.

BRANCO, W. & FRAAS, E. 1905, Das kryptovulkanische Becken von Steinheim. *Kaiserlich Preusse Akademie Wissenschaften Abhandlung*, Berlin, 1–64.

BRAY, J. V. G. ET AL. 1966. Shatter cones at Sudbury. *Journal of Geology*, **74**, 243–245.

BROCK, B. B. 1965. Discussion of a paper by W. I. Manton. *Annals of the New York Academy of Sciences*, **123**(2), 367–1257.

BUCHER, W. H. 1936. Cryptovolcanic structures in the United States. *In*: *Proceedings of the 16th International Geological Congress, USA*, **2**,1055–1084.

—— 1963. Cryptoexplosion structures caused from without or from within the earth? ('Astroblemes' or 'Geoblemes?'). *American Journal of Science*, **261**, 597–649.

CAMERON, A. G. W. 1997. The origin of the Moon and the single impact hypothesis V. *Icarus*, **126**, 126–137,

CANNON, W. F. 1961. The impact of uniformitarianism. *Proceedings of the American Philosophical Society*, **105**(3), 301–309.

CARUSI, A., GEHRELS, T., HELIN, E. F. ET AL. 1994. Near-Earth objects: present search programs. *In*: GEHRELS, T. (ed.) *Hazards Due to Comets and Asteroids*. University of Arizona Press, Tucson, 127–128.

CHATTERJEE, S. & RUDRA, D. K. 1996. KT events in India: impact, rifting, volcanism and dinosaur extinction. *Memoirs of the Queensland Museum*, **39**(3), 489–532.

CHLADNI, E. F. F. 1787. *Entdeckungen über die Theorie des Klanges*. Weldnanns Erben und Reich, Leipzig.

—— 1794. *Über den Ursprung der von Pallas Gefundenen und anderer ihr ähnlicher Eisenmassen, und Über Einige Damit in Verbindung stehende Naturerscheinungen.* Johann Friedrich Hartknoch, Riga.

CHYBA, C. F., OWEN, T. C. & IP, W.-H. 1994. *In*: GEHRELS, T. (ed.) *Hazards due to comets and asteroids*. University of Arizona Press,Tucson, 9–58.

DAVIS, M., HUT, P. & MULLER, R. A. 1984. Extinction of species by periodic comet showers. *Nature,* **308**, 715–717.

DAVIS, W. M. 1926. *Biographical memoir of Grove Karl Gilbert 1843–1918*. National Academy of Science Biographical Memoirs, **21**. US Govt Printing Office, Washington DC.

DE BOURNON, J. L. COMTE 1802. Mineralogical descriptions of the various stones said to have fallen upon the Earth; and description of various kinds of native iron. *Philosophical Transactions of the Royal Society, London,* **92**, 180–186, 203–210.

DE BUFFON, G. L.-C. 1749. *Histoire naturelle, général et particulière, avec la description du Cabinet du Roi.* Tome Premiere. l'Imprimerie Royale, Paris.

DE LAUBENFELS, M. W. 1956. Dinosaur extinction: one more hypothesis. *Journal of Paleontology,* **30**, 207–218.

DE MAUPERTUIS, PI. L. M. 1750. Essay de Cosmologie. IN: *Les Oeuvres de M. de Maupertius.* George Conrad Walther, Dresden (1752), 3–55.

DIETZ, R. S. 1946. Meteorite impact origin of the moon's surface features. *Journal of Geology,* **54**, 359–374.

—— 1947. Meteorite impact suggested by the orientation of shatter-cones at the Kentland, Indiana, Disturbance. *Science,* **105**, 76.

—— 1959. Shatter cones in cryptoexplosion structures (meteorite impact?). *Journal of Geology,* **67**, 496–505.

—— 1959. Meteorite impact suggested by shatter cones in rock. *Science*, **131**, 1781–1784.

—— 1962. Sudbury structure as an astrobleme. [Abstract], Preprinted from Transactions of the American Geophysical Union, **43**(4), 445–446.

—— & BUTLER, L. 1964. Shatter-cone orientation at Sudbury, Canada. *Nature,* **204**, 4955.

—— 1995. Letter to Ursula Marvin, 5 April.

FISCHER, A. G. & ARTHUR, M. A. 1977. Secular variations in the pelagic realm. *In:* COOK, H. E. & ENOS, P. (eds) *Deep-water carbonate environments*. Society of Economic Paleontologists and Mineralogists, Special Paper, **25**, 9–25.

FRENCH, B. M. 1967. Sudbury Structure, Ontario: some petrographic evidence for origin by meteorite impact. *Science,* **156**, 0094–1098.

—— & SHORT, N. M. (eds) 1968. *Shock Metamorphism of Natural Materials.* Mono Book Corporation, Baltimore.

GEIKIE, A. 1897. *The Founders of Geology*. Macmillan, London.

GIFFORD, A. C. 1930. The origin of the surface features of the Moon. *Scientia*, **48**, 69–80.

GILBERT, G. K. 1893. The Moon's face: a study of the origin of its features. *Bulletin of the Philosophical Society of Washington,* **12**, 241–292.

—— 1896. The origin of hypotheses, illustrated by the discussion of a topographic problem. *Science,* **3**, 1–24.

GLEN, W. 1996. Observations on the mass-extinction debates. *In*: RYDER, G., FASTOVSKY, D. & GARTNER, S. (eds) *The Cretaceous–Tertiary Event and Other Catastrophes in Earth History.* Geological Society of America Special Paper, **307**, 39–54.

GOULD, S. J. 1965. Is uniformitarianism necessary? *American Journal of Science,* **263**, 223–228.

—— 1987. *Time's Arrow, Time's Cycle: Myth and Metaphor in the Discovery of Geological Time.* Harvard University Press. Cambridge, MA.

GRIEVE, R. A. F. 1997. Target Earth: evidence for large-scale impact events. *In:* REMO, J. L. (ed.) *Near-Earth Objects: The United Nations International Conference*. Annals of the New York Academy of Science, **822**, 319–352.

——, RUPERT, J., SMITH, J. & THERRIAULT, A. 1995. The record of terrestrial impact cratering. *GSA Today,* **5**(10), 194–196.

HAGER, D. 1953. Crater Mound (Meteor Crater), Arizona, a geologic feature. *Bulletin of the American Association of Petroleum Geologists,* **37,** 821–857.

HALLAM, A. 1984. The causes of mass extinctions. *Nature,* **308**, 686–687.

HALLEY, E. 1694. Some farther thoughts upon the same subject [the universal deluge]. *Philosophical Transactions of the Royal Society,* **33**, (1724–1725), 123–125.

—— 1705. Astronomiae cometicae synopsis. *Philosophical Transactions of the Royal Society,* **24**, 1882–1889.

HALLIDAY, I., BLACKWELL, A. T. & GRIFFIN, A. A. 1984. The frequency of meteorite falls on the Earth. *Science,* **223**, 1045–1047.

HAMILTON, W. 1795. An account of the late eruption of Mount Vesuvius. *Philosophical Transactions of the Royal Society,* London, **85,** 73–116.

HILDEBRAND, A. R. 1997. Personal communication.

——, PENFIELD, G. T., KRING, D. A., PILKINGTON, M., CAMARGO, A., JACOBSEN, S. B. & BOYNTON, W. V. 1991. Chicxulub Crater: a possible Cretaceous–Tertiary boundary impact crater on the Yucatán Peninsula. *Geology,* **19**, 867–871.

HILLS, J. G. 1981. Comet showers and the steady-state infall of comets from the Oort cloud. *Astronomical Journal,* **86**, 1730–1740.

HOLLAND, H. D. 1997. Personal communication.

HOOKE, R. 1665. *Micrographia*. John Martyn & James Allestry, London.

HOWARD, E. C. 1802. Experiments and observations on certain stony and metalline substances, which at different times are said to have fallen on the Earth; also on various kinds of native iron. *Philosophical Transactions of the Royal Society, London*, **92,** 168–175, 179–180, 186–203, 210–212.

HUTTON, J. 1788. On the theory of the Earth; or an investigation of the laws observable in the composition, dissolution, and restoration of the globe. *Transactions of the Royal Society of Edinburgh,* **1,** 209–304.

—— 1795. *Theory of the Earth with Proofs and Illustrations*. 2 vols. Creech, Edinburgh.

KRING, D. A. 1993. The Chicxulub impact event and possible causes of K/T boundary extinctions. *In*: BOAZ, D. & FORNAN, M. (eds) *Proceedings of the First Annual Symposium of Fossils of Arizona.* Mesa Southwest Museum and the Southwest Paleontological Society, Mesa, Arizona, 63–79.

KRINOV, E. L. 1952. *Giant Meteorites, Tunguska and Sikhote-Alin.* Translated by J. S. Romankiewic. Pergamon Press, Oxford and New York.

LYELL, C. 1830–1833. *Principles of Geology. Being an Attempt to Explain the Former Changes of the Earth's Surface by References to Causes Now in Operation.* 3 vols. James Murray, London.

LYELL, K. M. 1881. *Life, Letters and Journals of Sir Charles Lyell.* 3 vols. John Murray, London.

MCLAREN, D. J. 1970. Presidential address: Time, life, and the boundaries. *Journal of Paleontology,* **44**, 801–815.

MARK, K. 1987. *Meteorite Craters*. University of Arizona Press, Tucson.

MARSDEN, B. G. 1997. Personal communication.

MARVIN, U. B. 1986. Meteorites, the Moon, and the history of geology. *Journal of Geological Education,* **34**, 140–165.

—— 1990. Impact and its revolutionary implications for geology. *In*: SHARPTON, V. L. & WARD, P. D. (eds) *Global Catastrophes in Earth History; An Interdisciplinary Conference on Impacts, Volcanism, and Mass Mortality.* Geological Society of America Special Paper, **247**, 147–154.

—— 1992. The meteorite of Ensisheim:1492 to 1992. *Meteoritics,* **27**, 28–72.

—— 1993. The Meteoritical Society: 1933 to 1993. *Meteoritics,* **28**, 261–314.

—— 1996. Ernst Florens Friedrich Chladni 1756–1827 and the origins of modern meteorite research. *Meteoritics and Planetary Science,* **31,** 545–588.

MORGAN, J. *ET AL.* 1997. Size and morphology of the Chicxulub impact crater. *Nature,* **390**, 472–476.

NAPIER, W. M. 1987, The origin and evolution of the Oort cloud. *In*: CEPLECHA, Z. & PECINA, P. (eds) *Interplanetary Matter*. Publications of the Astronomical Institute of the Czechoslovak Academy of Sciences, **67**(2), 13–20.

—— & CLUBE, S. V. M. 1979. A theory of terrestrial catastrophism. *Nature,* **282**, 455–459.

NEWTON, I. 1687. *Philosophiae Naturalis Principia Mathematica.* Royal Society, London.

—— 1704. *Opticks: Or a Treatise of the Reflexions, Refractions, Inflexion and Colours of Light.* 4 vols. S. Smith & B. Walford, London.
NININGER, H. H. 1942. Cataclysm and evolution. *Contributions to the Society for Research on Meteorites*, **1**, 27–29.
ÖPIK, E. J. 1958. On the catastrophic effects of collisions with celestial bodies. *Irish Astronomical Journal,* **5**, 34–36.
PETAEV, M. I. 1992. Meteorite Sterlitamak: a new crater-forming fall. [Abstract] *Meteoritics,* **27**, 276.
PLAYFAIR, J. 1802. *Illustrations of the Huttonian Theory of the Earth.* Creech, Edinburgh.
PROCTOR, R. A. 1873. *The Moon; Her Motions, Aspects, Scenery and Physical Condition.* Longmans, Green & Co., London.
RAMPINO, M. R. & CALDEIRA, K. 1993. Major episodes of geologic change: correlations, time structure and possible causes. E*arth and Planetary Science Letters,* **114**, 215–227.
—— & STOTHERS, R. B. 1984. Terrestrial mass extinctions, cometary impacts and the Sun's motion perpendicular to the galactic plane. *Nature,* **308**, 709–711.
RAUP, D. M. 1986. *The Nemesis Affair*. W. W. Norton, New York.
—— 1991. *Extinction: Bad Genes or Bad Luck?* W. W. Norton, New York.
—— & SEPKOSKI, J. J., JR 1984. Periodicity of extinctions in the geologic past. *Proceedings of the National Academy of Sciences, U.S.A.*, **81**, 801–804.
RYDER, G, FASTOVSKY, & GARTNER, S. (EDS) 1996. *New Developments in the Cretaceous–Tertiary Event and other Catastrophies in Earth History.* Geological Society of America Special Paper, **307**.
SCHINDEWOLF, O. H. 1962. Neokatastrophismus? *Zeitschrift der Deutschen Geologischen Gesellschaft,* **114**, 430–435.
SCHWARTZ, R. D. & JAMES, P. B. 1984. Periodic mass extinctions and the Sun's oscillation about the galactic plane. *Nature,* **308,** 712–713.
SHARPTON, V. L. & WARD, P. D. (EDS) 1990. *Global Catastrophes in Earth History: An Interdisciplinary Conference on Impacts, Volcanism, and Mass Mortality.* Geological Society of America Special Paper, **247**.
——, MARÍN, L. E., CARNEY, J. L. *ET AL.* 1996. A model of the Chicxulub impact basin based on evaluation of geophysical data, well logs, and drill core samples. *In*: RYDER, G., FASTOVSKY, D. & GARTNER, S. (eds) *New Developments in The Cretaceous-Tertiary Event and other Catastrophes in Earth History.* Geological Society of America Special Paper, **307**, 5574.
SHAW, H. 1994. *Craters, Cosmos, and Chronicles: A New Theory of the Earth.* Stanford University Press, Palo Alto, CA.
SHEA, J. H. 1982. Twelve fallacies of uniformitarianism. *Geology,* **10**, 455–460.
SHIGERU, I., CANUP, R. M., & STEWART, G. R. 1997. Lunar accretion from an impact-generated disk. *Nature,* **389**, 353–357.
SHOEMAKER, E. M. 1960. Penetration mechanics of high velocity meteorites, illustrated by Meteor Crater, Arizona. *In*: *21st International Geological Congress, Det Berlingske Bogtrykken Copenhagen*, 418–434.
SIGGURDSON, H., D'HONDT, S., ARTHUR, M. A., BRALOWER, T. J., ZACHOS, J. C., FOSSEN, M., & CHANNELL, J. E. T. 1991. Glass from the Cretaceous–Tertiary boundary in Haiti. *Nature,* **349**, 482–487.
SILVER, L. T. & SCHULTZ, P. H. (EDS) 1982. *Geological Implications of Impacts of Large Asteroids and Comets on the Earth.* Geological Society of America Special Paper, **190.**
SOLDANI, D. A. 1794. *Sopra una Piogetta di Sassi Accaduta nella sera de' 16. Giugno del MDCCXCIV in Lucignan d'Asso nel Sanese. Dissertazione*. Pier Francisco Rossi, Stampatore, con Approviazione, Siena.
SOUTHEY, R. 1797. *Letters Written during a Short Residence in Spain and Portugal*. Joseph Cottle, Bristol, 355–358.
SPENCER, L. J. 1933. Meteoric iron and silica glass from the meteorite craters of Henbury (central Australia) and Wabar (Arabia). *Mineralogical Magazine,* **23**, 387–404.
SWISHER, C. C., III *ET AL.*1992. Coeval $^{40}Ar/^{39}Ar$ ages of 65.0 million years ago from Chicxulub crater melt rock and Cretaceous–Tertiary boundary tektites. *Science,* **257**, 954–958.
TATA, D. 1794. *Memoria Sulla Pioggia di Pietre avvenuta nella Campagna Sanese il Dì 16. di Giugno de questo corrente anno.* Aniello Nobile, Naples.

TAYLOR, S. R. 1992. *Solar System Evolution: A new perspective*. Press Syndicate, University of Cambridge, UK.

THADDEUS, P. & CHANAN, G. A. 1985. Cometary impacts, molecular clouds, and the Sun's perpendicular motion perpendicular to the galactic plane. *Nature,* **314**, 73–75.

THOMSON, G. W. 1794*a*. Seven letters. *In:* SOLDANI, D. A. *Sopra una Piogetta di Sassi Accaduta nella sera de' 16. Giugno del MDCCXCIV in Lucignan d'Asso nel Sanese. Dissertazione*. Pier Francisco Rossi, Stampatore, con Approviazione, Siena. 237–263, 275–282.

—— 1794*b*. Letter on mineral composition of Siena stone. *In*: TATA, D. *Memoria sulla Pioggia di Pietre avventa nella Campagna Sanese il Di 16. di Giugno de questo Corrente anno. Aniello Nobile, Naples,* 51–70.

TOPHAM, E. 1797. Letter to Mr. Urban. *Gentlemen's Magazine,* **67**, 549–551.

UREY, H. C. 1973. Cometary collisions and geological periods. *Nature,* **242**, 32–33.

WETHERILL, G. W. & SHOEMAKER, E. M. 1982. Collision of astronomically observable bodies with the Earth. *In*: SILVER, L. T. & SCHULTZ, P. H. (eds) *Geological Implications of Impacts of Large Asteroids and Comets on the Earth.* Geological Society of America Special Paper, **190**, 1–14.

WHEWELL, W. 1832. *Principles of Geology* ... By Charles Lyell, Esq. F.R.S., Professor of Geology in King's College, London. Vol II. London. *Quarterly Review,* **47**, 103–132.

WHISTON, W. 1696. *A New Theory of the Earth, from Its Original to the Consummation of All Things*. R. Roberts, London.

WHITMIRE, D. P. & JACKSON, A. A., IV 1984. Are periodic mass extinctions driven by a distant solar companion? *Nature,* **308**, 713–715.

—— & MATESE, J. J. 1985. Periodic comet showers and Planet X. *Nature,* **313**, 36.

WILHELMS, D. E. 1993. *To a Rocky Moon: A Geologist's History of Lunar Exploration.* University of Arizona Press, Tucson.

WILLIAMS, J. L. 1802. Account of the explosion of a meteor, near Benares, in the East Indies and of the falling of some stones at the same time, about 14 miles from that city. *Philosophical Transactions of the Royal Society, London,* **92**,175–179.

Vestiges of a beginning and the prospect of an end

IAN W. D. DALZIEL*

Institute for Geophysics and Department of Geological Sciences, University of Texas at Austin, 4412 Spicewood Springs Road, Building 600, Austin, TX 78759-8500, USA

Abstract: 'No vestige of a beginning, ...' In one sense the first half of James Hutton's famous statement of 1788 holds true today – the oldest parts of Earth's crust identified in two centuries of 'modern' study look not unlike those being formed at present. Yet the age of the planet can now be determined as close to 4.5 billion years, and radiometric ages of vestigial rocks and minerals approach 90 per cent of that value. The history of the planet is becoming clearer. We can now accurately reconstruct the geography of Pangea in early Mesozoic times. Remnants of older rifted continental margins suggest the existence of previous supercontinents for which hypothetical reconstructions have been proposed – a global-scale Huttonian process of tectonic renewal. Their mode of fragmentation and comparison with the other terrestrial planets suggest a functional connection between surficial plates and deep-seated mantle plumes, which may extend back to the Archaean. The fossil record, geochemistry, and molecular biology provide a timeline for life on Earth which does extend to the Archaean, almost as far as the oldest rocks and minerals. The history of endogenic tectonism, environmental change and biological evolution was punctuated, and to some extent at least influenced, by bolide impacts.

Like Hutton, in the rocks we can still read 'no prospect of an end', though astrophysical evidence indicates the demise of the Earth, or at least of its biosphere, will inevitably come 5000 million years into the future when our Sun will become a red giant, enveloping all its planets in a gaseous holocaust. Detection of complex organic molecules in the comas of comets that recently traversed the inner Solar System has shown, however, that the basic chemical building blocks of life are present in interstellar space. Evidence is steadily building up for the existence of planets around other stars of the Milky Way. Hence life need not be limited in either space or time by the existence of the Earth itself. Indeed, contemporary cosmology entertains possibilities that the entire universe that we recognize may be boundless, permanently expanding, or perhaps even part of a continuum of evolving universes. In this ultimate sense, therefore, the concluding sentence of the *Theory of the Earth* by the 'founder of modern geology' can be considered as valid today as it was 200 years ago.

Into the abyss of time

The geological system of Dr Hutton, resembles, in many respects, that which appears to preside over the heavenly motions. In both, we perceive continual vicissitude and change, but confined within certain limits, and never departing from a certain mean condition, which is such, that, in the lapse of time, must become just equal to the deviations from it on the other. In both a provision is made for duration of unlimited

* Also affiliated with the Tectonics Special Research Centre, Department of Geology and Geophysics, University of Western Australia.

DALZIEL, I. W. D. 1999. Vestiges of a beginning and the prospect of an end.
In: CRAIG, G. Y. & HULL, J. H. (eds) *James Hutton – Present and Future*. Geological Society, London, Special Publications, **150**, 119–155.

> extent, and the lapse of time has no effect to wear out or destroy a machine, constructed with so much wisdom. Where the movements are all so perfect, their beginning and end must be alike invisible. (Playfair 1802, p. 440)

The last sentence of James Hutton's *Theory of the Earth* concludes, 'The result, therefore, of our present enquiry is, that we find no vestige of a beginning, – no prospect of an end.' (Hutton 1788.) In recognizing that extrapolation into the past of geological processes that he observed in his own rural surroundings in the Scottish Borders required that the Earth be far older than previously appreciated, and to have been subjected to many episodes of what we now call orogenesis or tectonism, he laid the foundation for modern geology. He appreciated that the planet we live on is dynamic. By analogy with present processes, moreover, Hutton deduced the enormity of the period of time required for the deformation, uplift and erosion of the Silurian greywackes at Siccar Point on the Berwickshire coast of southeastern Scotland prior to deposition of the unconformably overlying strata of the Old Red Sandstone (Fig. 1). For his companions in the field, it was in contemplation of the time when the superincumbent red sandstones were being deposited on the upright greywackes, and of 'an epocha still more remote' when the rock now vertical 'lay in horizontal planes at the bottom of the sea', that 'revolutions still more remote appeared in the distance', according to Professor John Playfair in his biography of Hutton (1805). Indeed, wrote Playfair in a justifiably famous and often quoted passage,'The mind seemed to grow giddy by looking so far into the abyss of time.' (Playfair 1805, p. 73.)

Fig. 1. The unconformity at Siccar Point, southeast Scotland. Old Red Sandstone strata rest unconformably on vertical beds of Silurian greywacke. For scale, a thickness of 2–3 m of Old Red Sandstone is shown. (Photo courtesy of Robert H. Dott, Jr).

There is nothing particularly unusual about the oldest rocks we can recognize in the field 200 years later. Indeed, chemical peculiarities in mafic volcanics aside, they appear very similar to some being formed at present. Thus in this restricted sense it is still true that 'with respect to human observation, this world has neither a beginning nor an end' (Hutton 1785). Nonetheless, in a broader context we are now in a position to say that vestiges of a beginning for the Earth do indeed exist in rocks far older than those cropping out beneath the Siccar Point unconformity – or indeed any rocks with which James Hutton and his associates were remotely acquainted (Fig. 2). This has come about partly through the application of Huttonian principles in the geological mapping of all six continents, erection of a relative geologic timescale, and radiometric dating to establish a numerical or 'absolute' scale for the Earth (e.g. Harland *et al.* 1990). It is also dependent on considering the Earth and Moon together, and as part of the Solar System, of the Milky Way Galaxy and of the universe as a whole. This is hardly a perspective new to the 'Space Age' and dawn of the twenty-first century, no matter how far our knowledge and technology have advanced over the past 200 years. The quotation above from John Playfair's '*Illustrations of the Huttonian Theory*' indicates that it was appreciated by Hutton and his associates in the eighteenth century.

Geochemical evidence that there exist terrestrial rocks and minerals with an antiquity of ~4.0 billion years, and for an isotopic model age ~0.5 billion years older for the Earth

Fig. 2. Assynt district of the northwest Highlands of Scotland looking north from Stac Pollaidh (Stack Polly). A glacially-exhumed hummocky surface of Archaean–Mesoproterozoic Lewisian Gneiss is unconformably overlain by flat-lying sandstone layers of the Neoproterozoic Torridon Group forming the mountains of Suilven (left) and Canisp (right). The Torridonian strata are overlain with slight angular unconformity by Cambrian platform sediments of Laurentian stratigraphic and faunal affinities (see text), which form the eastward- (right-) dipping slope of Canisp. (Photo by the author.)

as a whole, is supported by knowledge of the Moon, the other terrestrial planets, and meteorites. A wealth of data on lunar specimens returned by the Apollo and Luna missions to this remarkable blue planet, as it first appeared to us all in the photographs taken from the Apollo spacecraft (Fig. 3), and on meteorites confirm that the solar system originated within the Milky Way Galaxy (Fig. 4) close to 4.5 billion years before present. Moreover, this age is compatible with the age of the universe determined as between 10 and 20 billion years, perhaps 12–13 billion years (Harris *et al.* 1998), from the red shift of retreating galaxies and the temperature of dark matter in space recorded by the Cosmic Background Explorer spacecraft (COBE). The elements of which the Earth, its sister planets and their satellites are principally composed, indeed all elements apart from the hydrogen and helium that originated with the universe, were created in the interior of stars. The relative abundances of the elements reflect contributions from many different types of star. Individual grains of dust from stars that existed before our solar nebula collapsed to form the solar system have been identified in meteorites. Hence an age of ~4.5 billion years for the Earth and the solar system is quite consistent with current understanding of the cosmos.

In the rocks James Hutton knew, and indeed in all rocks on Earth, we still find no prospect of an end. It is astrophysical data, comparing our Sun with other stars of our own galaxy and beyond, that point to an inexorable demise of Earth as we know it ~5.0 billion years into the future. Thus we humans, whose very genus evolved a mere 2.5 million years in the past, inhabit Earth at 'half-time' in its lifespan as a planet of ~10 billion years.

Does all this mean that technical advances in the 200 years since the death of the 'founder of modern geology' have superseded his conclusion regarding the beginning and

Fig. 3. Earthrise from the Moon with the ascent stage of the Apollo Lunar Module. (NASA photo).

Fig. 4. The Sun against the backdrop of the Milky Way Galaxy with the dying comet SOHO 6 streaking towards the star from 'eight o-clock'. A photograph obtained using the large angle spectrometric coronagraph (LASCO) of the Solar and Heliospheric Observatory (SOHO). Taken in December 1996 with the Sun in front of the constellation Sagittarius and heading towards Capricorn, this is one of the first direct views of the Sun in its place in the galaxy from the Earth's perspective. A disc blocks the solar surface (white circle) out to three solar radii. Solar streamers, source of the solar wind, blow out as far as 20 million km from the surface. (Photo courtesy of NASA, the European Space Agency, and the United States Naval Research Laboratory.)

end of the Earth? Again the answer depends on the context. If taken from a purely 'local' point of view, even one embracing the solar system and the Milky Way, the answer is affirmative. Some present-day ideas regarding the origin and fate of the universe, however, can be viewed as quite in keeping with the conclusion that James Hutton reached two centuries ago in his *Theory of the Earth*, namely that the beginning and the end are still 'alike invisible' – as expressed by John Playfair in his *Illustrations of the Huttonian Theory* quoted above. Before considering this mind-stretching possibility, however, we must first review what has been learned about Earth history since James Hutton tramped over the rocks of the Southern Uplands and Highlands of Scotland in the 1700s, pondering their meaning for us all.

The dynamic blue planet

History

The deformation and uplift of the Silurian strata that James Hutton and his companions viewed and interpreted at Siccar Point represent the final phase of the Caledonian mountain building in what he referred to as 'the Scottish Alps'. It was to be the abrupt southwestern termination of this ancient Caledonian orogenic belt at the Atlantic coast of Ireland which formed one of the main lines of evidence leading in the present century to the full appreciation of the dynamic nature of the Earth as a planet anticipated in his work.

The Appalachian mountain belt that lies along the eastern seaboard of North America, and is likewise abruptly terminated in mirror image at the Atlantic coast of the island of Newfoundland, was recognized early as a possible former continuation of the Caledonides, implying possible subsequent tectonic separation of the European and North American continents (Wegener 1915; Bailey 1929; Holmes 1944; Kay 1966; Figs 5, 6, 7(a)). The formation of the Atlantic, Indian, Arctic, and Southern Ocean basins by sea-floor spreading during Mesozoic and Cenozoic times, the result of the divergence of rigid plates forming the lithospheric shell of the planet, was demonstrated by marine geophysical investigations, ocean drilling, and satellite altimetry derived gravity images in the second half of this century (Fig. 5). This permitted accurate reconstruction of the long-hypothesized supercontinent Pangea for early Mesozoic times (Fig. 6). It also led to understanding of the basic cause of mountain building during the formation of the Alps, Himalayas, Andes and other mountain ranges during the Mesozoic and Cenozoic, namely, plate boundary interaction (e.g. Dewey & Bird 1970). Relative motion of lithospheric plates has now been measured by satellite laser ranging, very long baseline interferometry, and geodetic measurements utilizing the satellites of the Global Positioning System.

Consideration of the Palaeozoic 'Scottish Alps' also led us back to understanding of the nature of the planet prior to the formation of the Mesozoic and Cenozoic lithosphere that floors today's ocean basins. One of the main keys to the cause of the early Palaeozoic orogenesis in the Appalachian–Caledonian mountain belt lies in the benthic fauna of the Cambrian strata unconformably overlying the crystalline Archaean–Mesoproterozoic

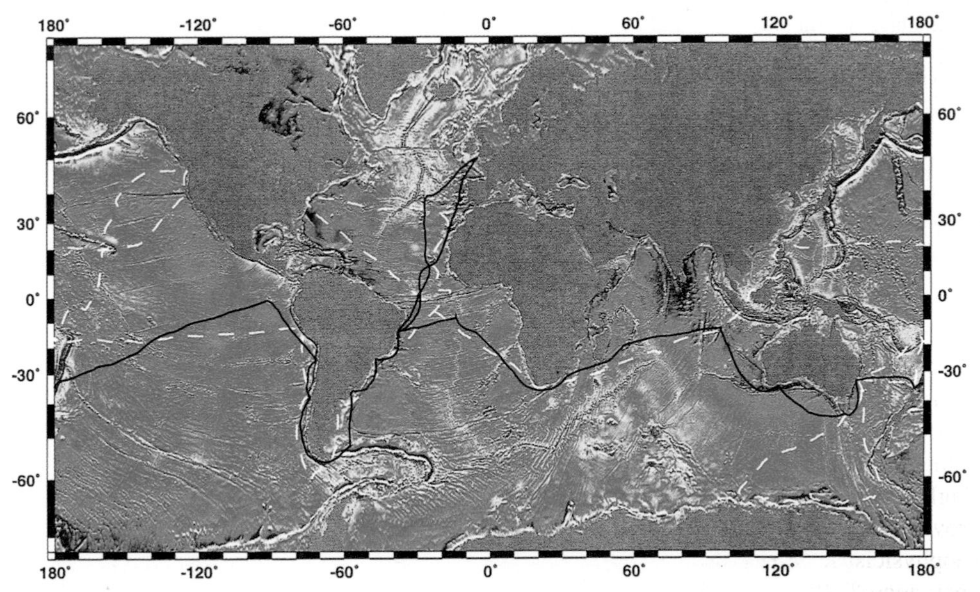

Fig. 5. Satellite altimetry-derived gravity field of the ocean basins (Sandwell & Smith 1995; mercator projection, red/yellow – positive values, blue/purple negative values). Superimposed are journeys of Charles Darwin aboard H.M.S. *Beagle* (solid black line) and James Dwight Dana participating in the United States Exploring Expedition (dashed white line). (PLATES, Institute for Geophysics, University of Texas at Austin.)

Fig. 6. Pangea reconstructed immediately prior to break-up in the Mesozoic using ocean floor magnetic anomalies and fracture zones; orthographic projection keyed to Laurentian south pole Representative palaeomagnetic poles (with alpha 95 confidence circles are shown for different continents: b – Baltica; i – India; G – Gondwana; l – Laurentia; s – Siberia; EA – East Avalonia (England, Wales, southern Ireland, Brittany); F – 'greater' Florida terrane; WA – West Avalonia – Avalon platform, Nova Scotia, and coastal New England).

Lewisian basement and Neoproterozoic sedimentary strata of the Torridon Group along the western boundary of the Caledonian orogenic belt in the northwest Highlands of Scotland (Fig. 2). Eighty years after the publication of the *Theory of the Earth*, Salter (1859) noted the North American affinities of this fauna. The similarities of the Cambrian and Lower Ordovician strata containing the fauna, mainly carbonates, with rocks of the same age in North America were emphasized by Benjamin Peach and his colleagues in their classic memoir on *The Geological Structure of the North-West Highlands of Scotland* (Peach *et al.* 1907). It was largely the contrast between these supposedly warm water deposits of northwestern Scotland and western Newfoundland with their 'Pacific' benthic fauna, and the apparently colder water facies including 'Atlantic' benthic fossils of England, Wales, the eastern seaboard of Newfoundland, the Canadian Maritime provinces, and coastal New England (Walcott 1889; Fig. 7(a)) that led the Canadian geophysicist J. Tuzo Wilson to ask the question 'Did the Atlantic Ocean open, close, and open again?' (Wilson 1966). Although Argand and others had previously suggested the presence of an early Palaeozoic ocean along the line of the Caledonian and Appalachian mountain chains, it was Wilson's question that first resulted in the plate tectonics paradigm being used to explain orogens that existed prior to the Mesozoic–Cenozoic formation of the present oceanic lithosphere (e.g. Dewey 1969).

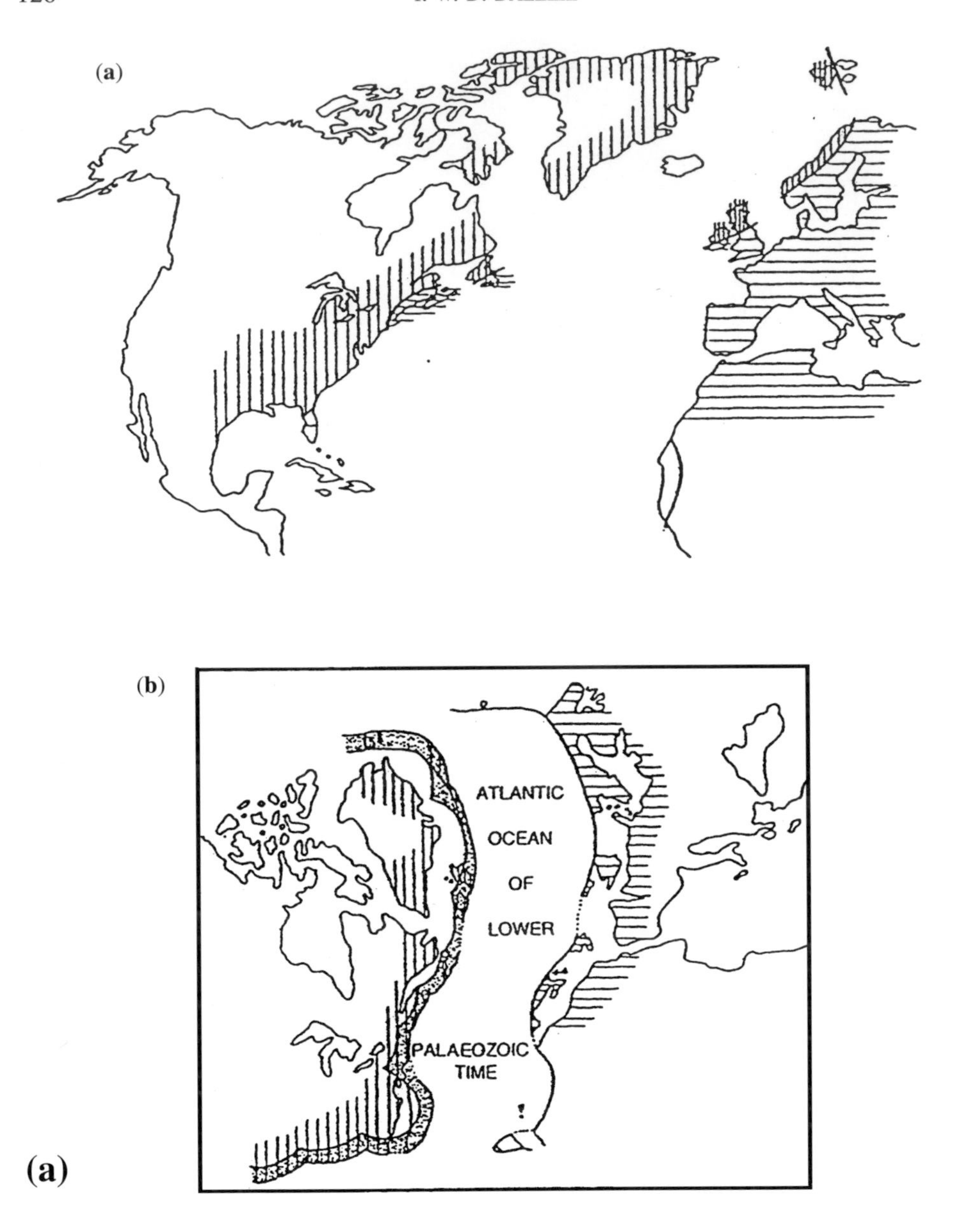

Fig. 7. (**a**) Present North Atlantic Ocean basin (a) and traditional view of early Palaeozoic palaeogeography of Laurentia, Baltica, and Gondwana (b) after Wilson (1966; reprinted with permission from *Nature*, copyright (1996) Macmillan Magazines Ltd). The 'Atlantic Ocean of Lower Palaeozoic Time' is now known as the Iapetus ocean (see Fig. 8). Horizontal and vertical shading shows the distribution of 'Atlantic' and 'Pacific' benthic faunas respectively (see text). Stipple indicates Ordovician island arcs. The boundary between the faunal provinces marks the suture where the Iapetus Ocean closed along the Appalachian–Caledonian orogen; note the truncation at the continental margins of Ireland and Newfoundland (see text). (**b**) Palaeomagnetically-acceptable alternative palaeogeographic relations of Laurentia relative to Gondwana through Paleozoic times (from Dalziel 1995, courtesy of *Scientific American Inc.*; see Dalziel 1991, fig. 1 for full explanation). The Silurian–Devonian hiatus represented by Hutton's unconformity at Siccar Point (Fig. 1) reflects the collision of Baltica with Laurentia in the Caledonian–Scandian orogeny shown at ~422 million years.

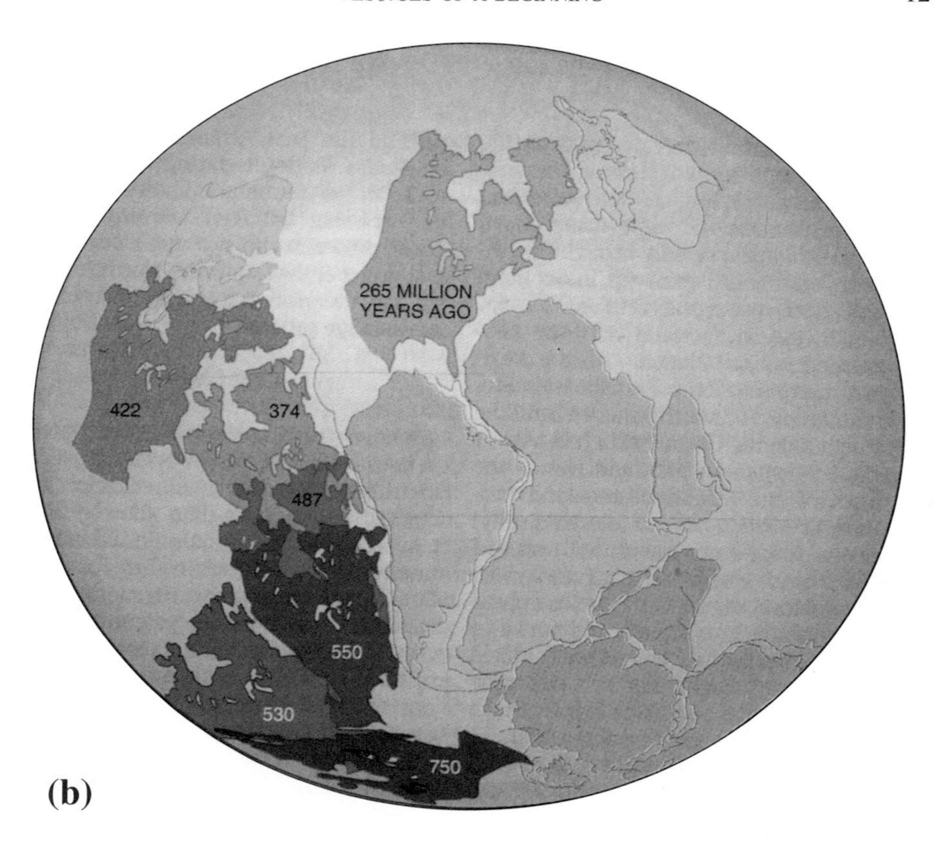

(b)

Wilson's suggestion was that Laurentia, ancestral North America, had rifted from Europe and northwest Africa at the end of Precambrian times in almost exactly the position in which it subsequently united with them to form Pangea in the late Palaeozoic (Fig. 7(a)). For a quarter of a century, this has dominated tectonic and palaeogeographic reconstructions of the Palaeozoic and late Precambrian time interval of Earth history, ~250–1000 million years before present. Geological mapping and isotopic dating of the Palaeozoic orogens and Precambrian cratons had been gradually leading to better understanding of orogenic processes through time and of older geological history, so most geologists were willing to accept that plate tectonics has operated since at least the end of the Archean eon (i.e. since ~2.5 Ga). Nonetheless, very few workers attempted palaeogeographic reconstructions that departed from the traditional Wilsonian view that juxtaposed the proto-Appalachian and proto-Caledonian margins of Laurentia with northwestern Africa and Europe (see, for example, McKerrow & Scotese 1990). Even fewer considered palaeogeography back to the time of the critical Precambrian–Cambrian boundary, let alone beyond that. Thus palaeogeographic reconstructions were limited to barely more than 10 per cent of the history of the Earth. An exception was the reconstruction by Piper (1982) of what he regarded as a long-lasting Proterozoic supercontinent. This reconstruction was based, however, on palaeomagnetic data that were for the most part poorly constrained with regard to the age of magnetization. Hence, the idea never attained general acceptance, even as a useful working hypothesis.

In the last decade of the twentieth century thinking has changed dramatically. Following the ideas of Canadian workers that the Pacific margins of Laurentia and Australia might have been opposed prior to the opening of the Pacific Ocean basin (e.g. Bell & Jefferson 1987), and publication of reconstructions juxtaposing the proto-Appalachian and proto-Andean margins on stratigraphic, faunal and palaeomagnetic grounds (Bond *et al.* 1984; Hartnady 1986), Eldridge Moores, of the University of California at Davis, and I suggested possible correlations between the Laurentian and East Antarctic cratons (Moores 1991; Dalziel 1991). Together with Paul Hoffman, I went on to suggest that opening of the Pacific Ocean basin during the Neoproterozoic to earliest Palaeozoic might have been balanced on a globe of constant radius by closing of ocean basins within the amalgamating supercontinent of Gondwanaland (Dalziel 1991, 1992*a*, *b*; Hoffman 1991). I pointed out that it is palaeomagnetically acceptable for Laurentia to have moved clockwise during the Palaeozoic around the proto-Andean margin of the newly amalgamated Gondwanaland to its Caledonian collison with Baltica

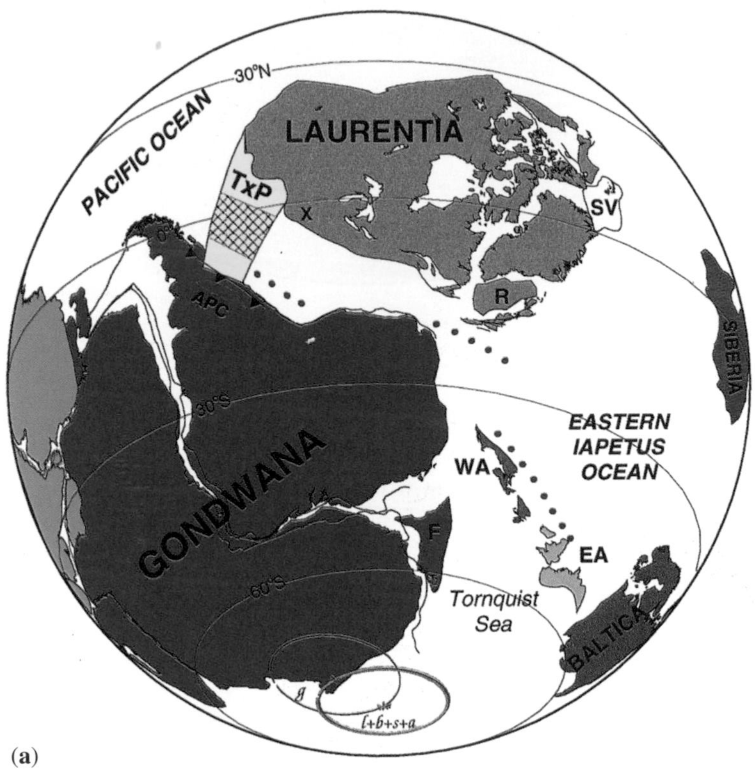

Fig. 8. Hypothetical supercontinents on orthographic projection keyed to Laurentian south pole: Artejia (**a**) in the Ordovician; Pannotia (**b**) in the latest Neoproterozoic; and Rodinia (**c**) in the early Neoproterozoic (Dalziel 1997). Palaeomagnetic pole with alpha 95 confidence circles as in Fig. 6, plus: a – Avalonia. Legend as in Fig. 6, plus: APC – Argentine Precordillera; F/MP – Falkland/ Malvinas Plateau; R – Rockall Plateau; TxP – hypothetical Cambrian to mid-Ordovician Texas plateau; x – Carolina terrane. Green zones (c) – Grenvillian orogens (1100–900 Ma); horizontal shading (b) – zone of latest Precambrian orogenic collision; red dots (a) – island arcs; red lines (c) – dyke swarms mentioned in text; modified from Dalziel (1997); for full explanation see figs 11 and 12 of original article. Reproduced with permission of Geological Society of America. Note that the position of the Kalahain Craton within Rodinia (**c**) has been modified to reflect probable collision with the Texas margin of Laurentia between 1150 and 1120 Ma (Dalziel *et al.* 1998).

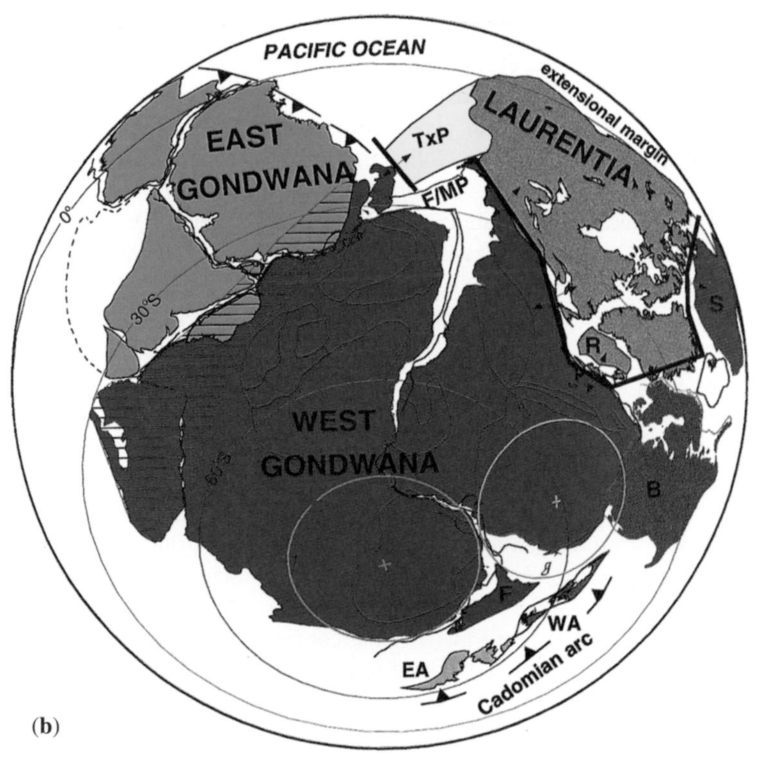
PACIFIC OCEAN
extensional margin
EAST
GONDWANA
TxP
LAURENTIA
F/MP
0°
30°S
S
R
WEST
GONDWANA
60°S
B
F
WA
EA
Cadomian arc

(**b**)

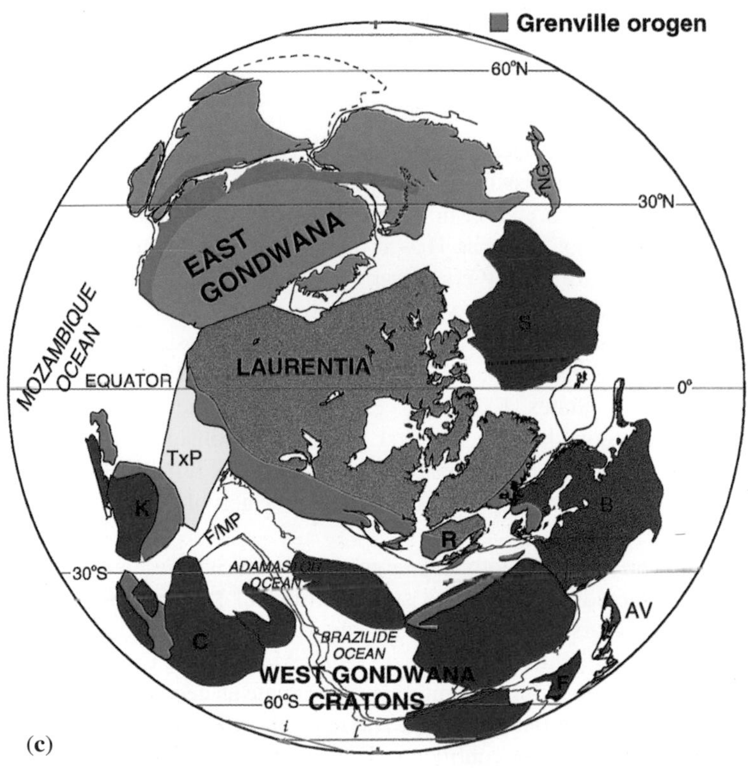
Grenville orogen
60°N
30°N
NG
EAST
GONDWANA
MOZAMBIQUE
OCEAN
S
LAURENTIA
EQUATOR
0°
TxP
K
B
F/MP
R
30°S
ADAMASTOR
OCEAN
AV
BRAZILIDE
OCEAN
C
WEST GONDWANA
CRATONS
60°S
F

(**c**)

and its Ouachita–Alleghanian–Hercynian–Uralian collision with Gondwanaland and Pangea to amalgamate Pangea (Fig. 7(b)). Dalla Salda *et al.* (1992*a*) suggested that an early Palaeozoic collisional orogen in South America might be explained by interaction between the proto-Appalachian and proto-Andean margins during this intercontinental relative motion in Ordovician times. Collision might have resulted in the transfer of the Precordilleran terrane of northwest Argentina (Fig. 8(a)), which like northwest Scotland has a Cambrian–Lower Ordovician carbonate platform with a 'Pacific' benthic fauna, from the area of the Ouachita embayment of Laurentia to Gondwanaland (Dalla Salda *et al.* 1992*b*; Dalziel *et al.* 1994*b*, 1996).

These ideas are still being debated and tested, but they have already led to reconstructions of three hypothetical supercontinents during the Neoproterozoic and Paleozoic eras: Artejia – in the mid-Ordovician; Pannotia – at the Precambrian–Cambrian boundary; Rodinia – in the early Neoproterozoic (Fig. 8; see Dalziel 1997 for a review). The first two would have been very fleeting configurations, the latter may have existed for some 200 million years. Still earlier entities have been suggested, for example an amalgamation of the Superior, Wyoming and Karelia cratons (Heaman 1997), and Vaalbara, resulting from the juxtaposition of the Kapvaal craton of southern Africa and the Pilbara craton of Western Australia, in Archaean to Palaeoproterozoic times (Cheney 1996).

Hypothetical though these pre-Pangea supercontinents are, there may lie in them a tectonic thread that can lead us back in time to the early stages of the history of the Earth. This thread lies in the processes by which supercontinental assemblages like Pangea, which arise from time to time by the amalgamation of individual smaller cratonic entities, are broken up.

Processes

It has been known for several decades that there are two principal ways in which the heat in the interior of the planet is dissipated at the surface. The dominant one is cooling of the young oceanic lithosphere formed at midocean ridges (Vine & Matthews 1963), and the other is in discrete hot spots such as Hawaii and Iceland (Morgan 1971, 1972; Wilson 1963, 1973). The latter are fed by comparatively narrow plumes of hot material originating in the mantle beneath the lithosphere (Wolfe *et al.* 1997) and generating lines of volcanoes and seamounts as the overlying plate moves and subsides. The prominent lines of volcanic islands in the Pacific Ocean (Fig. 5) had fascinated James Dwight Dana in the course of the United States Exploring Expedition in the nineteenth century. In contemplating their origin, he was the first scientist to consider in tectonic terms the potential global significance of these features, which directly reflect what we now refer to as surficial plate tectonics and deep-seated mantle plume activity (Dana 1843, 1847, 1849; Dott 1997).

A relation between the hot spots and large igneous provinces, including continental flood basalts that immediately pre-date supercontinental fragmentation, has also been recognized for many years (e.g. Burke & Dewey 1973; Burke & Kidd 1980; Hill 1991; Coffin & Eldholm 1994; White & McKenzie 1995; Mahoney & Coffin 1997). What has not been clear is whether the plumes, which may originate as deep as the D″ layer immediately above the core–mantle interface (e.g. Davies 1997; Lay *et al.* 1998), play an active role in the fragmentation of supercontinents. The answer to this question may lie in major dyke swarms, because these provide evidence of the state of stress in the lithosphere at the time of their formation. That is to say, they furnish clues to the dynamics of supercontinental fragmentation, rather than the kinematics and the magmatic 'plumbing' as do the seafloor fabric and geochemistry of the igneous rocks, respectively. Also, as they span the entire age range of the Earth (Ernst *et al.* 1995*a*, *b*), they are perhaps unique in contributing to understanding of the planet's tectonic history from the earliest times. They may thus provide a broadly uniformitarian tectonic link to the 'vestiges of a beginning' that are to be found in radiometric dating of rocks and minerals as discussed below.

Association of major dyke swarms with incipient formation of ocean basins is well known, most notably in the case of the dykes of the North Atlantic Tertiary igneous province. There the most prominent dyke swarms strike at a high angle to the continental margin of the North Atlantic Ocean basin in the British Isles, and parallel to the margin in a major crustal flexure along the coast of Greenland (Holmes 1944). May (1971) pointed out that a giant dyke swarm close to 200 million years old radiating through 360° can be reconstructed when the Central Atlantic Ocean is closed to juxtapose North America, South America and Africa in the computer-generated reconstruction of Bullard *et al.* (1965; Fig. 9). Impressed by the many prominent dyke swarms exposed in the recently deglaciated Laurentian shield, Canadian workers have drawn attention to several different types of map pattern represented (for review, see Ernst *et al.* 1995*a*, *b*). They have also long suggested that at least some of the swarms may permit location of the margins of ancient ocean basins that were subsequently closed by craton–craton collision (Halls & Fahrig 1987).

Recent surveys of Venus and Mars have revealed radiating patterns of lineaments on the same scale as the Central Atlantic giant radiating swarm. These are interpreted as systems of grabens located above radiating dyke swarms emplaced in extensional fractures. These fractures lie within circular upward flexures of the lithosphere believed to be caused by hot plumes of low-density magma that have risen from the planetary interiors (Fig. 10; Head 1990; Stofan *et al.* 1992; Ernst *et al.* 1995*b*; Mège & Masson 1996; Ernst & Buchan 1997; Head & Coffin 1997). The commonly observed near-perfect axial symmetry of these 'arachnoids' on Venus, in particular, is ascribed to the fact that the surface of that planet appears (from the comparatively low density of impact craters) to have been renewed in some sort of 'mantle turnover' event as recently as 0. 5 billion years or even 0.3 billion years. If some of the large igneous provinces on Earth are indeed also the result of the arrival of the heads of deep mantle plumes at the base of the lithosphere (e.g. Ernst *et al.* 1995*b*; Ernst & Buchan 1997; Head & Coffin 1997; Davies 1997), it seems likely that the comparative rarity of radial symmetry of associated radial dyke swarms may be the result of both the structural inhomogeneity of the terrestrial lithosphere and the anisotropic nature of the ambient stress system within most lithospheric plates (Dalziel & Lawver 1997, and in prep.), as measured at the present time (Zoback 1992).

Geometrically rigorous reconstruction of Pangea fragmentation through time confirms earlier observations that emplacement of large igneous provinces including dyke swarms, and associated topographic uplift, immediately preceded opening of major segments of ocean basin within Pangea. This is notably the case for the Central Atlantic and the Southwest Indian Ocean basins in the Jurassic, the South Atlantic Ocean basin in the Early Cretaceous, the separation of Madagascar from India in the mid-Cretaceous, the opening of the Labrador Sea in the latest Cretaceous, the separation of the Seychelles microcontinent from India at the end of the Mesozoic, and the recent opening of the Red Sea (Dalziel & Lawver 1997, and in prep.; Thompson 1998; Fig. 11).

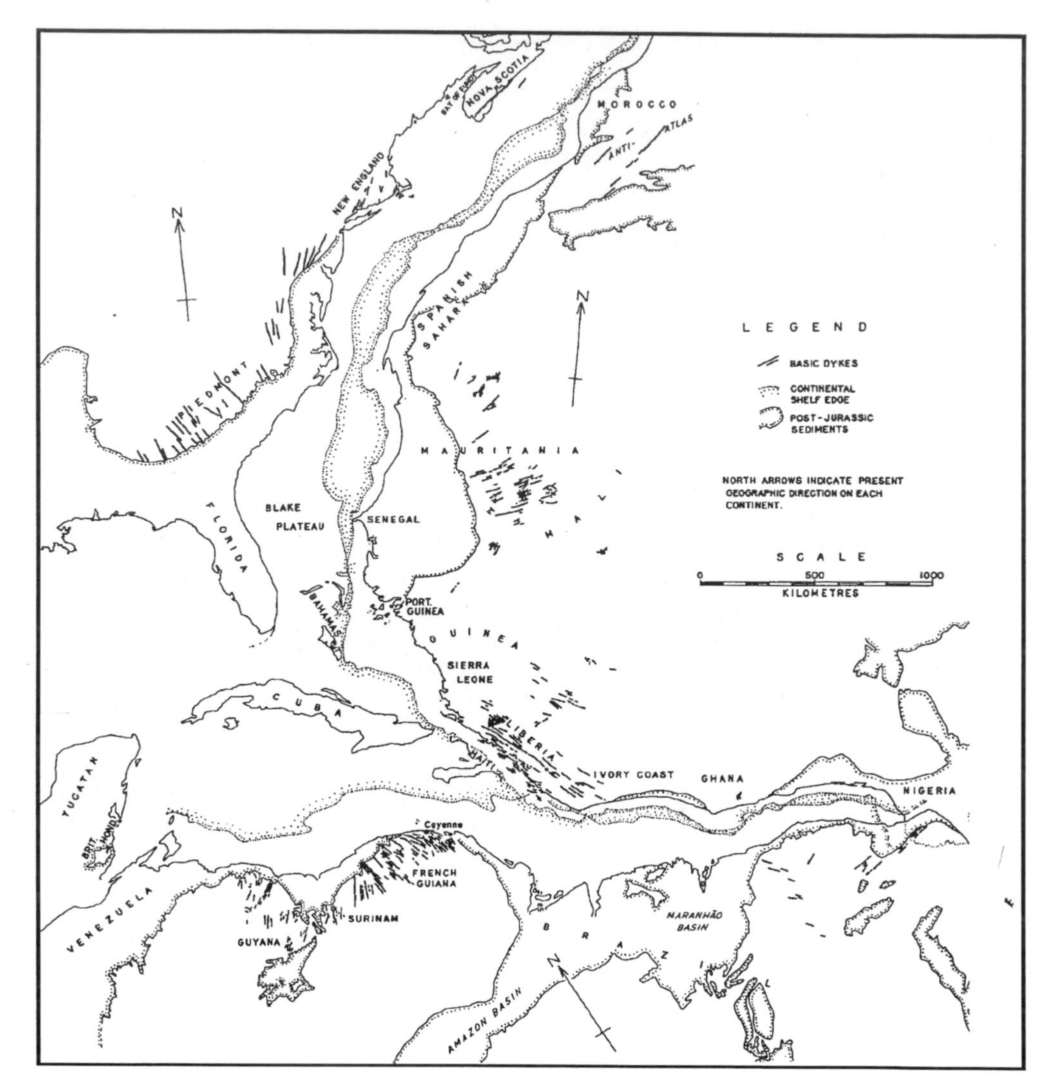

Fig. 9. Central Atlantic giant radiating dyke swarm of May (1971) on computer-fitted reconstruction of the Atlantic bordering continents by Bullard *et al.* (1965). Reproduced by permission of Geological Society of America.

Finite element modelling (e.g. Bott 1992) suggests that the extensional stress generated as part of a regime resulting from subduction along opposed margins of a supercontinent, acting alone, is unlikely to overcome the strength of the continental lithosphere. Addition of a component of extension associated with flexure of the lithosphere above a mantle plume head arriving below, however, may force rifting and initiation of a new ocean basin. The question arises whether giant radiating dyke swarms and large igneous provinces with continental flood basalts and various dyke swarms result from arrivals of mantle plume heads at the base of the lithosphere, or rather merely represent the first manifestation of passive adiabatic decompression melting as a continent broke up due to other causes such as regional lithospheric extension (White & McKenzie 1995) – a classic ‘chicken or egg’

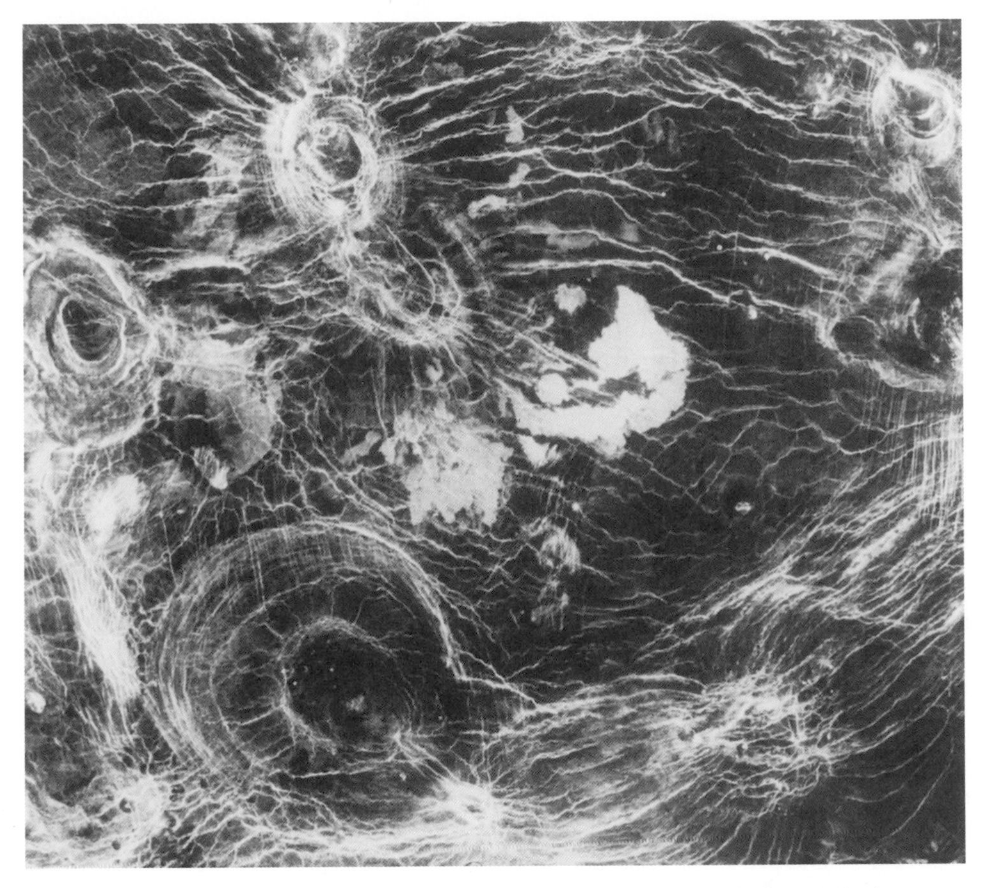

Fig. 10. Coronae and radiating graben (arachnoids) on Venus; Magellan mission, synthetic aperture radar image. The coronae range in width from 60 to 2600 km, with a median width of 200 km (Stofan *et al.* 1992). (NASA image.)

conundrum. Three lines of evidence suggest that the impact of mantle plumes plays a critical active role:

(1) geochemical evidence, especially involving helium isotopes, of a deep mantle source to some large igneous provinces (Basu *et al.* 1993, 1995);
(2) large igneous provinces that can be tied forward in time to present-day hot spots, through diachronous volcanic traces in the ocean floor, or the location of a present-day hot spot, or both (Wilson 1963, 1973; Morgan 1971, 1972; Fig. 11);
(3) spatially singular aspects of the igneous province such as a giant radiating dyke swarm emplaced prior to continental separation, or movement of small plates off a rising flexural dome in the lithosphere at the time of the igneous activity (e.g. southwest Indian Ocean basin: May 1971; Cox 1989; Dalziel 1992*a*; Dalziel & Grunow 1992; Storey 1995; Storey *et al.* 1996; Lawver *et al.* 1997).

There are cases where the separation of major segments of Pangean lithosphere do not appear to be related to hot-spot plume activity, for example the separation of Australia

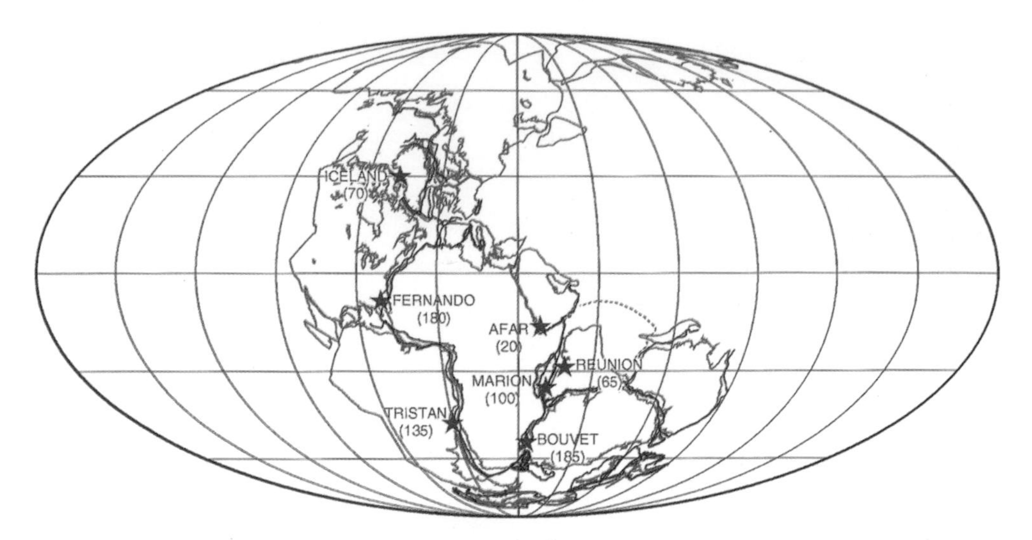

Fig. 11. Pangea (mollweide projection), showing location of selected present-day hot spots of the Atlantic and Indian ocean basins in their positions relative to adjacent continents at times (in Ma) immediately prior to separation by seafloor spreading at their respective locations (PLATES, Institute for Geophysics, University of Texas at Austin; Dalziel and Lawver, in prep.).

from East Antarctica and of the New Zealand microcontinent from West Antarctica during the Cretaceous. The separation in these cases may be the result of major plate organization, fracture propagation from one developing midocean ridge system to another, or ridge–crest subduction. Conversely, there are major igneous provinces that may be plume related yet did not result in continental fragmentation. In the case of the Siberian traps in the late Palaeozoic and the Keeweenawan volcanics in the late Mesoproterozoic, this may be due to the existence of an ambient compressional stress field in the continental lithosphere related to a contemporaneous continental collision (Uralian and Grenvillian, respectively).

As pointed out by the Canadian workers (Halls & Fahrig 1987), major radiating swarms of dykes like those associated with large igneous provinces, which may have resulted from impingement of mantle plumes actively responsible for the fragmentation of Pangea, seem to have emanated from locations along the margins of Precambrian cratons. This suggestion that the processes active in the fragmentation of Pangea may also have been active in the breakup of earlier supercontinental entities was recently strengthened by the discovery of a swarm of mafic dykes radiating through 120° of arc from the Mackenzie Mountains in the Northwest Territories of Canada to the Beartooth Mountains of Montana and the Tetons of Wyoming in the United States. The dykes are the same age, 780 million years, and share the same palaeomagnetic pole. They converge toward the area of present-day Vancouver Island, and were suggested by Park *et al.* (1995) to have a possible counterpart in the Gairdner dyke swarm of southern Australia (see small red lines digitized to scale on reconstruction of Rodinia; Fig. 8(c)). Although recent precise dating of the Gairdner swarm makes this unlikely (Wingate *et al.* 1998), the fact that the North American swarm is of the correct age to be related to the opening of the Pacific Ocean basin (Dalziel 1992*b*, 1997; Powell *et al.* 1993) suggests that a plume or plumes may have been active in the fragmentation of the early Neoproterozoic supercontinent Rodinia, regardless of its precise configuration.

Swarms associated with craton margins as old as the Archaean–Proterozoic boundary have been identified by Heaman (1997). In this case, the suggested configuration of a very ancient Superior, Wyoming, and Karelia supercontinent is open to considerable doubt on palaeomagnetic grounds. The presence of dyke swarms emanating from three separate cratonic margins of Archaean–Proterozoic boundary age does, however, suggest that plumes may have played a role in supercontinental fragmentation back to that time. The role of plumes in the Archaean is debatable, as indeed are the scale and even the basic operation of plate tectonics at that time (Campbell & Griffiths 1992; Nutman *et al.* 1996; Davies 1997). The closest analogue to the tectonics of the early Earth may be on Io, the moon of Jupiter, where temperatures of over 1800 K generated by enormous gravitational forces have been recorded by an instrument aboard the spacecraft Galileo. Thus highly magnesian lavas like Archaean komatiites may be forming, and crustal recycling is likely to be too rapid for the formation of continents. The widespread sedimentary cover of the Pilbara and Kaapval cratons in particular, however, indicates that major continents did exist on Earth by the end of the Archaean.

My colleague Lawrence Lawver and I believe that there may be geological evidence of a possible functional relation between deep mantle plumes and surficial plates (Dalziel & Lawver 1997, and in prep.). The location of Mesozoic–Cenozoic subduction zones around most of the Pacific margin is either along Neoproterozoic to earliest Palaeozoic rifted continental margins, for example those of North and South America and Antarctica, or at island arc systems recently separated from such margins, for example in the case of the western Pacific margin. Seismic tomography suggests that the slabs of oceanic lithosphere being subducted extend down to the D″ layer immediately above the core–mantle interface (Grand *et al.* 1997; van der Hilst *et al.* 1997; Lay *et al.* 1998). It is the weight of these downgoing slabs that appears to drive the motions of the plates forming the surface of the planet and 'plate-scale' flow in the mantle (Davies 1997).

If continental margins were created primarily as a result of the impingement of rising plumes from the deep mantle beneath continents as argued here, then plumes not only result in the midocean ridges where the newly formed material of the diverging plates has added surface area to the planet. They have also generated the zones of weakness along which the subduction of surface plates will occur in the future. There may therefore be a functional relation between the two thermal boundary layers of the Earth, the cold layer of surficial plates, and the hot core–mantle boundary at depth where evidence of plume generation has recently been reported (Shen 1997). The scenario envisaged is that the plumes play an active role in the formation of continental margins that are initially the site of plate generation, but subsequently become the locus of plate destruction. The recycling of the plates back into the mantle is the primary driving force of surficial plate tectonics and plate-scale flow in the mantle (Davies 1997), and the recycling in turn may play a role in the generation of new plumes at the D″ layer at the core–mantle interface (Lay *et al.* 1998). This model has to be reconciled with the evidence from geochemistry, which points to a two-layered mantle having been in existence for at least part of Earth history (Allègre 1997). Certainly slabs now penetrating the lower mantle are locally deflected at the 600 km discontinuity (for discussion, see Davies 1997; Lay *et al.* 1998).

The 'memory' of the mantle recoverable by seismic tomography may go back only as far as the Mesozoic (Grand *et al.* 1997). It is the rock record on the continents, to which Hutton's *Theory of the Earth* led us, that takes us back tectonically nearer to the beginning of the Earth. That beginning, however, is only revealed directly by geochemical studies applied to rock units determined by mapping to be relatively old in relation to their neighbours.

Vestiges of a beginning

The planet and the solar sytem

Radiometric dating using the Rb–Sr and K–Ar decay schemes has for several years enabled us to bracket the hiatus represented by Hutton's unconformity at Siccar Point (Fig. 1), basically the result of Laurentia–Baltica collision (Fig. 7(b)), as between ~425 Ma and 400 Ma. These are the approximate ages of the deformed Silurian strata and of the overlying Old Red Sandstone (Harland *et al.* 1990). It is the isotopes of lead, however, that have been called 'the hourglass of the solar system'. From a model describing the evolution of those isotopes in closed systems emerges the figure of ~4.5 billion years as the age of the Earth. The general approach was developed in the 1940s,

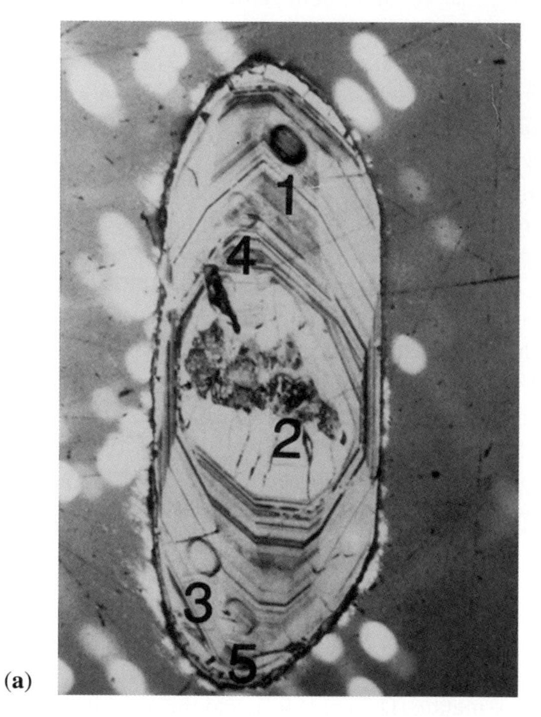

Fig. 12. (**a**) Vestiges of a beginning; polished section of zircon grain 0.5 mm long from the Acasta gneiss showing typical multi-layered structure (Bowring *et al.* 1989, grain #11). The elliptical pits were excavated by the ion beam used for the age measurements. Numbers refer to analyses yielding ages (in Ma): 1 – 3967 ± 4; 2 – 3868 ± 2; 3 – 3919 ± 6; 4 – 3965 ± 2; 5 – 3938 ± 10. (Photo courtesy of *Geology*.) (**b**) Concordia diagrams showing ion probe Pb–U analyses of zircon grains from the Acasta gneiss approaching ages of 4.0 Ga (Bowring *et al.* 1989). More recently dated grains do attain that value (Bowring *et al.* 1997). Circles in A are analyses from different areas of grain #11 (a); triangles are conventional analyses. Reproduced by permission of Geological Society of America.

and is known as the 'Holmes–Houtermans model', although its foundation was first laid down by the Russian scientist E. K. Gerling in 1942 following the development of the mass spectrometer, and the demonstration that the decay paths of the different U isotopes terminate at different isotopes of Pb. For a detailed account of the unravelling of the uranium–lead 'hourglass', the reader is referred to the comprehensive and readable book by G. Brent Dalrymple entitled *The Age of the Earth* (Dalrymple 1991).

Recent detailed studies of U and Pb isotopes in crystals from volcanic ash layers in Neoproterozoic and Cambrian strata in Namibia have pinned down the base of the Cambrian system represented by the strata overlying the Torridonian strata and Lewisian basement of northwestern Scotland (Fig. 2) at close to 544 Ma (Bowring *et al.* 1993). The Lewisian rocks themselves, although in part Archaean, are not the oldest rocks on Earth. The current contender for the oldest dated rock unit is the Acasta gneiss in the Slave province of the Northwest Territories of Canada. Zircon crystals in this gneiss (Fig. 12(a)) have been dated at over 3.9 Ga, actually 3962 ± 3 Ma (Bowring *et al.* 1989; Fig. 12(b)). Indeed some of the crystals have now been reported as reaching the 4.0 Ga mark (Bowring *et al.* 1997). All these crystals are believed by Sam Bowring and his colleagues to have

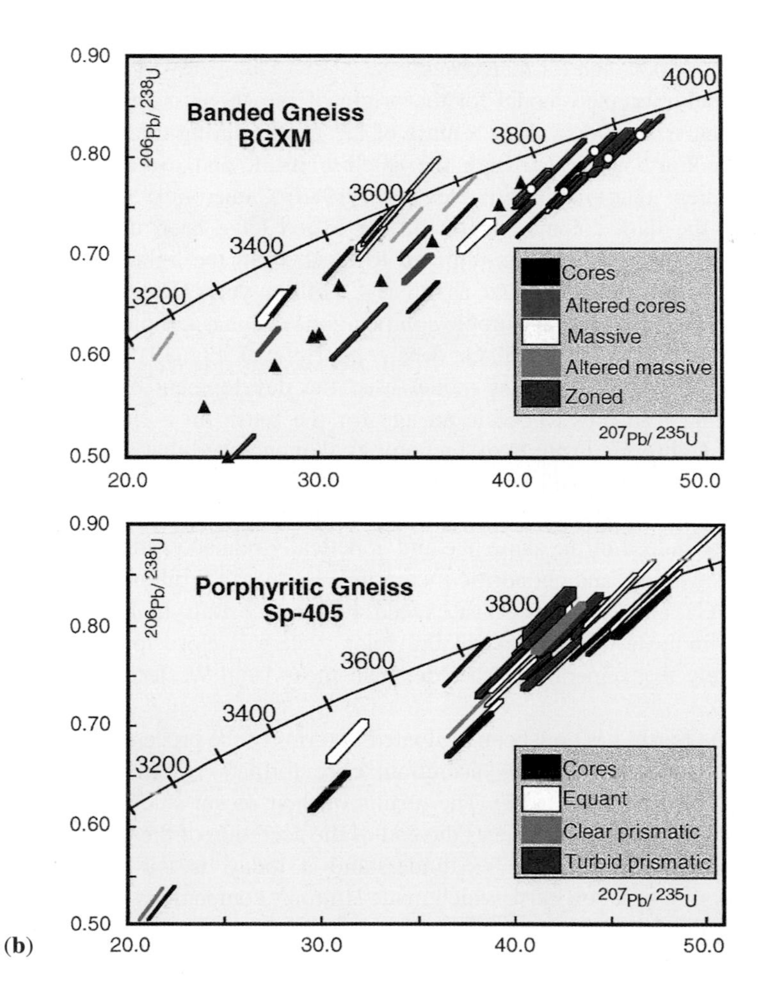

(b)

formed at the same time as their host rock, thus making the tonalitic to granitic protolith of the Acasta gneisses putatively the oldest dated rocks on the planet. Rocks in Enderby Land, Antarctica, Greenland and Labrador approach the same age. Hence there are preserved vestiges of ancient continental crust nearly 4.0 billion years old, but they are small. The largest remnant is the 3.8 Ga supracrustal sequence at Isukasia in Greenland. Either the earliest crust was not extensive, or it has been largely reworked by subsequent tectonism and meteorite bombardment (for discussion, see Bowring *et al.* 1989, p. 975).

The oldest dated minerals have been identified in the Pilbara craton of Western Australia, in quartzites at Mt Narryer and conglomerates at Jack Hills. These strata are part of a thick sequence of waterlain sedimentary rocks in the vicinity of orthogneisses dated at 3.6 Ga. Most of the zircons in the quartzites at Mt. Narryer have been dated at ~3.5–3.75 Ga, but four crystals have near concordant U–Pb ages between 4.1 and 4.2 Ga (Froude *et al.* 1983). One zircon from Jack Hills registers an age of 4276 ± 6 Ma (Compston & Pidgeon 1986). These old crystals are all interpreted as resistant grains recycled from a rock unit as yet unidentified, but one that could still be found. We can expect that older rocks and crystals will be reported from time to time, but the ages obtained will probably not be very much older than 4.2–4.3 Ga. The reason a substantially older date is unlikely, even for a recycled mineral grain, lies in the ages obtained for rocks returned from the Moon, and for meteorites.

The most widely accepted model for the origin of the Moon is that the impact of a planet at least the size of Mars ($0.12 \times$ mass of the Earth) during the later stages of the accretion of the Earth generated both the satellite itself, and the momentum of the Earth–Moon system (Hartman 1986; Stevenson 1987; Cameron 1988; Melosh 1989). Rocks forming the dark coloured maria of the Moon have been dated in the range 3.0–4.0 Ga. Some of the specimens returned to Earth from the lighter, rugged-looking lunar highlands or terrae, however, are as old as 4.5 billion years (Dalrymple 1991). Data from a new study of the tungsten isotopic compositions of lunar samples indicate that the Moon formed between 4.52 and 4.50 Ga (Lee *et al.* 1997; cf. Fig. 13)

The original Holmes–Houtermans model used the development of lead isotopes in ancient and young lead ores to obtain an age for the Earth. In a classic paper, C. C. Patterson of the California Institute of Technology demonstrated that a Pb isochron with a slope of 4.55 ± 0.07 Ga could be constructed using the Pb isotope data from several meteorites and modern ocean sediments. This constituted the first evidence that meteorites and the Earth are indeed of the same age and genetically related (Patterson 1956). Ages of most iron, stony iron, and chondritic meteorites are over 4.0 billion years, clustering around 4.4–4.5 Ga, and a few even just exceed 4.6 Ga (see Dalrymple 1991). All these data, therefore, indicate that the age of the solar system is close to 4.5 billion years, making it unlikely that minerals much older than those from Western Australia will be found on Earth.

The 'age of the Earth' has now been evaluated in terms of the processes of solar system and planetary formation, including accretion, core formation, and extraction of the atmosphere by Allègre *et al.* (1995). The results of their recent study using Pb–Pb and I–Xe terrestrial ages point to 4.45 Ga as the end of the accretion of the planet and its early differentiation (Fig. 13). This, as we understand it today, is the full depth of the measurable 'abyss of time' on Earth which made Hutton's companions giddy that day 200 years ago along the Berwickshire coast, as they contemplated the meaning of the Siccar Point unconformity that he was demonstrating.

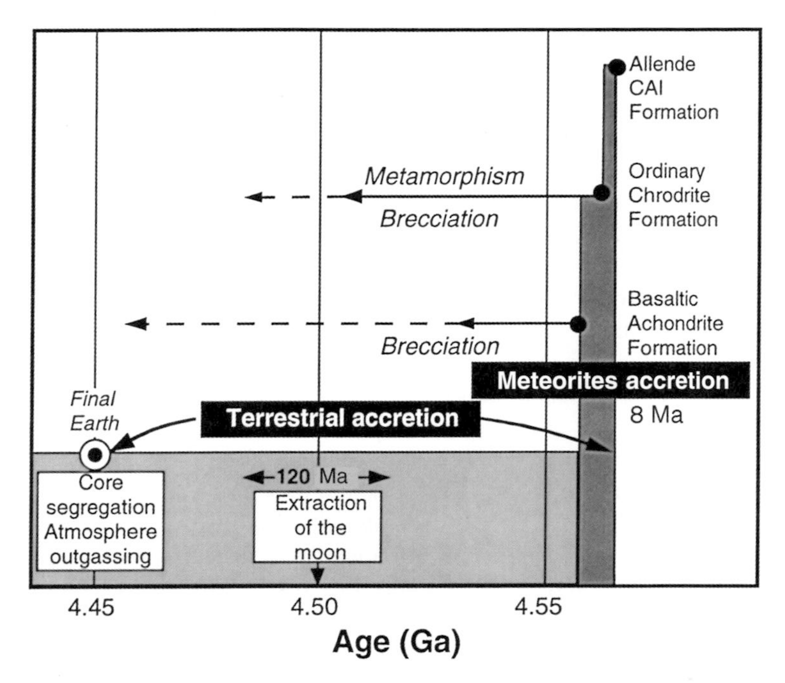

Fig. 13. Isotopically determined stages in the accretion of the Earth in relation to the early history of the Solar System. Reprinted from Allègre *et al.* (1995) with permission from Elsevier Science.

Life

There would be no wonder over the abyss of time if there were no living creatures on Earth capable of pondering it. It is the very existence of intelligent life that provides an immediate connection between Earth's past and its future by contemplation of both. I should not, therefore, move on to consider the future of the planet and the solar system without brief mention of the history of life. Critical to the cosmic view of Earth adopted by Hutton and his associates is the biological history within the context of the tectonic history. It is this interplay of the physical and biological history of the Earth that to me appears to be lacking, or at least unsatisfying, in most discussions of the contemporary idea that the Earth is a self-regulating 'mega-organism', the Gaia hypothesis (Lovelock 1979; Margulis 1993; Margulis & Sagan 1995). In his highly readable and stimulating self-styled 'unauthorized biography' of biological evolution, Richard Fortey puts it his way: 'Life made the surface of the Earth what it is, even while it was Earth's tenant.' (Fortey 1997.) But did the tenant control the property, or merely modify it and continue to thrive there – but within the framework of the landlord's periodic remodelling?

Charles Darwin, whose geological studies in the course of the voyage of HMS *Beagle* (Darwin 1839, 1844) tend to be overlooked, or at least understandably overshadowed by his biological observations, ranks with James Dwight Dana as a pioneer of truly global Earth science (Fig. 5). Darwin was hence well acquainted with contemporary knowledge of the history of the solid Earth as well as the history of life. His field experience prior to his voyage had been limited to 'geologizing' in Wales on excursions with Adam Sedgwick, the Woodwardian Professor at Cambridge University. Nonetheless, while becoming acquainted with Huttonian principles through the uniformitarian writing of

Charles Lyell while at sea, his self-imposed 'on-the-job' training was well underway by the time of *Beagle*'s landfall in the Cape Verde Islands, and his shrewd observations continued from there throughout the voyage. Visits to outcrops that he studied in southernmost South America have brought this home to me personally. As his ideas on evolution took shape after returning to England, therefore, he was conscious of the fact that fossil evidence for the myriad of complex life he had encountered appeared late and suddenly in the geological record, especially given the complexity of the fossils in Cambrian strata such as those overlying the old gneisses of the northwest Highlands of Scotland (Fig. 2). He wrote, 'to the question why we do not find rich fossiliferous deposits belonging to these assumed earliest periods prior to the Cambrian system, I can give no satisfactory answer' (Darwin 1859). Had he known the age of the base of the Cambrian System to be 544 Ma in an overall Earth history of 4.5 Ga, and had he been aware of the startlingly rapid appearance and development of Cambrian life (Bowring *et al.* 1993), I suspect that his disquiet would have been all the more profound.

Precambrian life is now known to have started long before Cambrian time (Bengston 1995). The comparatively sudden appearance of well-developed, hard-shelled and varied life forms at the base of the Cambrian is still a puzzle to modern scientists, however, as demonstrated by the wide variety of explanations put forward in recent literature to explain it. These explanations range from changes in the atmospheric chemistry and oceanic circulation and composition, to global orogenesis, massive slip of the entire crust and mantle over the core (so-called 'true polar wander'), and even changes in the obliquity of the planet to the ecliptic. Recently the problem has been addressed by molecular phylogeneticists, and data from this new approach appear to be changing the face of the long-standing debate. Calculations using ribosomal DNA suggest that divergence between different lineages of Bilateria extend back well into Neoproterozoic time (545–1000 Ma), and that simultaneous radiations occurred in the Cambrian as a result of some external cause (Balavoine & Adoutte 1998). There is now, moreover, a well-established metazoan fossil record for the Neoproterozoic, and a record of microscopic single-celled organisms extending back into the Archaean (Schopf 1992, 1993; Knoll 1994; Xiao *et al.* 1998). The Pilbara craton of northwestern Australia is once again the critical locality. The oldest undisputed life forms on Earth have been found there. Volcanic and sedimentary strata between ~3.0 and 3.5 Ga include a unit named the Warrawoona group, which contains a formation called the Apex Basalt. Cherts associated with the basalts have been found to contain prokaryotic morphotypes (Schopf 1993; Fig. 14). The basalts have been dated at 3450 ± 16 Ma.

It has recently been reported, however, that there may be evidence of even older life on the planet. The Itsaq Gneiss Complex within the Isua supracrustal belt in southwestern Greenland contains the metamorphosed remains of the oldest known sedimentary strata (in Greenlandic, 'Itsaq' actually means 'ancient thing'). These sediments, including banded iron formations and metachert, indicate that there was something like an ocean when they were deposited, certainly as long ago as 3.7 Ga, and possibly 3.85 Ga or slightly earlier. They also point to an atmosphere with substantially less oxygen than at present, a situation gradually changed as evolution progressed – perhaps the best example of Gaia at work? Although the strata are too highly altered to preserve biological structures like those in the cherts of the Pilbara craton, analyses of their carbon isotopes yield a value for the ratio of $^{13}C/^{12}C$ that is within the range characteristic of biological debris from sediments deposited at 2.7–3.5 Ga (Mojzsis *et al.* 1996).

This evidence from the Isua supracrustals appears to extend the age of life on Earth

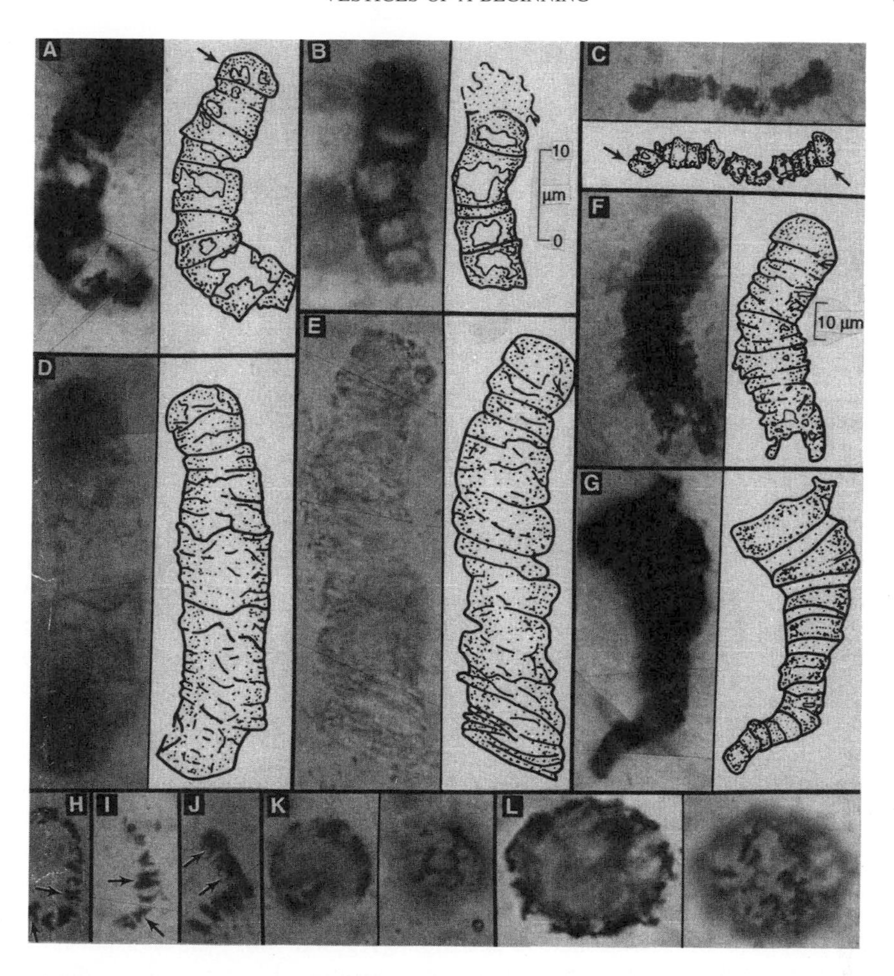

Fig. 14. Carbonaceous microfossils (with interpretive drawings) from the early Archaean Apex chert, Pilbara craton, Western Australia (Schopf 1993). Magnification of D, E, I and J as in scale in E, and of all others as in scale in A. A–E *Primaevifilum amoenum* (Schopf 1992); F–J P. conicoterminatum (Schopf 1993). Reproduced by permission of Cambridge University Press.

back to the oldest known sedimentary strata, and hence almost to the end of the 'late heavy bombardment' by giant meteorites that was experienced by all the terrestrial planets of the inner solar system. The asteroid impacts may have sterilized the Earth, indicating a remarkably fast emergence of life, or else the organic material represents a biota destroyed in the later stages of the bombardment, to be replaced by the single-celled organisms that were our ancestors. As discussed later, impacting bolides may have actually delivered complex organic molecules to this planet, as well as possibly playing a major role in influencing life through later events, most notably the one at the Cretaceous–Tertiary boundary (Alvarez *et al.* 1980). There can now be no doubt that impacts of major bolides have occurred throughout the history of the planet, though the influence of these events on evolution as well as on the origin of life is a matter of intense debate.

The evidence for a major impact at the Cretaceous–Tertiary boundary in the shallow epicontinental seas of the Yucatan Peninsula of Mexico is now overwhelming (Hildebrand *et al.* 1991; Morgan *et al.* 1997). There is also evidence of a major impact in North Africa close to the Jurassic–Cretaceous boundary, the Morokweng impact crater. Were a large proportion of the boundaries in the geological timescale extraterrestrially determined? On the other side of the globe from the Yucatan, however, there was a major K–T boundary eruption of basalt to form the Deccan Traps of India, possibly as a result of the arrival of a plume from the deep mantle (Basu *et al.* 1993, 1995). The fact that similar magmatic events occurred at the times of other major biological extinctions, for example the Triassic–Jurassic boundary, and the end of the Palaeozoic era, leaves open the possibility that the internal heat of the planet itself may have played a role in extinctions (Courtillot *et al.* 1988; Courtillot 1990; Olsen *et al.* 1997). Again, just what is the relative importance of endogenic versus extraterrestrial events on the development of the biosphere? In my view, this is perhaps the single most important question in contemporary Earth science.

The prospect of an end

Popular contemplation of the future of the Earth understandably focuses on the comparatively short-term issue of climate change and specifically 'global warming'. Geologists are used to thinking of long-term changes between global 'greenhouse' climatic regimes in early Palaeozoic and Mesozoic times, 'icehouse' regimes in the late Palaeozoic and Quaternary, the possibility even of a 'snowball Earth' at times in the Precambrian, and certainly a low-oxygen atmosphere early in the history of the planet. To our community, therefore, the change in climate under debate seems a comparatively minor one. Indeed, that very fact cannot help but colour in an unusual way our personal contemplation of its possibly catastrophic effects on human civilization. We are used to looking for geological explanations for global change – just what changes are driven by humankind? Only a few years ago, for example, I was informed by several distinguished colleagues in the field of climate research that the idea of volcanic activity influencing climate was a result of the fixation of the geological community with volcanoes – then came the eruptions of Mount Pinatubo and Monte Hudson with their undisputed effects on atmospheric temperature and chemical composition. Likewise, the influence of bedrock on the behaviour of continental ice sheets was barely considered until the acquisition of data indicating the possible presence of active volcanoes beneath the West Antarctic Ice Sheet (Blankenship *et al.* 1993) and the Gjálp subglacial eruption at Vatnajökull in Iceland (Gudmundsson *et al.* 1997). For most people contemplating the future of the planet, however, local changes in weather and crop supplies, landslides, earthquakes, volcanic eruptions and possible melting of ice sheets and global sea-level rise are understandably the main concerns.

For some, particularly residents of the west coast of the United States, thoughts of earthquakes are associated with the idea that western California may 'drop into the ocean' as a result of seismic activity along the San Andreas fault system. Of course, extrapolation of present motion along the fault predicts the northward motion of the Salinian block along the western margin of the continent as has apparently, if debatably, happened to several other terranes in Mesozoic and Cenozoic times. Extrapolation of present day plate motion 100 million years into the future – generating a wider Atlantic Ocean basin, a narrower Pacific, and Australia potentially colliding with Siberia after major sinistral transpressional orogenic activity along the Pacific margin of Asia (Fig. 15) – was beyond the realm of James Hutton's view of the Earth 200 years ago. Even this scenario, however, does not constitute 'the prospect of an end'.

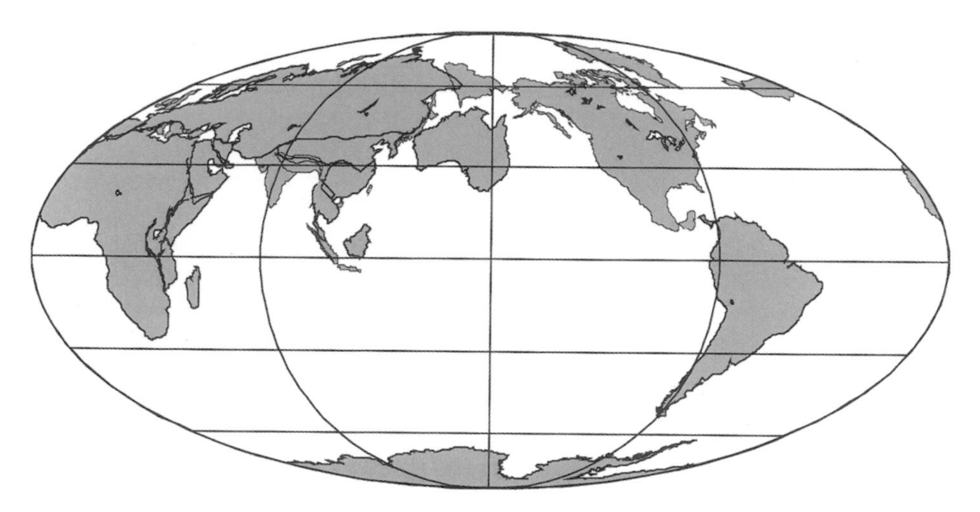

Fig. 15. Geography 100 Ma into the future if present plate motions continue: mollweide projection. (PLATES, Institute for Geophysics, University of Texas at Austin)

Sixty-five million years have elapsed since the Chicxulub impact of an extraterrestrial body with Earth, the event widely related to the termination of the Cretaceous period and the Mesozoic era, regardless of the extent to which the contemporary greenhouse state was already in decline. Future impacts of extraterrestrial bolides with Earth are certain. It is likely that on an average of every 100 million years there will be a major one on the scale of Chicxulub. Even if such events have a catastrophic effect on the existing life forms of the time, including potentially humankind, the history of the biosphere over the past 4 billion years indicates that such an event is unlikely to result in the destruction of the planet, or indeed of all life. As Richard Fortey puts it, 'Life will probably cope' (Fortey 1997). Here again, were Hutton alive today, he would be likely to reach the same conclusion regarding the Earth's fate as he did in 1788.

The lithosphere, the upper thermal boundary layer of the planet, is at present approximately 100 km thick. It will gradually thicken as further cooling takes place. Eventually, it may thicken to a critical value at which subduction of oceanic lithosphere is no longer possible. There will then be no water returned to the mantle, and circulation there will cease. The Earth will no longer be a dynamic planet, and its surface may come to look more like that of Mars or Venus – but it will still be a rocky 'terrestrial' planet, and the effect of the change on the biosphere is unclear. Consideration of surficial processes, most critically long-term decrease in atmospheric CO_2 (the present fossil-fuel induced increase notwithstanding), points to the demise of a plant-based biosphere in approximately 1 to 1.5 billion years' time. According to this scenario, in ~2.5 billion years' time Earth may lose all its water into Space as has Venus (Caldeira & Kasting 1992).

It is the astronomical and astrophysical evidence that places the ultimate time limit on the existence of life on Earth and indeed of the planet as a discrete entity in the solar system. The Sun plots near the centre of the 'main sequence' of stars, those in the stable hydrogen-burning phase on a Hertzsprung–Russell diagram, a plot of the surface temperature of a star versus its luminosity (Fig. 16). Approximately 90 per cent of the stars in the Milky Way plot along this line. The larger a star is, the hotter it burns, but the shorter its

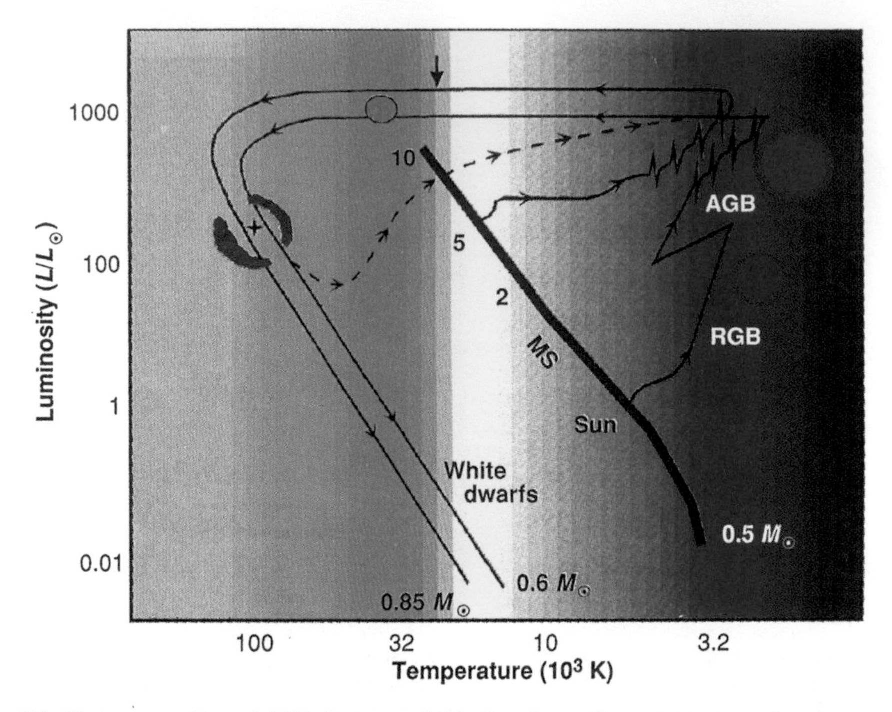

Fig. 16. Hertzsprung–Russel (HR) diagram, which plots the surface temperature of a star versus its luminosity (*L*) (L_0 is the luminosity of the Sun). About 90 per cent of stars in the Milky Way lie on a single narrow band running diagonally from hot, bright stars to faint cool ones. This is known as the main sequence (*M* numbers indicate star masses in units of the mass of the sun, M_0). Giants and supergiants are much more luminous at a given colour at the cool end of the diagram. Well below the main sequence are the white dwarfs. The position of a star in the HR diagram is mainly determined by two parameters, mass and age (by age, the stage of evolution is meant). Different stars evolve at different rates and therefore reach similar stages of evolution with different ages in years. The two solid lines are evolutionary tracks (arrows show direction of evolution) of stars that leave the main sequence at the mass of the Sun (M_0) and five times that mass $5M_0$, become red giants (RGB is red giant branch and AGB is asymptotic giant branch) and end as white dwarfs of 0.6 and 0.85 M_0, respectively. Between the thick vertical arrow that marks the onset of photo-ionization and the white dwarf regime, these stars are the central stars of gaseous 'planetary nebulae' (so-called because their often faint discs resemble Uranus and Neptune, but actually envelopes thrown off stars in advanced evolutionary stages). Spikes in the diagram represent thermal pulses, and the dashed line represents a 'born again' evolution wherein a particular type of PNe returns to the AGM regime and retraces its evolutionary path to a white dwarf. Diagram and explanation reprinted with permission from Weinberger & Kerber (1997). Copyright (1997) American Association for the Advancement of Science.

time in the main sequence. When a star has used up its hydrogen, there is a change in its mode of energy production and it moves up and right on the diagram. A star the size of the Sun has a life of ~10 billion years as a main sequence star. As shown in Fig. 16, the Sun will eventually leave the main sequence and enter the red giant branch of stars. Thus ~5 billion years from now the Sun will turn into a red giant, expanding to 100 times its present diameter, destroying the Earth's atmosphere and consuming the lifeless planet before the outer layers of the expanded star are blown off in a gaseous holocaust creating a planetary nebula within which the central star declines to a white dwarf (Weinberger &

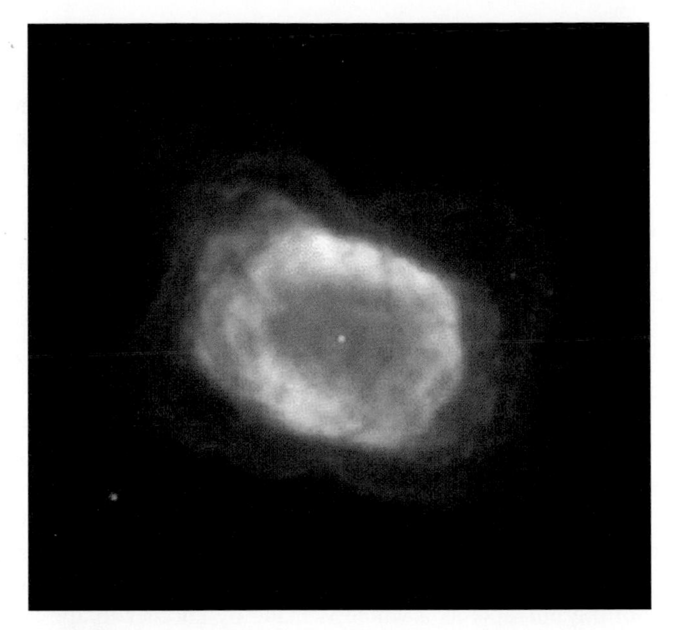

Fig. 17. The prospect of an end. Hubble Space Telescope/NICMOS image of a so-called 'galactic planetary nebula', NGC 7027, 3000 light years from Earth in the constellation Cygnus, the result of the 'death' of a star. The image captures an ionized gas cloud 14 000 astronomical units in diameter surrounded by an envelope of dust. In the case of the Sun, a gas cloud, propelling an envelope at speeds *c.* 100 000 km h^{-1}, will extend far beyond the outermost planet, Pluto. (Image courtesy of William B. Latter, California Institute of Technology and colleagues, and NASA.)

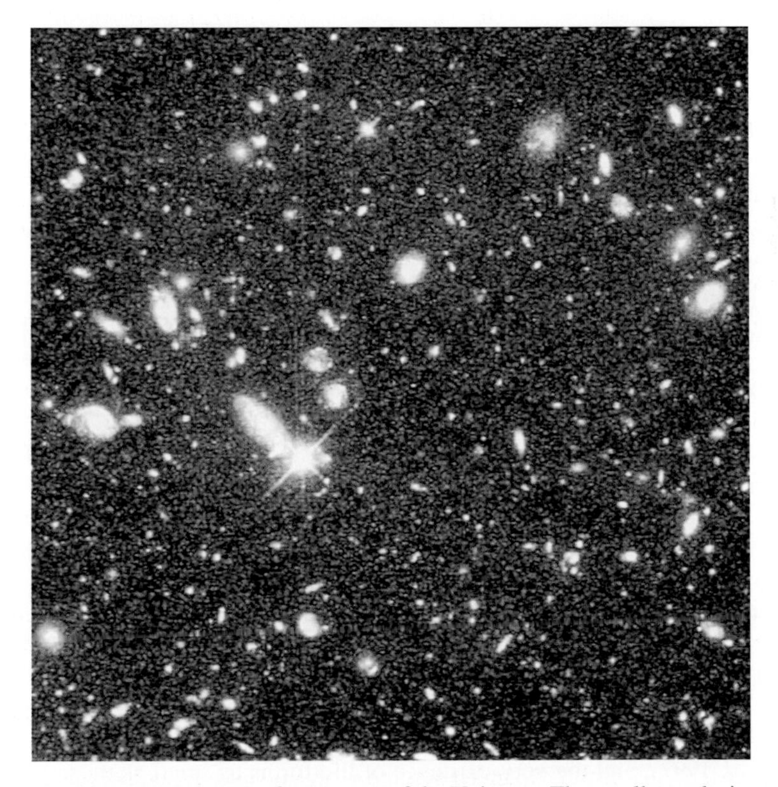

Fig. 18. Hubble 'deep field' image of a segment of the Universe. The smallest galaxies are seen as they were at over twice the age of the Earth and Solar System (see text). (Courtesy of NASA.)

Kerber 1997; Bobrowsky *et al.* 1998). This, therefore, is the 'prospect of an end' that our purely terrestrial studies could reveal neither to James Hutton two centuries ago, nor to modern students of the planet itself. Exactly this prospect is mirrored in a spectacular image recently obtained by the Hubble Space Telescope (Fig. 17).

The vestiges of geochemical evidence therefore point to a beginning at 4.5 Ga, and the astrophysical prospect of an end is 5.0 billion years into the future. On the nearly 4.0 billion year old 'tree of life' on this planet, the bipedal hominids from which our species is descended evolved from earlier life forms only within the most recent 5.0 million years. This is certainly a giddying thought for a self-styled technologically advanced civilization Humankind, therefore. exists poised remarkably close to the midpoint of the temporal span of the solar system. This leads to the most fundamental scientific question of all. However we evolved from the earliest life on this planet, whatever the fate of our species, whatever life forms may (or may not) evolve in the future from our species or the others that inhabit Earth with us at this midpoint, is all life confined to the time interval between the beginning and end of this one small blue dot in space, orbiting an unremarkable star? A striking connection between the origin of the Earth as a potential home for life, and the time–space scale of the universe as a whole is made by another image acquired by the Hubble Space Telescope, that of the 'Hubble deep field' (Fig. 18). This has a 'look back' time over twice the age of the solar system. The very faintest objects on the image are galaxies as they appeared at that time, approximately 3×10^{10} Ga. Galaxies only slightly larger than the faintest ones on the image appear as they were on the day of the Earth's birth.

Deeper into the abyss

Many scientists believe that life, even intelligent life, may exist elsewhere in the universe. A plaque has been placed on a spacecraft outward bound from the solar system, and a Search for Extraterrestrial Intelligence is being conducted. Both are based on the belief, indeed conviction, that there are civilizations at least as technologically advanced as our own elsewhere in the Milky Way Galaxy or beyond. Astronauts and samples returned from the Moon were quarantined lest they contaminate Earth with alien life forms. A fly-by of the Earth conducted by the spacecraft Galileo *en route* to Jupiter included a test of human ability to detect life on an 'alien' planet. Atmospheric oxygen and modulated radio emissions were detected, but, as pointed out by Carl Sagan and his colleagues, the same fly-by conducted a mere 200 years earlier would not have revealed the presence of a technologically proficient civilization (Sagan *et al.* 1993).

The first evidence claimed to indicate the presence of life beyond the confines of the Earth's atmosphere was reported in 1996 to have been found in a meteorite collected from a 'blue ice' area along the cratonic side of the Transantarctic Mountains. The chemistry of this particular meteorite, an impact-shocked igneous rock designated ALH84001 after the collection site in the Allen Hills, had been known to indicate a likely Martian origin. Analysis of Martian soil had failed to detect any evidence of recognizable life, but ALH84001 contains chemically and isotopically heterogeneous carbonate globules and associated organic and inorganic structures that have been interpreted as possible fossil remains of an ancient Martian biota (McKay *et al.* 1996). Several aspects of the evidence cited in favour of this conclusion have been vigorously disputed (e.g. Scott *et al.* 1997; Bradley *et al.* 1997), and the very existence of life forms as small as those postulated in the meteorite is highly controversial. Nonetheless, the Allen Hills meteorite report has dramatically transposed the question of extraterrestrial life from the realm of Hollywood fiction and the speculation of celebrated and far-thinking scientists such as Sir Fred Hoyle (1965), Francis Crick (1981) and Carl Sagan (1994), not only to news media headlines, but also to the mainstream scientific literature. There is evidence that Europa, the ice-covered moon of Jupiter, may have an 'ocean' favourable to at least primitive life forms (Carr *et al.* 1998).

In 1996 and 1997 the comet Hale-Bopp (C/1995 01) visited the inner part of the solar system. A mere 30–40 km in diameter, it carved a spectacular path (Fig. 19) through the night skies of the world and was viewed by countless millions of people. It also carved a major role in transforming studies of comets from traditional areas of study and speculation, to what Cruikshank (1997) refers to as a new paradigm, namely 'through cometary messengers from far beyond the plantary region of our solar system, life on Earth is connected to stardust'. Perhaps the late Carl Sagan would not have regarded this development as particularly startling, but he would certainly have been excited, and again fresh data have brought a somewhat ethereal question into the everyday scientific literature.

Fig. 19. Comet Hale-Bopp (C/1995 O1) over San Antonio, Texas, 29 March 1997. (Photo by Richard Miscke.)

Spectra obtained from ground-based radio telescopes showed the progressive release of CO, CH_3OH, HCH, H_2 (from OH), H_2S, CS, H_2CO, CH_3CN and HCN as the comet approached through 6.9–1.4 astronomical units from the Sun (Biver *et al.* 1997; Fig. 20). The more volatile species were relatively more abundant in the tail of the comet further from the Sun. As pointed out by Cruikshank (1997), the list of molecules now known to occur in comets is close to that of ices that occur in the dense clouds of the interstellar medium. He draws attention, in particular, to methanol (CH_3OH) found in the coma of Hale-Bopp, and often (after H_2O) the second or third most abundant component in both interstellar and cometary ices. This is particularly significant as it is the starting point of a rich chain of photochemical reactions. There is a possibility that some of the material could have reacted under the effect of light to form molecules that are chemical pathways to amino acids, the building blocks of terrestrial life.

Traditional views of the origin of life on Earth have centered on sea water – Darwin's 'warm little pond' referred to in his famous letter to Joseph Hooker in 1871 (see Fortey 1997, p. 35). More recently attention has turned to hot volanic vents on the ocean floor and in terrestrial hot spots such as Yellowstone. The data from the comets, however, certainly make it possible that not only carbon but also the basic organic chemical

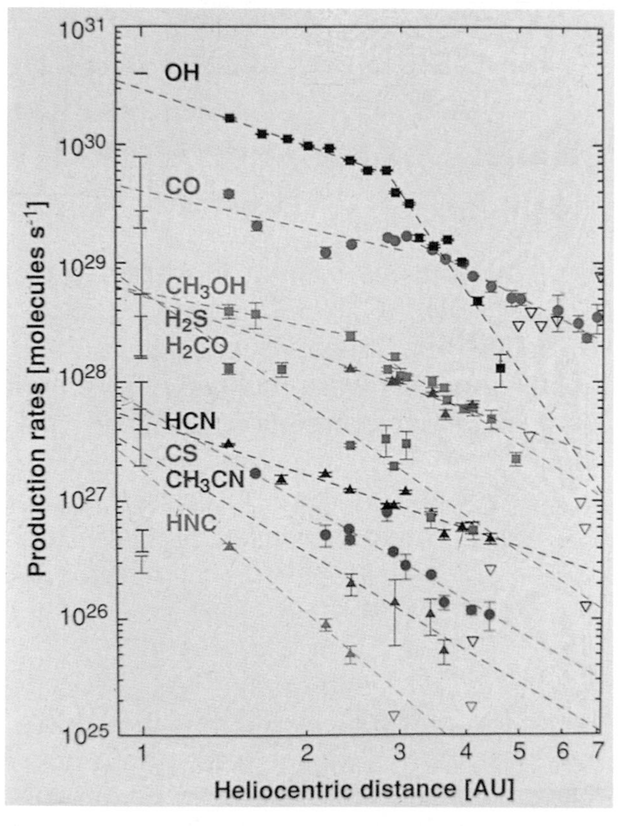

Fig. 20. Emissions recorded from coma of Comet Hale-Bopp (C/1995 01). Reprinted with permission from Biver *et al.* (1997). Copyright (1997) American Association for the Advancement of Science.

Fig. 21. Near-infrared image of newborn Taurus Molecular Ring, star 1 binary (TMR-1, image centre) revealing a long thin nebula pointing towards a faint companion object (TMR 1C, bottom left), which could be the first extra solar planet to be imaged directly. The NASA Hubble Space Telescope image was obtained on 4 August 1997, the day before the start of the Hutton/Lyell Bicentennial Conference in Edinburgh.

compounds necessary for the development of life are present in the outer reaches of the solar system and in the interstellar medium. They may, therefore, have arrived here during the pre-Archaean meteoritic bombardment, and could actually have arrived on more than one occasion. Life may indeed be a 'cosmic imperative' as suggested by Christian de Duve in the subtitle to his book, *Vital Dust,* on evolution from a cell biologist's standpoint (de Duve 1995), although Paul Davies takes a somewhat sceptical view of this concept in his recent book, *The Fifth Miracle* (Davies 1998). Evidence for the existence of planets orbiting other stars in the Milky Way is becoming stronger (Fig. 21). There may well prove to be countless other potential planetary 'homes' for interstellar organic material. But are there other 'blue dot' planets, and even if there is life on another planet, will it have evolved beyond the unicellular stage that dominated on Earth for so long?

Finally, and I am sure I am not alone in feeling that this point stretches the mind to and indeed beyond its limit, we must take into account various ideas currently under discussion by cosmologists. While geochemical and astrophysical data clearly delimit the life span for the Earth from 4.5 Ga in the past to ~5.0 Ga into the future, and despite the absence of empirical evidence, the hypotheses of a boundless or eternally self-reproducing universe have been put forward on theoretical grounds (Hawking 1988; Smolin 1992;

Linde 1994; Ferris 1997; Ryle 1997). Even as I write, a debate has sprung up over new observations of the most distant galaxies, indicating that the universe is expanding at an accelerating rate due to a previously unknown force, and that it may do so in perpetuity (Perlmutter *et al.* 1998).

Hence, at the end of this discourse on the life of our planet I have to conclude that, taken at its full scope, modern scientific enquiry by an interdisciplinary global community of scientists presently reaches the same conclusion as that of the almost solitary James Hutton 200 years ago in Edinburgh. In this sense, there is still 'no vestige of a beginning, and no prospect of an end'. This takes us a long way from Siccar Point with the east wind off the North Sea blowing in our faces. For the present, at least, it forces us to consider ourselves as part of a universe that, having neither a beginning nor end, 'would simply be' (Hawking 1988, p. 141).

Conclusions

In this contribution to the celebration of James Hutton's life and work, I have tried to put his view regarding evidence for a beginning and an end to the Earth in a modern context. One can view the issue at three levels. First, the geological evidence, as he himself would have viewed it in the field, still reveals 'no vestige of a beginning and no prospect of an end'. Second, geochemical evidence from the Earth, the Moon and meteorites clearly points to a beginning of the solar system at close to 4.5 Ga, and the astrophysical evidence points to an end of this planet, or at least of its biosphere, at ~5.0 billion years in the future. Third, cosmological considerations, although thus far in the absence of any direct observational or experimental evidence, raise the possibility, that the universe containing the solar system, and galaxy may be boundless or part of a perenially expanding continuum or 'multiverse'. In this ultimate sense, Hutton's statement of two centuries ago may be considered as close to the greater truth as cosmologists contemplate it today, than the rocks, the geochemistry, or stars in the Milky Way and beyond can themselves reveal.

For geologists two centuries after the death of the 'Founder of modern geology', I believe that the lesson is clearly that we must follow the approach of Hutton and Playfair more assiduously than ever in considering the Earth that we study in the context of the solar system, the Milky Way Galaxy and the universe – Playfair's 'heavenly motions'. It is in this all-embracing context , with fresh opportunities opening up almost daily, that our study of the rocks here on Earth, and the evolution of this planet, attain their full and most exciting value. Most critically, we can thereby contribute to interlocking causal relationships across disciplines in the natural and social sciences, the 'consilience' called for by E. O. Wilson (1998*a*, *b*), a return to the approach of the age of Enlightenment which may now be required to deal with issues urgently facing humankind. Two hundred years after James Hutton's death, I believe this to be the *raison d'être* of twenty-first century 'modern geology'.

Some of the ideas outlined in this paper were developed in collaboration with my colleague Larry Lawver, and with others while I was a Gledden Senior Research Fellow in the Department of Geology and Geophysics at the University of Western Australia under the sponsorship of Professor Chris Powell, now Director of the Tectonics Special Research Centre. Funding was partly provided by the United States National Science Foundation through the Office of Polar Programs (Grant DPP 9117996, and the Tectonics Program of the Earth Science Division (Grant No. EAR 9418256). I thank Sam Bowring, Richard Buffler, Robert Dott, Jr, Richard Ernst, Daniel Jaffey, Richard Miscke, John Myers and Yosio Nakamura, who went out of their way to provide me with illustrations for my lecture at the Hutton Symposium in Edinburgh, some of which are reproduced here. Lisa Gahagan and Gwen Watson undertook computer illustrations. James Connelly, Robert H. Dott Jr. and Todd Housh made helpful comments on an early version of the manuscript. Constructive comments by Michael Johnson and an anonymous reviewer improved the final paper.

References

ALLÈGRE, C. J. 1997. Limitation on the mass exchange between the upper and lower mantle: the evolving convection regime of the Earth. *Earth and Planetary Science Letters*, **150**(1–2), 1–6.

——, MANHÈS, G. & GÖPEL, C. 1995. The age of the Earth. *Geochimica et Cosmochimica Acta*, **59**(8), 1445–1456.

ALVAREZ, L. W., ALVAREZ, W., AZARO, F. & MICHEL, H. V. 1980. Extraterrestrial cause for the Cretaceous–Tertiary extinction. *Nature*, **208**, 1095–1108.

BAILEY, E. B. 1929. *The Palaeozoic Mountain Systems of Europe and America*. British Association for the Advancement of Science Reports, 96th Annual Meeting, Glasgow, 57–76.

BALAVOINE, G. & ADOUTTE, A. 1998. One or three Cambrian radiations? *Science*, **280**, 397–398.

BASU, A. R. ET AL. 1993. Early and late alkali igneous pulses and a high-^{3}He plume origin for the Deccan flood basalts. *Science*, **261**, 902–906.

—— ET AL. 1995. High-^{3}He plume origin and temporal–spatial evolution of the Siberian flood basalts. *Science*, **269**, 822–825.

BELL, R. T. & JEFFERSON, C. W. 1987. An hypothesis for an Australia–Canadian connection in the Late Proterozoic and the birth of the Pacific Ocean. *In*: *Proceedings of the Pacific Rim Congress 1987*. Australian Institute of Mining and Metallurgy, Parkville, Victoria, Australia, 39–50.

BENGSTON, S. (ED.) 1995. *Early Life on Earth*. Columbia University Press, New York.

BIVER, N. ET AL. 1997. Evolution of the outgassing of Comet Hale-Bopp (C/1995 O1) from radio observations. *Science*, **275**, 1915–1918.

BLANKENSHIP, D. D. ET AL. 1993. Active volcanism beneath the West Antarctic ice sheet and implications for ice-sheet stability. *Nature*, **361**, 526–529.

BOBROWSKY, M. ET AL. 1998. Birth and early evolution of a planetary nebula. *Nature*, **392**, 469–471.

BOND, G. C., NICKESON, P. A. & KOMINZ, M. A. 1984. Breakup of a supercontinent between 625 Ma and 555 Ma: new evidence and implications for continental histories. *Earth and Planetary Science Letters*, **70**, 325–345.

BOTT, M. H. P. 1992. The stress regime associated with continental break-up. *In*: STOREY, B. C., ALABASTER, T. & PANKHURSt, R. J. (eds) *Magmatism and the Causes of Continental Break-up*. Geological Society, London, 125–136.

BOWRING, S. A. ET AL. 1993. Calibrating rates of Early Cambrian evolution. *Science*, **261**, 1293–1298.

——, WILLIAMS, I. S. & COMPSTON, W. 1989. 3.96 Ga gneisses from the Slave province, Northwest Territories, Canada. *Geology*, **17**(11), 971–975.

—— ET AL. 1997. An overview of the geologic framework of the Acasta gneisses. *In*: *Geological Association of Canada/Metrological Association of Canada Annual Meeting. Abstract Volume.* GAC/MAC, Ottawa, A–16.

BRADLEY, J. P., HARVEY, R. P. & MCSWEEN, J. 1997. No 'nanofossils' in martian meteorite. *Nature*, **390**, 454.

BULLARD, E. J., EVERETT, J. E. & SMITH, A. G. 1965. The fit of the continents around the Atlantic. *Philosophical Transactions of the Royal Society, London*, **A258**, 41–51.

BURKE, D. & KIDD, W. S. F. 1980. Volcanism on earth through time. *In*: STRANGWAY, D. W. (ed.) *The Continental Crust and its Mineral Deposits.* Geological Association of Canada Special Paper, 503–522.

BURKE, K. & DEWEY, J. F. 1973. Plume-generated triple junctions: key indicators in applying plate tectonics to old rocks. *Journal of Geology*, **81**, 406–433.

CALDEIRA, K. & KASTING, J. F. 1992. The Lifespan of the biospere revisited. *Nature*, **360**, 721–723.

CAMERON, A. G. W. 1988. Origin of the Solar System. *Annual Reviews in Astonomy and Astrophysics*, **26**, 441–472.

CAMPBELL, I. H. & GRIFFITHS, R. W. 1992. The changing nature of mantle hotspots through time: implications for the chemical evolution of the mantle. *Journal of Geology*, **92**, 497–523.

CARR, M. H. ET AL. 1998. Evidence for a subsurface ocean on Europa. *Nature*, **391**, 363–368.

CHENEY, E. S. 1996. Sequence stratigraphy and plate tectonic significance of the Transvaal succession of southern Africa and its equivalent in Western Australia. *Precambrian Research*, **79**, 3–24.

COFFIN, M. F. & ELDHOLM, O. 1994. Large igneous provinces: crustal structure, dimensions, and external consequences. *Reviews of Geophysics*, **32**, 1–36.

COMPSTON, W. & PIDGEON, R. T. 1986. Jack Hills, evidence of more very old detrital zircons in Western Australia. *Nature*, **321**, 766–769.

COURTILLOT, V. E. 1990. A volcanic eruption. *Scientific American*, **263**, 85–92.

—— ET AL. 1988. The Deccan flood basalts and the Cretaceous/Tertiary boundary. *Nature*, **333**, 843–846.

COX, K. G. 1989. The role of mantle plumes in the development of continental drainage patterns. *Nature*, **342**, 873–877.

CRICK, F. 1981. *Life Itself: Its Origin and Nature*. Simon & Schuster, New York.

CRUIKSHANK, D. P. 1997. Stardust memories. *Science*, **275**, 1895–1896.

DALLA SALDA, L. H., CINGOLANI, C. A. & VARELA, R. 1992*a*. The Early Paleozoic orogenic belt of the Andes in southwestern South America: result of Laurentia–Gondwana collision? *Geology*, **20**, 617–620.

——, DALZIEL, I. W. D., CINGOLANI, C. A. & VARELA, R. 1992*b*. Did the Taconic Appalachians continue into southern South America? *Geology*, **20**, 1059–1062.

DALRYMPLE, G. B. 1991. *The Age of the Earth*. Stanford University Press, Stanford, CA.

DALZIEL, I. W. D. 1991. Pacific margins of Laurentia and East Antarctica–Australia as a conjugate rift pair: evidence and implications for an Eocambrian supercontinent. *Geology*, **19**(6), 598–601.

—— 1992*a*. Antarctica: a tale of two supercontinents? *Annual Review of Earth and Planetary Sciences*, **20**, 501–526.

—— 1992*b*. On the organization of American plates in the Neoproterozoic and the breakout of Laurentia. *GSA Today*, **2**(11), 237–241.

—— 1995. Earth before Pangea. *Scientific American*, **272**, 58–63.

—— 1997. Neoproterozoic–Paleozoic geography and tectonics: review, hypothesis, environmental speculation. *Geological Society of America Bulletin*, **108**(1), 16–42.

—— & GRUNOW, A. M. 1992. Late Gondwanide tectonic rotations within Gondwanaland: causes and consequences. *Tectonics*, **11**, 603–606.

—— & LAWVER, L. A. 1997. A functional relation between deep-seated mantle plumes and surficial plates since Archean time? *Geological Society of America, Abstracts with Programs*, **29**(6), A48.

——, KNOLL, A. & MOORES, E. 1994*a*. Late Precambrian tectonics and the dawn of the Phanerozoic (Penrose Conference Report). *GSA Today*, **4**(1), 8–9.

——, ET AL. 1994*b*. Paleozoic Laurentia–Gondwana interaction and the origin of the Appalachian–Andean mountain system. *Geological Society of America Bulletin*, **106**(2), 243–252.

—— ET AL. 1996. The Argentine Precordillera: a Laurentian terrane? (Penrose Conference Report). *GSA Today*, **6**(2), 16–18.

—— ET AL. 1998. Laurentia–Kalahari collision and the assembly of Rodinia. *Geological Society of America, Abstracts with Programs*, **90**(7), A124.

DANA, J. D. 1843. On the areas of subsidence in the Pacific, as indicated by the distribution of coral islands. *American Journal of Science and Arts*, 1st series, **45**, 131–135.

—— 1847. Origin of the grand outline features of the Earth. *American Journal of Science and Arts*, 2nd series, **3**, 381–398.

—— (ED.) 1849. Atlas, Geology. U.S. Exploring Expedition, 10. (1838–42) George P. Putnam, New York.

DARWIN, C. 1839. *Narrative of the Surveying Voyages of His Majesty's Ships 'Adventure' and 'Beagle' between the Years 1826 and 1836, Describing Their Examination of the Southern Shores of South America, and the 'Beagle's Circumnavigation of the Globe. Journal and Remarks*, 1832–1836, **3**. Henry Colburn, London.

—— 1844. *Geological Observations on the Volcanic Islands Visited during the Voyage of H.M.S. 'Beagle'...* . Smith, Elder & Co., London.

—— 1859. *On the Origin of Species by Means of Natural Selection.* J. Murray, London.

DAVIES, G. F. 1997. Plates, plumes, mantle convection, and mantle evolution. *In*: *The Earth's Mantle: Composition Structure, and Evolution.* Cambridge University Press, Cambridge, 228–258.

DAVIS, P. 1998. *The Fifth Miracle.* Allen Lane, The Penguin Press, Ringwood, Vic, Australia.

DE DUVE, C. 1995. *Vital Dust: Life as a Cosmic Imperative.* HarperCollins, New York.

DEWEY, J. F. 1969. Evolution of Appalachian/Caledonide orogen. *Nature*, **211**, 124–129.

—— & BIRD, J. M. 1970. Mountain belts and the new global tectonics. *Journal of Geophysical Research*, **75**, 2615–2647.

DOTT, R. H. 1997. James Dwight Dana's old tectonics–global contraction under divine direction. *American Journal of Science*, **297**, 283–311.

ERNST, R. E. & BUCHAN, K. L. 1997. Giant radiating dyke swarms: their use in identifying pre-Mesozoic large igneous provinces and mantle plumes. *In*: MAHONEY, J. J. & COFFIN, M. F. (eds) *Large Igneous Provinces: Continental, Oceanic, and Planetary Flood Volcanism.* American Geophysical Union, Washington, 297–334.

——, —— & PALMER, H. C. 1995*a*. Giant dyke swarms: characteristics, distribution and geotectonic applications. *In*: BAER, G. & HEIMANN, A. (eds) *Physics and Chemistry of Dykes.* A. A. Balkema, Rotterdam, 3–22.

——, HEAD, J. W., PARFITT, E., GROSFILS, E. & WILSON, L. 1995*b*. Giant radiating dyke swarms on Earth and Venus. *Earth Science Reviews*, **39**, 1–58.

FERRIS, T. 1997. *The Whole Shebang: A State-of-the-Universe(s) Report.* Simon & Schuster, New York.

FORTEY, R. 1997. *Life: An Unauthorised Biography.* HarperCollins, London.

FROUDE, D. O. ET AL. 1983. Ion microprobe identification of 4,100–4,200 Myr-old terrestrial zircons. *Nature*, **304**, 616–618.

GRAND, S. P., VAN DER HILST, R. D. & WIDIYANTORO, S. 1997. Global seismic tomography: a snapshot of convection in the Earth. *GSA Today*, **7**(4), 1–7.

GUDMUNDSSON, M. T., SIGMUNDSSON, F. & BJÖRNSSON, H. 1997. Ice–volcano interaction of the 1996 Gjálp subglacial eruption, Vatnajökull, Iceland. *Nature*, **389**, 954–957.

HALLS, H. C. & FAHRIG, W. F. (EDS) 1987. *Mafic Dyke Swarms.* Geological Association of Canada Special Papers, **34**.

HARLAND, W. B. ET AL. 1990. *A Geologic Time Scale 1989.* Press Syndicate of the University of Cambridge, Cambridge and New York.

HARRIS, W. E. ET AL. 1998. Constraints on the Hubble Constant from observations of the brightest red giant stars in a Virgo-cluster galaxy. *Nature*, **395**, 45–47.

HARTMAN, W. K. (ED.) 1986. *Origin of the Moon.* Lunar and Planetary Institute, Houston.

HARTNADY, C. J. H. 1986. Was North America ("Laurentia") part of south-western Gondwanaland during the late Proterozoic era? *Suid-Afrikaanse Tydskrif vir Wetenskap*, **82**, 251–254.

HAWKING, S. W. 1988. *A Brief History of Time.* Bantam Books, New York.

HEAD, J. W. 1990. Processes of crustal formation and evolution on Venus: an analysis of topography and crustal thickness variations. *Earth, Moon and Planets*, **50/51**, 25–55.

—— & COFFIN, M. F. 1997. Large igneous provinces: a planetary perspective. *In*: MAHONEY, J. J. & COFFIN, M. F. (eds) *Large Igneous Provinces: Continental, Oceanic, and Planetary Flood Volcanism.* American Geophysical Union, Washington, 411–438.

HEAMAN, L. M. 1997. Global mafic magmatism at 2.45 Ga: remnants of an ancient large igneous province? *Geology*, **25**(4), 299–302.

HILDEBRAND, A. R. ET AL. 1991. A possible Cretaceous–Tertiary boundary impact crater on the Yucatan Peninsula, Mexico. *Geology*, **19**, 867–871.

HILL, R. I. 1991. Starting plumes and continental break-up. *Earth and Planetary Science Letters*, **104**, 398–416.

HOFFMAN, P. F. 1991. Did the breakout of Laurentia turn Gondwanaland inside out? *Science*, **252**, 1409–1412.

HOLMES, A. 1944. *Principles of Physical Geology.* T. Nelson, London.

HOYLE, F. 1965. *Galaxies, Nucleii, and Quasars.* Heinemann, London.

HUTTON, C. 1785. *Concerning the System of the Earth, Its Duration, and Stability.* Royal Society of Edinburgh, Edinburgh.

HUTTON, J. 1788. Theory of the Earth. *Transactions of the Royal Society of Edinburgh*, **1**, 209–304.
KAY, M. 1966. *North Atlantic–Geology and Continental Drift.* American Association of Petroleum Geologists Memoir, **12**.
KNOLL, A. H. 1994. Proterozoic and Early Cambrian protists: evidence for accelerating evolutionary tempo. Proceedings of the National Academy of Sciences, 6743–6750.
LAWVER, L. A., DALZIEL, I. W. D. & GAHAGAN, L. M. 1997. A mantle plume look at the Permo-Jurassic tectonic history of the South Atlantic Region. *Eos Transactions of the American Geophysical Union*, **78**(46), F721.
LAY, T. *ET AL.* 1998. The core-mantle boundary layer and deep Earth dynamics. *Nature*, **392**, 461–463.
LEE, D.-C., HALLIDAY, A. N., SNYDER, G. A. & TAYLOR, L. A. 1997. Age and origin of the Moon. *Science*, **278**, 1098–1103.
LINDE, A. 1994. The self-reproducing inflationary universe. *Scientific American*, **271**(5), 48–55.
LOVELOCK, J. E. 1979. *Gaia: A New Look at Life on Earth.* Oxford University Press, Oxford.
MCKAY, D. *ET AL.* 1996. Search for past life on Mars: possible relic biogenic activity in martian meteorite ALH84001. *Science*, **273**, 924–930.
MCKERROW, W. S. & SCOTESE, C. R. (EDS) 1990. *Palaeozoic Palaeogeography and Biogeography.* Geological Society Memoirs, 12.
MAHONEY, J. J. & COFFIN, M. F. (EDS) 1997. *Large Igneous Provinces.* Geophysical Monograph Series, American Geophysical Union, Washington.
MARGULIS, L. 1993. *Symbiosis in Cell Evolution.* Freeman, New York.
—— & SAGAN, D. 1995. What is Life? Simon & Schuster, New York.
MAY, P. R. 1971. Pattern of Triassic–Jurassic diabase dykes around the North Atlantic in context of predrift position of the continents. *Geological Society of America Bulletin*, **82**, 1285–1292.
MÈGE, D. & MASSON, P. 1996. A plume tectonics model for the Tharsis province, Mars. *Planetary Space Science*, **44**(12), 1488–1546.
MELOSH, H. J. 1989. *In*: NEWSOM, H. E. & JONES, J. J. (eds) *Origin of the Earth.* Oxford University Press, Oxford, 69–83.
MOJZSIS, S. J., ARRHENIUS, G. *ET AL.* 1996. Evidence for life on Earth before 3,800 million years ago. *Nature*, **384**, 55–59.
MOORES, E. M. 1991. Southwest U.S.–East Antarctic (SWEAT) connection: a hypothesis. *Geology*, **19**(5), 425–428.
MORGAN, J. *ET AL.* 1997. Size and morphology of the Chicxulub impact crater. *Nature*, **390**, 472–476.
MORGAN, W. J. 1971. Convection plumes in the lower mantle. *Nature*, **230**, 42–43.
—— 1972. Deep mantle convection plumes and plate motions. *American Association of Petroleum Geologists Bulletin*, **56**, 203–213.
NUTMAN, A. P. *ET AL.* 1996. The Itsaq gneiss complex of southern West Greenland; the world's most extensive record of early (3,900–3,600 Ma) crustal evolution. *Precambrian Research*, **78**, 1–39.
OLSEN, P. E. *ET AL.* 1997. Causal? Association of the Triassic–Jurassic mass extinction and Pangean flood basalt – a matter of timing. *Eos, Transactions of the American Geophysical Union*, **78**(46), F721.
PARK, J. K., BUCHAN, K. L. & HARLAN, S. S. 1995. A proposed giant radiating dyke swarm fragmented by the separation of Laurentia and Australia based on paleomagnetism of ca. 780 Ma mafic intrusions in western North America. *Earth and Planetary Science Letters*, **132**(1–4), 129–140.
PATTERSON, C. C. 1956. Age of meteorites and the Earth. *Geochimica et Cosmochimica Acta*, **10**, 230–237.
PEACH, B. N. *ET AL.* 1907. The geological structure of the north-west Highlands of Scotland. *Geological Survey of Scotland Memoirs*, 668.
PERLMUTTER, S. *ET AL.* 1998. Discovery of a supernova explosion at half the age of the universe. *Nature*, **391**, 51–54.
PIPER, J. D. A. 1982. The Precambrian paleomagnetic record: the case for the Proterozoic supercontinent. *Earth and Planetary Science Letters*, **59**, 61–89.
PLAYFAIR, J. 1802. *Illustrations of the Huttonian Theory of the Earth.* Cadell & Davies, London.

—— 1805. Biographical account of the late Dr. James Hutton F.R.S. Edinburgh. *Royal Society of Edinburgh Transactions*, **5**, 39–99.

POWELL, C. M., LI, Z. X., MCELHINNY, M. W., MEERT, J. G. & PARK, J. K. 1993. Paleomagnetic constraints on timing of the Neoproterozoic breakup of Rodinia and the Cambrian formation of Gondwana. *Geology*, **21**(10), 889–892.

RYLE, M. 1997. *Before the Beginning: Our Universe and Others.* Addison-Wesley, London.

SAGAN, C. 1994. *Pale Blue Dot: A Vision of the Human Future in Space*. Random House, New York.

——, THOMPSON, W. R., CARLSSON, R., GURNETT, D. & HORD, C. 1993. A search for life on Earth from the Gallieo spacecraft. *Nature*, **365**, 715–721.

SALTER, J. W. 1859. Durness limestone fossils. *Quarterly Journal of the Geological Society, London*, **15**, 374–381.

SANDWELL, D. T. & SMITH, W. H. F. 1995. Marine gravity field from declassified Geosat and ERS 1 altimetry. *EOS, Transactions of AGU, Fall Meeting Supplement*, 76.

SCHOPF, J. W. 1992. *In*: SCHOPF, J. W. & KLEIN, C. (eds) *The Proterozoic Biosphere*. Cambridge University Press, New York, 41-42.

—— 1993. Microfossils of the early Archean Apex Chert: new evidence of the antiquity of life. *Science*, **260**, 640–646.

SCOTT, E. R. D., YAMAGUCHI, A. & KROT, A. N. 1997. Petrological evidence for shock melting of carbonates in the Martian meteorite ALH84001. *Nature*, **387**, 377–379.

SHEN, Y. 1997. Seismic evidence for a lower mantle origin of the Iceland Plume. *Eos, Transactions of the American Geophysical Union*, **78**(46), F500.

SMOLIN, L. 1992. Did the universe evolve? *Classical and Quantum Gravity*, **9**, 173–191.

STEVENSON, D. J. 1987. Origin of the Moon – the collision hypothesis. *Annual Review of Earth and Planetary Sciences*, **15**, 271.

STOFAN, E. R. *ET AL.* 1992. Global distribution and characteristics of coronae and related features on Venus: implications for origin and relation to mantle processes. *Journal of Geophysical Research*, **97**(E8), 13 347–13 378.

STOREY, B. C. 1995. The role of mantle plumes in continental breakup–case histories from Gondwanaland. *Nature*, **377**, 301–308.

——, KING, E. C. & LIVERMORE, R. A. (EDS) 1996. *Weddell Sea Tectonics and Gondwana Break-up*. Geological Society, London.

THOMPSON, G. A. 1998. Deep mantle plumes and geoscience vision. *GSA Today*, **8**(4), 17–25.

VAN DER HILST, R. D., WIDIYANTARO, S. & ENGDAHL, E. R. 1997. Evidence for deep mantle circulation from global tomography. *Nature*, **386**, 578–584.

VINE, F. J. & MATTHEWS, D. H. 1963. Magnetic anomalies over oceanic ridges. *Nature*, **199**, 947–949.

WALCOTT, C. D. 1889. Stratigraphic position of the Olenellus fauna in North America and Europe. *American Journal of Science*, **38**, 29–42.

WEGENER, A. 1915. *Die Entstehung der Kontinente und Ozeane*. Friedr. Vieweg u Sohn, Braunschweig.

WEINBERGER, R. & KERBER, F. 1997. Planetary nebulae: understanding the physical and chemical evolution of dying stars. *Science*, **276**, 1382–1386.

WHITE, R. S. & MCKENZIE, D. 1995. Mantle plumes and flood basalts. *Journal of Geophysical Research*, **100**(B9), 17 653–17 585.

WILSON, E. O. 1998*a*. Integrated science and the coming century of the environment. *Science*, **279**, 2048–2049.

—— 1998*b*. *Consilience: The Unity of Knowledge*. Alfred A. Knopf, New York.

WILSON, J. T. 1963. Evidence from islands on the spreading of ocean floors. *Nature*, **197**, 536–538.

—— 1966. Did the Atlantic close and then re-open? *Nature*, **211**, 676–681.

—— 1973. Mantle plumes and plate motions. *Tectonophysics*, **19**, 149–164.

WINGATE, M. T. D., CAMPBELL, I. H. & COMPSTON, W. 1998. Ion microprobe U–Pb ages for Neoproterozoic basaltic magmatism in South Central Australia and the break-up of Rodinia. *Precambrian Research*, **87**, 137–162.

WOLFE, C. J. *ET AL.* 1997. Seismic structure of the Iceland mantle plume. *Nature*, **385**, 245–247.

XIAO, S., ZHANG, Y. & KNOLL, A. H. 1998. Three-dimensional preservation of algae and animal embroys in a Neoproterozoic phosphorite. *Nature*, **391**, 553–558.

ZOBACK, M. L. 1992. First- and second-order patterns of stress in the lithosphere: the World Stress Map Project. *Journal of Geophysical Research*, **97**(B8), 11 703–11 728.

The Dynamic Earth project and the next millennium

S. K. MONRO & A. J. CROSBIE
Dynamic Earth Charitable Trust, Dynamic Earth, PO Box 23086, Edinburgh EH8 8ZH, UK

Abstract: Two hundred and fifty years ago Edinburgh was a focus of intellectual ferment. The Enlightenment fired concern for an understanding of the science of the natural world. Hutton's *Theory of the Earth* not only provided a comprehensive view of the planet and its processes but also altered the perception of time. The next millennium will see a new global Enlightenment. The communications revolution is extending an awareness of science, but there is also an increased responsibility on scientists to make the results of their work understandable and accessible to the general public. Edinburgh's 'Dynamic Earth' exhibition will play a major part in delivering a better public understanding of the planet, generating that same sense of excitement felt by Hutton and his colleagues when first they looked into 'the abyss of time'. It will demonstrate that the Earth is a dynamic system, and show how landscapes are formed by a complex interaction between the geosphere, atmosphere, hydrosphere and biosphere and that these processes continue today. The challenge of Hutton's concept that 'the present is the key to the past' lies in what it implies about the future. The presentation within the Dynamic Earth will help visitors make up their own mind about what the future may hold.

James Hutton would notice a considerable difference in his part of Edinburgh today. The past 200 years have witnessed the expansion of the city, the development of industry on what, to him, would have been a rural fringe, and then its gradual decline in the twentieth century. Over the last decade, however, the area is once again being perceived as a setting where the old and the new, the historical and the modern can be blended into a harmonious whole.

The Dynamic Earth forms the centrepiece of a major urban regeneration plan, the Holyrood Project, steered by Lothian and Edinburgh Enterprise Limited, which will bring new vitality to the former industrial land at the lower end of the Royal Mile (Fig. 1). In place of the buildings of the former Holyrood Brewery and the old gasometers of British Gas, new houses, offices, shops, hotels and workshops are already taking form. Prominent within this new development will be a landmark building, the William Younger Centre (Fig. 2), housing the Dynamic Earth, which has attracted a substantial funding contribution from the Millennium Commission. This is to be a permanent exhibition and education centre which will help deliver a better public understanding of the processes that have shaped the Earth.

The Dynamic Earth concept

The primary objective of the Dynamic Earth exhibition is to present a holistic view of the planet Earth, demonstrating the interaction of forces that, through time, have created and

MONRO, S. K. & CROSBIE, A. J. 1999. The Dynamic Earth project and the next millennium. *In*: CRAIG, G. Y. & HULL, J. H. (eds) *James Hutton – Present and Future*. Geological Society, London, Special Publications, **150**, 157–167.

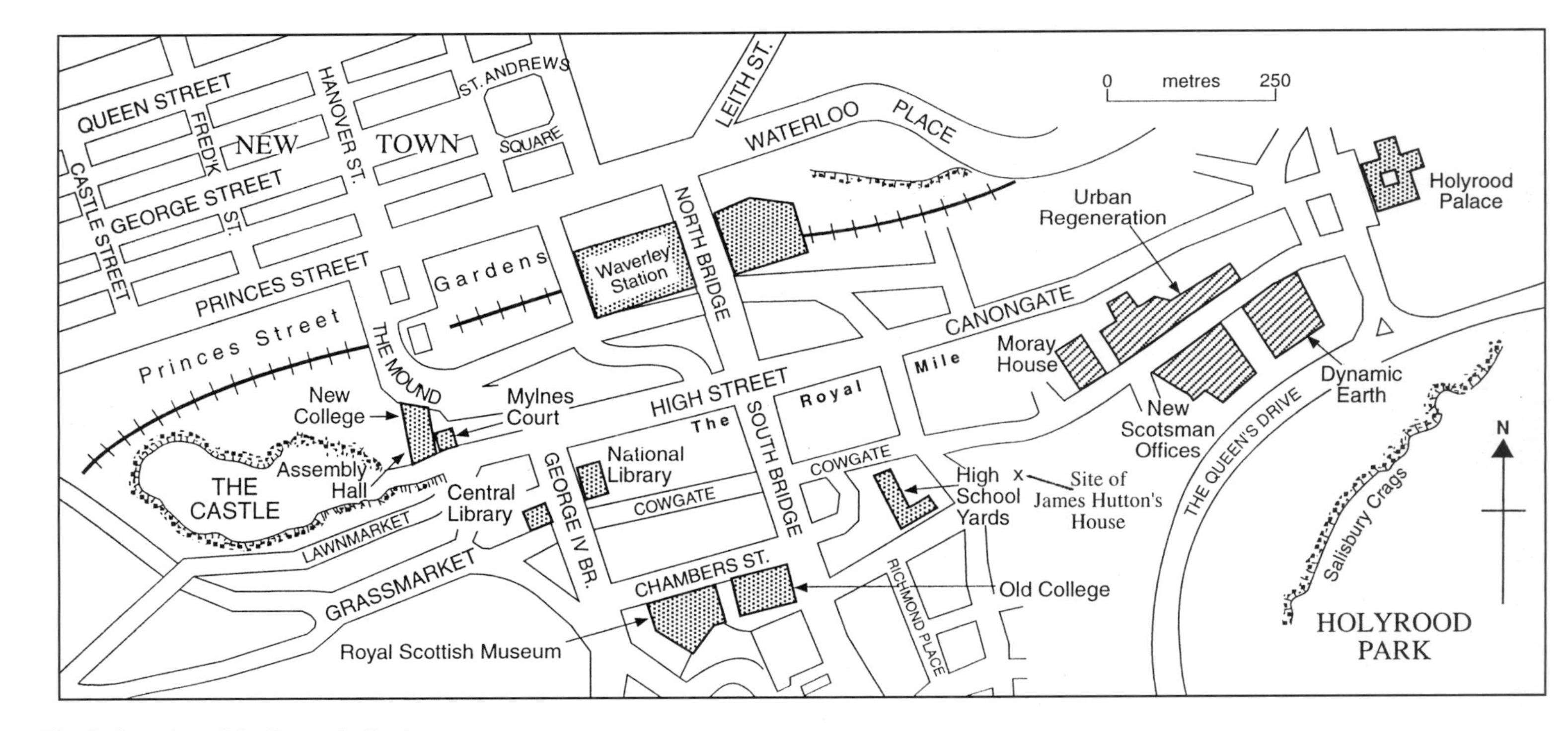

Fig. 1. Location of the Dynamic Earth.

shaped the Earth as we know it today. The approach adopted within the Dynamic Earth focuses on many areas of science including geography, geology, astronomy, biology and oceanography, making the exhibition unique not only in its breadth but also in communicating the complex relationship between these subject areas. This is the challenge for the next millennium. It is an exhibition that is more concerned with *process* than *product*; it includes few artefacts, but audio-visual presentations that recreate a process or translate the visitor into the heart of an environment are used extensively. The intention is to use technology to extend the visitor's experience, for example, taking them into volcanoes such as those in Iceland and Montserrat, and across the glaciers of Norway. James Hutton – the man, his times and his legacy – provides the key to the conceptual framework of the Dynamic Earth.

James Hutton, the man

James Hutton was an Edinburgh man through and through. Educated at the High School and the University, he was under no pressure to earn a living. His father, who died when Hutton was still young, was a wealthy merchant and Hutton inherited his business acumen. He was involved in a number of commercial enterprises, including the construction of the Forth and Clyde canal and owned considerable property, some of which would have fallen within the area of the present urban regeneration project. Therefore, the location of the Dynamic Earth, adjacent to the Palace of Holyrood and against the spectacular background of Salisbury Crags and Arthur's Seat, is singularly fitting. It looks out on part of the evidence that inspired Hutton's *Theory of the Earth* and lies close to the home where he set his ideas on paper.

The city of Edinburgh was very different at the end of the eighteenth century. Until the Jacobite rising of 1745, the city was tightly confined to the crag and tail ridge surmounted by the Castle to the west and running down to Holyrood Palace to the east, with a substantial population of 57 000 in 1755, concentrated in tall tenements, sometimes as high as 16 storeys, and with all the environmental consequences, most notably, 'gardez-loo'. It has to be said that the drainage at that time must have made the site of the Dynamic Earth less than salubrious. After the 1745 rebellion, the population rapidly grew to 85 000 in 1792 and the compressed population and intellectual energy were released by the planned creation and development of the New Town of Edinburgh. This physical expansion was complemented by an intellectual ferment – the Enlightenment – which made the city in one phrase 'a hotbed of genius'. It led to the founding of the Royal Society of Edinburgh, where both the arts and the physical sciences were established and in which Hutton was a major figure.

Edinburgh, however, is appropriate for the Dynamic Earth not only because it was Hutton's residence but also because it is a superb example of how geological forces, in the form of fire, ice and water, can shape a landscape and give character to a city. The evolution of Edinburgh as a beautiful scenic town was a conscious exercise by the city fathers in which the physical surroundings played an integral part. Equally, however, Scotland itself is an ideal location for such an exhibition as, within its limited compass, there is an unparalleled range of geological history, from some of the oldest rocks in the world to some of the youngest, post-glacial deposits.

Hutton was a genius and his perception of the heat engine of the Earth and the resultant processes led to his title as the 'Founder of modern geology'. Perhaps more significantly, in casting off the shackles of theology in measuring the age of the Earth, he demonstrated

Fig. 2. William Younger Centre housing the Dynamic Earth exhibition.

freedom of thought regardless of orthodoxy. It is worth recalling that more than half a century later, in 1857, Hugh Miller entitled his book *The Testimony of the Rocks; or Geology in Its Bearings on the Two Theologies, Natural and Revealed* (Miller 1857). The revolutionary significance of Hutton's concept of time was wittily highlighted by Louis Agassiz in his Memoir to Miller's earlier book *Foot-prints of the Creator*. Here he recalled the words of Sir David Brewster: 'The Geological Society of London, which doubtless sprung from the excitement in the Scottish metropolis, entered on the new field of research with a faltering step. The prejudices of the English mind had been marshalled with illiberal violence against the Huttonian doctrines. Infidelity and atheism were charged against their supporters; and had there been a Protestant Inquisition in England at that period of general political excitement, the geologists of the north would have been immured in its deepest dungeon.' (Miller 1849)

But Hutton was endowed with an enthusiasm and an insatiable curiosity about science which did not confine his interest to geology but extended it into all aspects of the living world. He had a holistic view of the Earth. He was also a communicator with a remarkable gift for generating lasting friendship. His greatest friend was Joseph Black, who was dissimilar to Hutton in many ways: it was said 'that Dr. Black dreaded nothing so much as error, and that Dr. Hutton dreaded nothing so much as ignorance' (Fergusson 1805). Hutton believed that exercising the mind on problems not only provided useful results but also led to personal fulfilment and pleasure (Morrison, in press).

The conclusion of the Abstract of James Hutton's *Theory of the Earth* reads 'there is opened to our view a subject interesting to man who thinks; a subject on which to reason with relation to the system of nature; and one which may afford the human mind both information and entertainment' (Hutton 1785). This statement chimes exactly with the aims and objectives of the Dynamic Earth, which is designed to be both a visitor attraction and an educational resource.

Edinburgh in the Enlightenment: a place of changing ideas

The Scottish Enlightenment flourished in the last quarter of the eighteenth century. It developed out of the European Age of Reason which had evolved during the preceding two centuries and provided intellectual liberation from the beliefs and practices of the Middle Ages. In Edinburgh, the peculiar social structure, in which all classes lived cheek by jowl in the close-knit society imposed by the buildings of the Old Town, was reflected in the continual cross-fertilization of ideas and great diversity of interests. Intellectual ferment is a social phenomenon and the reciprocal arrangements fostered polymaths who were both versatile and practical. Such was the reputation of this community that Thomas Jefferson, corresponding in 1789, expressed the view that 'in science, no place in the world can pretend to a competition with Edinbugh'.

Time is the commodity that is taken most for granted. Most individuals can grasp and imagine periods of time measured in decades, as these relate to the human life span. History allows us to study change over periods of time measured in hundreds of years, but grappling with millions and even thousands of millions of years stretches the imagination of the individual. In the early eighteenth century the thinking of Archbishop James Ussher was accepted, namely that the world was created on 23 October 4004 BC (Ussher 1658). This established 'truth' was, like so many other things, challenged during the intellectual ferment of the Enlightenment.

Hutton's theories regarding geological time were put to the test at the Siccar Point unconformity and demonstrated that, whatever the exact figure might be, the age of the Earth must be much greater than the 6000 years calculated by Archbishop Ussher. Hutton was able to use the natural environment as his laboratory. A hypothesis erected on the basis of observations made at Jedburgh and on Arran was confirmed at Siccar Point. Other fundamental concepts were explored in a similar way. The relationship between the rock of Salisbury Crags and the underlying sediments was evidence for the forceful emplacement of rocks in a molten state, contrasting with the then accepted mechanism for the formation of igneous rocks, namely that they were precipitated out of sea water on an ocean floor. Hutton used the power of observed field relations to make statements about the mechanisms of formation of the rocks and the period of time over which this took place. He could also ascribe the processes observed in the world today to the geological past giving rise to the Huttonian maxim, 'the present is the key to the past'.

Hutton came to the Earth sciences from a background as a chemist, a physician, a businessman, a farmer and a seasoned traveller, giving him a comprehensive view of the world in which he lived. Unlike today, when Töpffer's remark in 1841 that 'geologists are charming company – particularly for other geologists' (Craig & Jones 1982) remains apposite, Hutton kept company with the intellectual giants of the day: Robert Adam, Joseph Black, John Clerk of Eldin and his son, John Clerk, junior, Adam Ferguson, Sir James Hall of Dunglass, David Hume, John Playfair, William Robertson and Adam Smith. These were not the geologists of the time nor yet the scientists but represented a stratum of Edinburgh and Scottish society that was concerned to understand the world we live in, not only its geological, geographical, scientific and medical aspects but also from a social, political and economic perspective.

Others too followed on from Hutton in pushing out the frontiers of understanding. Louis Agassiz, the Swiss geologist, looked at the striations on the rocks by the Braid Burn of Edinburgh in 1840 and announced to the world from the pages of *The Scotsman* newspaper that this was the work of ice. Charles McLaren, the then editor of *The Scotsman*, was an enthusiastic amateur geologist and did much to further awareness of issues in the developing science through the pages of his publication. James Croll, a man before his time, had an interest in astronomy and calculated the precession of the planets round the Sun. He recognized the effect of the Earth's orbit on the amount of solar radiation which would impact on the surface, effectively identifying cycles of climate change and laying the foundations for the important work carried out later by Milankovitch. The Challenger Expedition, completed in 1876, had a major impact on Scottish scientific life. John Murray, as editor of the report, had immense influence in Edinburgh and stimulated all aspects of the natural sciences. This powerful heritage of intellectual activity in Edinburgh continues today in its universities, its Observatory, its museums, the Royal Botanic Gardens, the Zoo and the British Geological Survey.

The time of the Enlightenment was very ably summed up by Lord Cameron when he said that it was 'a world in which men of genius and talent rubbed shoulders, and indeed lived, in a community of intellect where the language of specialisation had not yet begun to erect those barriers which today, in increasing degree, inhibit the ease of effective communication in the world of thought and of the mind'. (Cameron 1967). The Dynamic Earth will help to break down these barriers.

The landscape of Edinburgh, carved by fire and ice

The city of Edinburgh is surrounded by a landscape that has been fashioned by the powerful forces of the Earth. The global processes of plate tectonics placed Edinburgh in the tropical regions between 400 and 300 million years ago and the sedimentary rocks formed at that time contain evidence of shallow tropical seas and hot humid coal forests. The colder conditions during the Ice Ages of the last 2 million years produced thick ice sheets, which shaped the surface and contributed to the rugged and diverse landscape in which Edinburgh is situated. Edinburgh is therefore an illustration of global processes that have been operative through geological time.

Unlike other scientists, those that are concerned with the natural world have the complete environment as a laboratory. In the heart of the city, the extinct volcano of Arthur's Seat is an example of a natural feature that can be enjoyed for its own sake yet provides an opportunity to understand the processes of volcanism. The known and the familiar are the best routes to comprehension. On a global scale the processes that have shaped the planet are less well known but an appreciation of the complex interaction between the geosphere, the atmosphere, the hydrosphere and the biosphere will ensure that an individual gains an enhanced perception of landscapes and the processes that lead to their formation.

The resources that support the community have also been sought from the rocks in and around the city. Salisbury Crags and other igneous sills in the city at Corstorphine Hill, Turnhouse Hill, Mons Hill and Dalmahoy Hill have all been quarried at some time to provide building or road stone. Quarrying at Salisbury Crags, however, was proceeding so rapidly in Hutton's time that the skyline of Edinburgh was being affected. Some of the original sections examined by Hutton were quarried away and it is fortuitous that extraction ceased when it did, maintaining the characteristic profile of the Crags and important exposures at the base of the intrusion. The sandstones of Edinburgh, most notably at Hailes and Craigleith, have been extensively quarried to provide the stone for many of Edinburgh's most important buildings and have also been exported to London and elsewhere. Water from the thick glacial deposits immediately adjacent to Arthur's Seat was the basis for the brewing industry of Holyrood. Energy resources, originally obtained from the coal deposits around Edinburgh, are now entirely won by opencast methods. Today, oil and gas from the North Sea provide much of our energy needs. The limestone and mudstone of East Lothian form the basis of a cement industry that underpins much of the civil engineering activity in Scotland.

The resources of the Earth remain an essential component in the fabric of modern society but many are finite and need to be utilized in a sensible way to ensure their longer-term availability. Decisions on the utilization of resources require that Earth science information is integrated with planning, economic and social science data as part of the strategic planning process. These are environmental issues that impinge on everyone. Coverage by the media frequently fails to communicate effectively with the general public and the messages are perceived as being too complex, too confusing and changing too often. It is one of the objectives of the Dynamic Earth to give visitors an insight into the science that underpins these issues so that informed judgements can be made.

The Dynamic Earth exhibition

The aim of the exhibition is to emphasize the dynamic nature of the planet. It begins by showing the ways the Earth is being monitored at the present day, set against a backdrop of geological time. This is followed by presentations on the main processes – geophysical, atmospheric, hydrological and biological – culminating in an examination of anthropogenic influences on the planet. The integrated role of these processes is demonstrated in the Earth's major environments.

Equally significant is the second objective of the Dynamic Earth, to create a national and international educational resource. The subject matter integrates well with the national curricula of both Scotland and England and Wales and this will be supported by an educational team and dedicated 'discovery rooms'. The rapid evolution of information technology provides exciting opportunities not only to explore related areas but also to disseminate the activities of the Dynamic Earth.

'The State of the Earth' (Fig. 3) is the first section of the exhibition and will look at the ways in which the Earth is being continually monitored to build up a picture of a dynamic planet. It will raise many questions in the mind of the visitor about the processes that cause this continual change.

'The Time Machine' will convey the concept of the immensity of geological time, taking the visitor from their present familiar surroundings, through the World Wars, the Roman invasion, the Stone Age, human origins, the age of dinosaurs, early life forms, to a planet devoid of life and finally to the beginnings of the universe in the Big Bang – where the story begins.

'How it all Started' takes the visitor from the Big Bang and the start of the physical universe to a planet capable of sustaining life. It will demonstrate the relative place of the Earth within the universe and the vast distances involved. 'The Restless Earth' is concerned with the internal processes on the planet: what causes volcanoes and

Fig. 3. Area of the exhibition concerned with 'The State of the Earth'.

earthquakes, how mountains are built up and why continents move. 'Shaping the Surface' examines the surface processes sculpting the landscape, particularly glaciation, which has been an important agent in moulding the scenery of Scotland. 'Casualties and Survivors' looks at the biological processes that make the planet as it is today. The evolution of the skeleton left fossilized evidence of a wide range of life forms. Some of these still have living relatives: these are the survivors. Others are only preserved as fossils and are the casualties. Mass extinctions have taken place in the past and will undoubtedly be a feature of the future. In this context will *Homo sapiens*, 'the human animal', be a casualty or a survivor?

The exploration of 'The Oceans' (Fig. 4) has been moved on immeasurably by remote sensing of the ocean floor. The use of satellite technology has greatly increased the understanding of the linkages between the oceans and the atmosphere and the transfer of momentum, energy and matter at the ocean–atmosphere interface. 'The Polar Regions' represent the extremes of cold climate yet, though the Arctic and the Antarctic are superficially very similar, one is oceanic and the other continental. 'From tundra to Tropical' portrays the contrast between areas of extreme climate and emphasizes that it is within these zones that human need has significantly modified the landscape. In 'The Tropical Regions' the visitor will experience the hot, wet environment of the tropical rain forest, where the Sun's energy encourages the greatest diversity of plant and animal life.

'The Showdome' is a summary of the exhibition, highlighting the dramatic processes that have shaped the planet Earth, many of which may be regarded as 'hazards' but, nevertheless, many of these are also the processes of renewal which rejuvenate the planet.

The exhibition will also have an external dimension. Links will be made, where appropriate, with other sites in Edinburgh such as the Zoo, the Botanical Gardens and the Royal Museum of Scotland, as well as The Helix in Newcastle, the National Space Science Centre in Leicester and other sites across the globe, so that the visitor can extend the voyage of exploration into the planet, how it formed, what it is made of, and the plants and animals that live on it.

The Dynamic Earth: a resource for the next millennium

The Dynamic Earth *is* a project for the millennium in that it is one of five major science centres that have been financially supported by the Millennium Commission. Recognition of the importance of science lies in the fact that approximately one-third of the Millennium Commission's budget has gone to scientific proposals, not least because of their fundamental significance for the future but particularly because of the need to encourage understanding and appreciation among the public. It is one of the objectives of the Dynamic Earth Charitable Trust 'to encourage and support the dissemination of knowledge on the Dynamic Earth'. This broadly based educational goal is a keystone of the Dynamic Earth.

The importance of the public understanding of science is mirrored in the mission statements of many of the research councils in the UK and also echoed in the findings of the Wolfendale report in 1995, which encouraged all those in the professional scientific and engineering community, who have an interest in creating wealth and enhancing our

Fig. 4. Area of the exhibition concerned with 'The Oceans'.

quality of life to participate in promoting the public understanding of science, engineering and technology. Government appreciation of the importance of this area can be measured by the financial support that is on offer to COPUS (Committee on the Public Understanding of Science) within the Science Budget. The Dynamic Earth Charitable Trust will ensure that the Dynamic Earth will play its part in furthering these objectives.

In Hutton's time, during the Enlightenment, Europe was unstable, nationalism was bursting forth, and this political activity was accompanied by a growing need for social change. Today, there is an equal need for enlightenment, to which the Dynamic Earth can contribute. Some examples will serve to illustrate the point. Firstly, there is now global awareness that we live on an isolated planet in which all systems are interrelated and change is no longer local. Compartmentalism in scientific disciplines is no longer valid as complex relationships are discerned and discrete actions raise varied and thorny ethical questions.

Secondly, the revolution in communications, which began with the printing press, is now leading to a surfeit of information with a growing need for a means to comprehend it. Satellite monitoring and new technology are expanding our knowledge of processes in the natural sciences but concurrently raise new questions and concerns. Presentation of issues as brief, snapshot items on television news leads to anxiety in the public mind and a growing desire for wider perspectives to assist in understanding and in formulating an appropriate response.

Thirdly, more than 50 per cent of the world's population are now classified as urban dwellers. Their perception of the planet is conditioned by the artificial environment in which they live and there is a diminishing understanding of the planet and nature.

Fourthly, the pace of change today is unprecedented. Previous revolutions, such as that from the Bronze Age to the Iron Age, the agricultural revolution or the industrial revolution heralded changes that took centuries to manifest themselves. Today, changing technology results in new attitudes and perceptions that have to be constantly revised. It is vital that the rhythms of time in the natural world are not forgotten and provide a baseline for measuring change.

Conclusion

James Hutton, with his dislike of ignorance, was fully aware of the need for enquiry and research. He was also conscious, in the prevailing attitude of his times, that nature was wise and benevolent and that the planet would go on changing, regardless of whether humankind was present or not. His legacy should perhaps have the last word in this presentation. In a 'Letter to the Earth' published in Sceance de la Terre, he supposedly wrote from his celestial abode (although the missive apparently bears marks of scorching!) as follows:

> '... We all look forward to meeting some of your young colleagues who have made such spectacular advances in plate tectonics, and I am especially glad to hear that they are using *my* heat to drive *their* plates ...
>
> Yours very truly, James Hutton'. (Craig & Jones 1982)

Hutton's precept 'to afford the human mind both information and entertainment' remains the key to fostering an enlightened awareness within the global community of our Dynamic Earth.

References

CAMERON, J. 1967. Scott and the community of intellect. *In: Edinburgh in the Age of Reason.* Edinburgh University Press, Edinburgh.

CRAIG, G. Y. & JONES E. J. 1982. *A Geological Miscellany.* Orbital Press, Oxford.

FERGUSON, A. 1805. Minutes of the life and character of Joseph Black MD. *Transactions of the Royal Society of Edinburgh,* **5**(3), 101–117.

HUTTON, J. 1785. Abstract of a Dissertation read in the Royal Society of Edinburgh upon the Seventh of March, and Fourth of April, MDCCLXXXV, concerning the System of the Earth, its Duration and Stability.

MILLER, H. 1849. *Foot-prints of the Creator.* W. P. Nimmo, Hay & Mitchell, Edinburgh.

—— 1857. *The Testimony of the Rocks; or Geology in its Bearings on the Two Theologies, Natural and Revealed.* Constable, Edinburgh.

MORRISON, I. 1998. Makkin Siccar – Dr James Hutton on the rocky road to Evolution. *COSMOS (Journal of the Traditional Cosmology Society)* **13**, 69–89.

USSHER, J. 1658. *Annales Veteris et Novi Testamenti.* J. Crook & G. Bedell, London.

Closing remarks for the Hutton bicentenary, Edinburgh

ROBERT H. DOTT, JR
Department of Geology and Geophysics, University of Wisconsin, Madison, WI 53706, USA

Quite a few things of note happened in 1797: Franz Schubert was born; Napolean defeated the Austrians and was appointed to command forces to invade England; John Adams became the second President of the United States; chromium was discovered; the first copper pennies and pound notes were issued in Britain; and Merino sheep were introduced to Australia. None of these seems more important, however, than the geological coincidence that brought us together for this outstanding Bicentennial Conference. In attempting to summarize our proceedings, I feel like that political foe whom Winston Churchill once characterized sardonically as 'having much to be humble about'.

I trust that all of the conferees join me in thanking the Royal Society of Edinburgh and the University of Edinburgh for being such gracious hosts. We owe a special debt of gratitude to Gordon Craig and his organizing committee, together with the Session Chairmen (Charles Waterston, Graham Shimmield, Barry Dawson, Tony Hallam and Dennis Dean), who helped the speakers to be most effective, and those who arranged the fine excursions (Norman Butcher, David Land, David McAdam, Donald McIntyre, Stuart Munro, Ian Rolfe, David Stephenson and Leonard Wilson).

I have a special gift of appreciation for Gordon by way of returning a favour he did me seven years ago. In 1990 I had the pleasure of presiding when the Geological Society of America's History Division honoured Gordon. What did he do after I presented our award to him, but counter by awarding me with a copy of Charles Lyell's notes for a lecture to be given in Philadelphia on 2 March 1842. This diverting token hooked me into a research project on Lyell's lectures and travels in America from 1841 to 1853, which I only completed this year – just in time to report briefly at the London portion of this conference. So, in return, I wish to award Gordon with a bottle of 'Piltdown Man Wine', which my wife and I obtained recently from the winery that now occupies the site of the famous Piltdown skull. One good hoax deserves another!

If memory serves, this is my fourth visit to Edinburgh. I have a rather spectacular history of failures when visiting these parts in spite of the fact that my paternal great-grandfather emigrated from just across the firth in Fife and that both of my wife's paternal grandparents came from near Kinnordy, seat of the Lyell family. During my first visit in 1963, after dining at the University Staff Club, my two hosts escorted me on a pilgrimage to Greyfriar's Churchyard to see Hutton's grave and a plaque, which I knew had been placed there in 1947 on the 150th anniversary of his death. It was about 10 o'clock at night, but in mid-summer at 56°N latitude it was still light. No amount of light nor of guides' confidence, however, was sufficient, for we failed to discover either grave or

DOTT, JR, R. H. 1999. Closing remarks for the Hutton bicentenary, Edinburgh.
In: CRAIG, G. Y. & HULL, J. H. (eds) *James Hutton – Present and Future*. Geological Society, London, Special Publications, **150**, 169–173.

plaque. Some time later, my hosts sheepishly informed me that Hutton was secured in some remote corner behind locked doors, safe from all his enemies and creditors, I suppose. On two other occasions, I also managed to miss finding the classic Siccar Point unconformity locality by getting into coves on either side; so it will be a special pleasure for me to be taken to that exact spot tomorrow. I am happy to report that I had better luck on the Isle of Arran, where I did manage to find Hutton's unconformity all by myself in 1986.

My second visit to Edinburgh was in 1971 to participate in a special meeting at which the new plate tectonic paradigm was featured. I was invited to speak of the implications of the new theory for sedimentology. How fitting to return here this week to assess some of the great past, present and future ideas about the Earth on the 200th anniversary of the death of the man who initiated the first great paradigm shift in the history of the geological sciences.

Donald McIntyre mesmerized us with his poetic description of Hutton's Edinburgh and how the climate of the Scottish Enlightenment and Hutton's friends influenced his theory. Ever since my first excursion into the history of geology 30 years ago (which excursion concerned Hutton), I have felt that the most important novelty of the theory was in regarding the entire Earth as dynamic and ever-changing due to internal heat, proposed as it was when the ruling neptunian paradigm considered the solid Earth to be completely passive; only the ocean changed.

This conference has highlighted the importance of knowledge gained since Hutton's death about the nature of the Earth's interior. During the late nineteenth century, a lively debate raged between two contending groups of Cambridge physicist-mathematicians about the character of the interior – was it solid or liquid? William Hopkins and his promising disciple, William Thomson, the future Lord Kelvin, led the 'solids', while Osmond Fisher and George Darwin led the 'liquids'. The latter were influenced by the evidence for polar flattening of the Earth and the need to account for magmas. The battle lines were sharpened by Kelvin's attack upon Lyell's thermodynamically impossible steady-state Earth, beginning in the 1860s. Osmond Fisher countered that, if the interior were liquid, much heat would have been dissipated through convection and Kelvin's calculation of age would be seriously in error. Soon the new theory of isostasy implied that the interior must not be quite 'as rigid as steel' as Kelvin was insisting, and the discovery of radioactivity at the end of the century – 100 years after Hutton's death – eventually would provide a new source of heat to unravel Kelvin's argument a bit further. Also at the turn of the century, compositional models for the interior were being refined by Eduard Suess and others using arguments based upon density and petrology just as the core–mantle boundary and the Moho were recognized by seismology.

Following from those long-ago discoveries, Don Anderson presented a new theory of the Earth, which was more specifically a story of the rise and fall of the plume theory. He transported us by 'fast-forward' to give a breathtaking look deep into the Earth's abyss, but then returned to the surface to suggest how the shallow and surface realms may be integrated in a more straightforward way than I would have expected. Long ago Don and I were lieutenants together in the United States Air Force, and I would like to share a story about him from that Palaeozoic era of our lives. He was engaged in studies on Thule Bay in northern Greenland of sea ice as a possible emergency landing surface for crippled aircraft. Don was out on the ice one day setting off explosions for seismic studies of ice thickness and strength when a small figure approached. It was an Innuit, who walked towards him until in range, then stopped, opened his parka, and took out a camera to photograph this weird foreign intruder, who obviously must be quite insane.

Early in our century, while geophysics was providing important new constraints for the structure of the inaccessible interior, geologists recognized that an impasse had been reached, which required knowledge of the properties and behaviour of Earth materials at high pressures and temperatures. In the United States, this challenge was met by a small group of far-sighted individuals, who in 1906 conceived the Geophysical Laboratory within the new Carnegie Institution of Washington created by Scottish-born millionaire-philanthropist, Andrew Carnegie. It was that laboratory which sponsored the experimental investigations based upon phase rule chemistry made famous by N. L. Bowen. Peter Wyllie brought us from Bowen up to the present after first noting Sir James Hall's pioneering experiments in those 'hot little crucibles' (and big cannon barrels) which his friend James Hutton so disparaged. As Peter has shown us, thanks to technologies that would boggle the minds of both James Hutton and Sir James Hall, it is now possible to take a vicarious Jules Vernian journey to the centre of the Earth by reproducing the thermochemical conditions for the core boundary as well as for Hutton's shallow little granite bodies, and even to model the chemical differentiation of the entire Earth. Similarly, Werner Schreyer took us on another deep *PT* trip through the changing environments of metamorphism. Both discussions mirrored nicely the Huttonian theory of cycles of burial, alteration, uplift and exhumation. Just imagine how Hutton and his Oyster Club cronies might have celebrated these achievements with rounds of malt whisky. I am impressed to realize that Edinburgh is still today at the frontier of igneous and metamorphic petrology.

It has often been said, perhaps *ad nauseum*, that geology is an historical science, and some revisionists have criticized Hutton for not being enough interested in geological and palaeontological history. But, as he 'read from the book of nature', surely Hutton was as much an historian of the Earth as are most of us. Each speciality approaches history differently; thus the petrologist may tell us about a complex history of an individual metamorphic mineral grain, while the geomorphologist deciphers the evolution of a landscape, and the palaeobiologist recounts the history of life. Ultimately, all of these histories must be interrelated.

Both Gordon Herries Davies and Celal Sengor have addressed our roles as historians and have reminded us that there are different perspectives and styles in the study of history. These differences are strongly coloured by cultural circumstances and they serve to warn us that ultimate historical truth is an elusive phantom like Hamlet's ghost or a hologram (choose your own metaphor); you see it for a moment, but you cannot permanently grasp it, for it keeps changing. An interesting difference in style of intellectual inquiry was highlighted by Playfair in contrasting Hutton with friend Joseph Black, quoted as follows: 'one would say that Dr. Black dreaded nothing so much as error, and that Dr. Hutton dreaded nothing so much as ignorance; that the one was always afraid of going beyond the truth, and the other of not reaching it'.

Ian Dalziel plumbed the historical depths of our current global paradigm, plate tectonics, by introducing us to the vestiges of supercontinents dating much farther back than anyone dreamt possible to discern in the 1970s. And his suggestion that the history of life on Earth has been linked closely with global tectonic history converges upon Andrew Watson's fascinating discussion, to which I shall return momentarily, but first an anecdote. The various wanderings of ancient plates that Ian told us about remind me of one of *his* wanderings when we were working together on South Georgia Island in 1973.

It was a particularly foggy day, but he and a student were determined to make a traverse a few miles across a low pass from one fjord to another. All seemed to be going well enough until, after an hour or so of walking, Ian realized that the lake visible through the mist on his right side was still there. That seemed odd because it was only a small lake. Just then the fog lifted in front of them for a moment, and, lo and behold, there was their boat just in front of them, which they had tied on the shore two hours earlier! Yes, the intrepid field geologists, like certain supercontinents, had gone right around in a circle. Our student made good use of this lesson learned from the mentor, however, proving Ian's prowess as a teacher. A few weeks later, after a particularly exuberant farewell party at our British Antarctic logistical base, the said student emerged in the dark of a moonless night a bit disorientated. Suddenly he realized that his right foot was wet. Slowly his brain registered that he must have stepped into the edge of the bay, and if he would just walk along keeping that same foot in the water, he could not miss our lodgings. This novel mode of navigation worked perfectly, and we then felt assured that he was PhD material.

Besides the 1797 Hutton–Lyell conjunction, there have been other notable historical coincidences. For example, Mark Twain, who mercilessly satirized scientific research in general and uniformitarianism in particular, began and also ended his life with Halley's Comet visible in the heavens. Ursula Marvin looked into the heavens with us here and explored another dimension of history involving unearthly objects, that geologists long ignored as of no relevance for them. Today, the 'falling sky' has taken centre stage to create – pardon the pun – the greatest splash in geology since plate tectonics. Ursula showed how difficult it was for people to believe in 'stones from the sky', and that, curiously, such acceptance dated from the very time of Hutton's *Theory of the Earth*. In the 17 years since the Alvarez hypothesis was first announced, the liveliest discussions in the earth Sciences have focused upon the K–T boundary impact event and its implications for possible mass extinctions of species. The new respectability of great impacts has also helped to foster that trendy term, 'Neocatastrophism'. Weathering and erosion processes as well as plate tectonics, which perhaps are all unique to the Earth, greatly obscured the fact that our planet had shared the early great bolide showering within the solar system. Some years ago, Ursula pointed out that that event challenged Lyellian uniformitarianism because it was caused by a process no longer acting on Earth; today we can add the apparent former presence of much liquid water on Mars as another non-uniformitarian historical phenomenon in the sense of Lyell. The study of other planetary bodies has greatly expanded our geological vistas and provided the clearest examples of the past being a key to the present. It seems especially poignant that the little Rover is probing the Martian surface even as I speak.

To my surprise, the issue of uniformitarianism versus catastrophism was little in evidence in this conference. Do we finally understand the many meanings of these old and much misused terms? Most geologists had already rejected Lyell's extreme uniformitarianism even before Kelvin mounted his thermodynamic challenge to a steady-state Earth. Without explicitly invoking the words, Kelvin in fact had opened a window for a new evolutionary directional view of the Earth as well as of life, an implication of his campaign which seems under appreciated. It was Thomas Huxley, ten years after Darwin's *Origin of Species* appeared, who put it into words, and ever since, I believe, this has been our guiding worldview.

Geologically short-term fluxes were illustrated for us in Maureen Raymo's discussion of climate change, which seems to be overtaking bolide impacts on our collective agenda of major issues. She prophesied the chilling inevitability of a next ice age, whether or not humankind is creating a serious greenhouse effect, which still seems to be debatable. While Milankovitch orbital factors surely provide an ongoing, truly cyclic control over climate, there are other important, but temporally irregular, factors, which include changing palaeogeography and atmospheric carbon dioxide. No geological phenomenon illustrates more clearly than climate change the complexity of interacting causes with their very different timescales and degrees of predictability. And in no other realm is geology so relevant to the welfare of humankind as in exploiting the geological record to help predict our climatic future, as Dr Raymo so eloquently showed.

Being co-author of a book titled *Evolution of the Earth*, first published 26 years ago, I was delighted to hear Andrew Watson's discussion of the coevolution of the Earth and of life with profound feedbacks and fluxes between. As Andrew indicated, the entire motivation of Hutton's design-filled theory was to provide a teleological explanation for how an ongoing habitat for life could be maintained in the face of the obvious decay of landscapes. We have long known that there has been some two-way feedback between life and the Earth, for example the release of free atmospheric oxygen through life processes. Today, however, as was noted by both Watson and Dalziel, we are provoked by the Gaia hypothesis to wonder if the feedback from life has been far more active and self-serving than was ever imagined before Lovelock. Here is yet another challenge for future interdisciplinary investigations. Testing of the self-regulatory implications of Gaia, for example, is critical to the ongoing debate between punctuated equilibrium and the older, progressional model of organic evolution.

Completion of the Dynamic Earth project described by Stuart Munro will be a most fitting follow-up to this bicentennial celebration, and how appropriate it is that the project is to be housed practically upon the site of the home of the man who, more than any other, initiated the concept of a dynamic Earth. Not only will the centre provide an exciting, multidisciplinary view of the Earth 200 years after Hutton, it will also provide an effective stimulus for looking to the future. Most importantly it aims to make our scientific knowledge accessible to the public, something that we neglect at our professional peril. I have been deeply impressed by the quality and extent of such outreach in the United Kingdom as evidenced by the fine array of popular publications displayed at this meeting. I commend these as examples for our profession to emulate everywhere.

So we have plumbed together the physical depths of the Earth and the chemical and *PT* depths of petrology, also the depths of the abyss of time and of space as well. There remain many unanswered questions, but that is just as well, for, to quote Robert Louis Stevenson, 'To travel hopefully is a better thing than to arrive.' Thanks to this Hutton–Lyell Conference and to *all* of its participants, we surely now have found many 'vestiges of the beginnings' of our science, but our look into its future suggests that there is, indeed, 'no prospect of an end' to our exciting endeavour to understand the Earth and its life.

Hutton Scholarship, 1992–1997

DENNIS R. DEAN
834 Washington Street, Apt 310, Evanston, IL 60202, USA

In my *James Hutton and the History of Geology* (Dean 1992), a study of Hutton's life, geological theorizing, and subsequent reputation, I endeavoured not only to include everything then known about these topics but also to point out what was not known. Since it appeared, some of these lacunae have been filled in. A number of publications, moreover, if not necessarily making original contributions themselves, have called attention to Hutton in the five years preceding and including the bicentenary of his birth. What follows is a review of this literature in so far as it is known to me.

Though Hutton's correspondence with James Watt has been known for some time, it remained unpublished till 1994–1995, when 13 letters (1774–1795) from or to Hutton were edited by Jean Jones, Hugh S. Torrens and Eric Robinson (1994–1995). The two problems with these letters, and why their publication was delayed, are that they seem only incidentally geological and that (in Hutton's case) their contents are often vulgar. Despite the fact that most of them cannot be dated precisely, the letters have some biographical value and probably reveal Hutton's private personality more vividly than anything else he wrote. The editors' annotations are exemplary. A most valuable letter is Watt's to Hutton, 9 December 1795, which establishes that pre-publication sheets of *Theory of the Earth* (1795, but probably January 1796) were in existence. There are also two letters from Hutton to George Clerk-Maxwell, one of which (it is not noted) was excerpted substantially by G. Y. Craig and E. J. Jones (1985).

One of the first scholars to mention my book in something other than a review was Rudolf Trümpy (1994), who discussed 'James Hutton und die Anfänge der modernen Geologie' in a volume of essays by various contributors devoted to the Scottish Enlightenment. Most of his material, including notes on some of Hutton's predecessors, his life, his theory (1788 and 1795), Playfair's *Illustrations* (1802), and certain of their successors, is no more than standard information and was apparently derived entirely from secondary sources. Trümpy's conclusion questions whether or not Hutton was (as I and others claim) *the* founder of modern geology, but he makes no attempt to answer what I said in my own conclusion (and which Hugh Torrens read before the Geological Society of America at their Hutton commemoration in New Orleans, 1995).

In a more argumentative mode, David J. Leveson (1996) examines Hutton's methodology in attempting to resolve the strong disagreement between scholars who, like me, see him as the founder of modern geology and others who regard him as an a priori religionist. Among the latter group, for Leveson, Stephen Jay Gould has been the most outspoken proponent. Utilizing quotations from Gould, Dean and (most extensively) Hutton himself, Leveson eventually sides with Dean.

The vexing debate as to how Hutton accounted for the subterranean fire or heat required by his geological theory was taken a step further by Douglas Allchin (1994) in a valuable essay on Hutton and phlogiston. Hutton defended the concept of phlogiston (an earlier

DEAN, D. R. 1999. Hutton Scholarship, 1992–1997. *In*: CRAIG, G. Y. & HULL, J. H. (eds) *James Hutton – Present and Future*. Geological Society, London, Special Publications, **150**, 175–179.

explanation of burning) in two publications of 1792 and 1794 that are difficult to find and rarely consulted in detail by historians of geology. In them, Allchin observes, Hutton accepted Lavoisier's discovery of oxygen but maintained that belief in phlogiston was still necessary to explain certain otherwise inexplicable phenomena.

In the 1794 publication, Hutton published the following geological remark:

> Fire, and the consumption of phlogistic substances, is a great and necessary operation in the oeconomy of this world. There is constant fire in the mineral regions;–fire which must consume the greatest quantities of fuel; the consolidation of loose materials, stratified at the bottom of the sea, depends upon the heat of that fire (pp. 320–321).

Hutton then went on to discuss how oxygen alone is not the cause of the light and heat emitted by burning coal. These statements lead Allchin to propose that 'For Hutton, the answer to the problem of geological heat was simple: subterranean coal burned and produced heat for uplift' (1994, p. 625).

Allchin was followed in this reasoning by David Oldroyd in one chapter of his *Thinking About the Earth: A History of Ideas in Geology* (1996), an attractive and stimulating book. But Oldroyd's evaluation of Hutton is eccentric, to say the least, and seems to depend almost entirely on passages not printed within Hutton's lifetime. He certainly ignores the greater part of Hutton's theory. Both authors, moreover, introduce confidence-shaking arguments into their essays: Allchin represents Hutton as writing against Werner (whom Hutton never mentions), and Oldroyd, after denegrating biographical scholarship, sends an in fact bedridden Hutton off to the Jura in 1794. Hutton never visited the Jura in his life.

Both Allchin and Oldroyd, but the latter especially, have failed to consider Hutton's geological writings more fully. In Chapter 2 of his *Theory of the Earth* (1795), Volume one, it is true, a flustered Hutton attempted to counter Richard Kirwan's objections by acknowledging that some mineral substance like coal might be the fuel on which subterranean fire subsists. His position is stated fully in I, ii, pp. 235–240, and most concisely on p. 239: 'I have inferred the former existence of an internal heat, a subterraneous fire, or a certain cause of fusion by whatever name it shall be called, and by whatever means it shall have been procured.' Hutton never claimed to know what was at work within the Earth and thought it unlikely that any such knowledge was possible. For him, we can know subterranean forces only by their effects.

With regard to coal and other mineral combustibles, Kirwan himself provides a powerful refutation (quoted by Hutton on p. 242) – the insufficiency of all known deposits – and is only then countered by Hutton's observation that coal regularly forms from dead plant life throughout time and is therefore a renewable resource. But this is nothing more than an attempt on Hutton's part to condemn Kirwan's logic, not to propose the answer he has already denied having. How could coal possibly form at the rate at which it would be consumed?

In the long final chapter of *Theory of the Earth*, Volume 1, Hutton discusses the nature of coal, emphasizing (incorrectly) that it has been consolidated through fusion. If fusion is the result of heat, as he believed, and coal the source of that heat, Hutton's theory would soon reduce to an infinite regression in which every bed of coal is solidified by the one below it until one arrives at the centre of the Earth and the realization that such a theory cannot be true. Hutton, therefore, did not claim that his necessary subterranean fire or heat derived from the ignition of coal, and no subsequent contemporary précis of his theory by friend or foe attested that he did.

A recent scholarly essay by Charles W. J. Withers (1994) on Hutton's unpublished and rarely discussed 'Elements of Agriculture' compares Hutton's opinions on farming with those of other Scottish improvers (on which Withers has written in previous essays). His general knowledge of the larger topic patently overshadows what little he says of Hutton in particular. Withers also attempts to relate Hutton's interests in agriculture and geology, but he succeeds only in restating what has already been said by others. It does not help that he claims the 1795 version of Hutton's geological theory to be, as compared with the 1788 one, 'much improved by the attention of Playfair', an erroneous notion easily refuted by textual comparison.

Two reprints of Volume 3 (1899) of Hutton's *Theory of the Earth* (1795) appeared in 1997. The first of these, issued by the Geological Society of London, is an unaltered reprinting of the original publication of that classic, as edited by Sir Archibald Geikie in 1899. A more ambitious attempt at the same project is Dennis R. Dean's edition of *James Hutton in the Field and in the Study*, which also reprints the whole of Geikie's edition, but in augmented form. The most important additions are a new preface (with comments on the 'lost drawings'), facsimile pages from the original manuscript, title pages and others from three foreign volumes on geology discussed at length by Hutton in this one, contemporary illustrations by Hutton's companion in the field, new letters by Playfair and Hall, and previously unpublished geological sections by Hutton and Playfair. Both editions include Geikie's index to all three volumes of Hutton's *Theory of the Earth*.

Also reprinted for the Hutton bicentenary were Hutton's 'Abstract' of 1785 (Craig 1997*a*), and the biographies, in *Transactions of the Royal Society of Edinburgh,* 1805, of Hutton by Playfair and of Joseph Black by Adam Ferguson (Craig 1997*b*). Both volumes include brief introductions by G. Y. Craig.

Of the several other publications intended specifically to commemorate the bicentenary of Hutton's death, a particularly attractive example is Donald B. McIntyre and Alan McKirdy's *James Hutton: The Founder of Modern Geology* (1997). Though by design introductory, and necessarily cramped for space, this 52-page booklet includes some new information, a number of apt quotations and a superb series of photographs in colour. Many of the geological snapshots were by McIntyre, who also contributed generously to Dean's edition of Hutton III and wrote most of the conference's field guide to Glen Tilt.

Norman E. Butcher (1997) has recently charted 'The ebb and flow of geology in Britain' in *Zeitgeist*, a new Edinburgh publication also intended for popular consumption. Written specifically with the Hutton bicentenary in mind, his somewhat depressing essay includes sections on 'Geology before Hutton' and 'James Hutton, founder of modern geology' (not to mention 'Twentieth century stagnation'). Butcher has significantly researched Hutton's Edinburgh residence (of which nothing now remains) on St John's Hill and was responsible for a great deal of the hard work that culminated on 6 August 1997 when a wonderfully appropriate bronze plaque and stone circle were unveiled on the site. There was a fine article in *The Scotsman* the next day. The same newspaper had published more generally on Hutton in its issue of 30 December 1996.

Among the many popular guides to Scottish geology which include Hutton, one must mention A. D. McAdam's and E. N. K. Clarkson's *Lothian Geology: An Excursion Guide. Hutton Bicentenary Edition* (1996). McAdam also wrote the brief conference field guide to Siccar Point. Like McIntyre & McKirdy, the anonymous pamphlet *Discovering Edinburgh's Volcano* includes a colour reproduction of the recently redated Hutton portrait by Henry Raeburn, whose work was the subject of a special exhibit in August 1997 at Edinburgh. Other recent publications by Scottish National Heritage (no date) and the

British Geological Survey also mention Hutton and the sites associated with him.

What remains to be done is a collected edition of Hutton's correspondence and the numerous references to him in the letters and diaries of others, from which a more complete biography might result. Eventually, one may even hope for a properly edited edition of his collected works, but such is not in sight.

References

ALLCHIN, D. 1992. Phlogiston after oxygen. *Ambix*, **39**, 110–116.
—— 1994. James Hutton and phlogiston. *Annals of Science*, **51**, 615–635.
BUTCHER, N. E. 1997. The ebb and flow of geology in Britain. *In*: *Zeitgeist: An Anthology of Popular Science Writing*. Science Reviews, Edinburgh, 200–220.
—— 1997. James Hutton's House at St. John's Hill, Edinburgh. *Book of the Old Edinburgh Clubs*, ns**4**, 107–112.
CRAIG, G. Y. (ed.) 1997*a*. *The 1785 Abstract of James Hutton's Theory of the Earth.* Edinburgh University Library, Edinburgh.
—— (ed.) 1997*b*. *James Hutton & Joseph Black: Biographies by John Playfair and Adam Ferguson, from Volume V of Transactions of the Royal Society of Edinburgh, 1805.* Royal Society of Edinburgh, Edinburgh.
—— & JONES, E. J. 1985. *A Geological Miscellany.* Princeton University Press, Princeton, NJ.
DEAN, D. R. 1992. *James Hutton and the History of Geology.* Cornell University Press, Ithaca and London.
—— (ed.) 1997. *James Hutton in the Field and in the Study*. Being an augmented reprinting of Vol. III of Hutton's *Theory of the Earth*, as first published by Sir Archibald Geikie (1899). Scholars' Facsimiles & Reprints, Delmar, NY.
GOULD, S. J. 1987. *Time's Arrow, Time's Cycle*. Cambridge University Press, Mass. and London
HUTTON, J. 1788. Theory of the Earth. *Transactions of the Royal Society of Edinburgh*, **1**, 209–304.
—— 1795. *Theory of the Earth, with Proofs and Illustrations.* 2 vols, Edinburgh.
—— 1799. *Theory of the Earth, with Proofs and Illustrations.* Volume 3. Ed. Archibald Geikie. London. Reprinted 1997.
—— 1792. *Dissertations on Different Subjects in Natural Philosophy*. Edinburgh.
—— 1794. *A Dissertation upon the Philosophy of Light, Heat, and Fire*. Edinburgh.
—— 1796–1797. Elements of Agriculture. Manuscript, 2 vols, 1045 pp. National Library of Scotland, Edinburgh.
JONES, J., TORRENS, H. S. & ROBINSON, E. 1994–1995. The correspondence between James Hutton (1726–1797) and James Watt (1736–1819) with two letters from Hutton to George Clerk-Maxwell (1715–1784). *Annals of Science*, **51**, 637–653; **52**, 357–382.
LEVESON, D. J. 1996. What was James Hutton's methodology? *Archives of Natural History*, **23**, 61–77.
MCADAM, A. D. Undated. *Edinburgh: A Landscape Fashioned by Geology*. British Geological Survey, Edinburgh.
—— & CLARKSON, E. N. K. 1996. *Lothian Geology: An Excursion Guide. Hutton Bicentenary Edition.* Edinburgh Geological Society, Edinburgh.
—— 1997. *Field Excursion Guide to Siccar Point: The Abyss of Time*. British Geological Survey, Edinburgh.
—— & STONE, P. Undated. *East Lothian and the Borders: A Landscape Fashioned by Geology*. British Geological Survey, Edinburgh.
MCINTYRE, D. B. & MCKIRDY, A. 1997. *James Hutton: The Founder of Modern Geology.* Stationery Office, Edinburgh.
—— & STEPHENSON, D. 1997. *Field Excursion Guide to Hutton Country: Scottish Highlands and Glen Tilt.* Royal Society of Edinburgh, Edinburgh.
OLDROYD, D. 1996. *Thinking About the Earth: A History of Ideas in Geology.* Harvard University Press, Cambridge, MA.
PLAYFAIR, J. 1802. *Illustrations of the Huttonian Theory of the Earth*. Edinburgh.
SCOTTISH NATIONAL HERITAGE. Undated. *Discovering Edinburgh's Volcano*. Edinburgh.

TRÜMPY, R. 1994. James Hutton und die Anfänge der modernen Geologie. *In*: BRÜHLMEIER, D., HOLZHEY, H. & MUDROCK, V. (eds) *Scottische Aufklärung: 'A Hotbed of Genius'*. Akademie Verlag, Berlin, 75–89.

WITHERS, C. W. J. 1994. On Georgics and geology: James Hutton's 'Elements of Agriculture' and agricultural science in eighteenth-century Scotland. *Agricultural History Review*, **42**, 38–48.

Index

Page numbers in *italics* refer to Tables or Figures